D1554122

The Story of Evaliz

# SHUKAR BALAN:

# THE WHITE LAMB

By

Mela Meisner Lindsay

Published under the auspices of the
American Historical Society of Germans from Russia
631 D Street, Lincoln, Nebraska 68502

Library of Congress Catalog
Card Number: 75-39490
International Standard Book Number 0-914222-02-3


Second Edition, 1978
Third Printing, 1979
Fourth Printing, 1980
Fifth Printing, 1982
Sixth Printing, 1983


Printed by
Augstums Printing Service, Inc.
Lincoln, Nebraska

## To

My father and mother who lived it; my brother, Theodore, and sisters, Elizabeth and Nathalia, who lie in Russian soil; my brother Arthur, and sisters, Lydia, Bertha, Othelia, Martha, Rachel, and Hilda, who make one happy family; and all Russian-Germans, who have become true American citizens.

To Blanche Y. McNeal, my writing teacher, who inspired me to begin it; Louise DeTolla, who drove me to supply page after page; George M. Osborne, who willed me to finish it; Magdalena Schwien and Wilhelm Dietz, whose "remembering" added much to the folklore; Frank B. Walker, a Western Kansas cattleman, who made the journey to America possible; my husband James for his forbearance; my children, James E. Jr., Robert D., and Marlene; and, to the memory of these words from Goethe: "Begin the web; God will supply the thread," I dedicate this book.

# PREFACE

While this is a factual novel based on the experience of a people as a whole, and especially of my mother and father who lived it, it also contains characters, conversations, and events drawn entirely from my own imagination.

While the story concentrates on Evaliz, a peasant girl of sixteen, who wills her life to be something other than that of an ox of the field, and longs for America, it is also the story of all *Russland-Deutschen*, the descendants of the German colonists who settled in the Volga region in the 1760's during the reign of Catherine the Great. *The White Lamb* details the day-by-day struggle of these people who have come to know Russia as their homeland, but accept nothing that is Russian, preferring to remain wholly German in their communities, their homes, and their churches.

The first half of the book ends after the Russo-Japanese War of 1904-05 which, a disaster for Russia, brought many a Russian soldier back from the Manchurian front to plunder, sack, and burn the rich estates, to tear the earrings from the earlobes of the elite. Seeing the nightly fires against the sky and hearing the dirge of funeral hymns, my story people flee to America. The second half of the book deals with the "Ploughing of the Prairie" in western Kansas, and ends in the early 1920's.

I was born in Russia, near the Don Cossack border, and though I do not remember that part, I knew my story people personally and have drawn on materials given to me piecemeal, over a span of more than thirty years by "Old Time" immigrants who have now passed on. It is my conviction that we, the present generation, must now fill in the gap of our missing history. *The White Lamb* is designed to speak not only for Evaliz, but to give voice to the heart-song of a thousand Evalizes like her who cannot speak for themselves, and to unfold for future generations experiences too real to be forgotten!

Mela Meisner Lindsay
Denver, Colorado
May, 1976

# CONTENTS

*Part Two.* AMERICA, MY AMERICA

# PART ONE

# *IN RUSSIA*

*LORD, my heart is not haughty, nor mine eyes lofty: neither do I exercise myself in great matters, or in things too high for me. Surely I have behaved and quieted myself, as a child that is weaned of his mother: my soul is even as a weaned child.*

*Psalm 131:1-2*

# CHAPTER 1

## Women Also Dream

On this spring day in Russia, 1893, we, the young people of the village, are gathering flowers of the field for the wedding. And as Nathalia and I, apart from the others, wander over the blowing steppes of Saratov, tears fall on Nathalia's bridal bouquet. Nathalia, so fair and golden, my very best friend.

"*Ach*, Evaliz!"* she cries, holding the flowers to her young bosom. "I do not want to marry this man who is like a stranger to me. I do not want to marry any man yet. I am afraid! But my father gave his word."

I see the great tears in her blue eyes, brimming over, the sun brightening her wet eyelashes. Bitter tears creep down my own face. I think how she is so shy — too shy to be given in marriage. She is only seventeen. Too young to take her place beside robust women who were once brides like her, but who now do the work of men in the fields of their husbands' large *Familien*.

"My father won't do that to me," I say to her with sureness in my voice, "for my father is a kind man."

*Evaliz — a contraction of the name Eva Elizabeth, pronounced āf'-lis.

"*Ach*, Evaliz, you are only sixteen, too young to know," Nathalia says pityingly through her tears. "But even a kind father does not pride himself with unmarried daughters in his house."

Suddenly, I think how I, too, have many sisters and brothers, and I know my father will not keep them always. The boys will bring wives into the *Familie*, but the girls will have to go.

My fingers tremble as I pick the tender flowers for the church altar. I look at Nathalia. Her eyes are on me, but they do not see, for tears. I turn away and look at the distant village — this German village on Russian soil. It is the custom of our Volga-German people to pledge the girls in marriage. Always, it will be this way. But always, in the eyes of the young, it will be a great sin.

Rancor stirs my heart as I think of the night less than a month ago, when two drunken fools came to Nathalia's house to make the marriage bargain. She told me about the smell of *Schnaps*, the brash words flowing from their stinking mouths, and my stomach recoils, even now.

Bah! Marriage-fixing may be their pride, but how I wish they had never been born.

Nathalia told me how their thick voices boomed at her father, "*Ja*, Herr Konrad, Karl makes the fine husband for your Nathalia. Finer than any other men in the village. *Donner*, but he has the good head on his shoulder. A little young, *ja*, but the strong back of an ox."

Nathalia's father believed them because they are his friends, and they are not so bad when they are sober.

I also remember what my young brother, Otto, said happened afterwards. How the *Freiers*, the matrimonial agents, went back to Karl and said all was fixed smooth as goose fat, and he need not even crook his little finger. "Haw! Haw!" they roared, proud of their accomplishment.

But Karl was tongue-tied.

"*Na, Kissel Donner Wetter*," they swore, "what kind of dumb-ox have we here? The sweetest, most tender damsel in all *Russland*, and he stands glass-eyed and the cat has his tongue. Haw! Haw!" And Karl received a hearty slap on his back for being the lunkhead he is.

I cannot keep the tears from falling while I pick the flowers that will not soften the fear in Nathalia's heart. I think of other times when we have picked blossoms and put them in our flaxen hair. Brides we pretended to be, so pretty and young. Once the boys sneaked up from behind and kissed us, their laughter ringing in our ears. Other girls liked the boys. They laughed when surprised with stolen kisses. But Nathalia and I did not like their teasing eyes,

2

bright with naughty light. Quickly we turned and ran back to the village, tearing the flowers from our hair.

And today we do not smile. A real wedding, a real bride: Nathalia! Her fingers tremble as I take her hand, so chill and cold. *Ach*, suddenly, we are like strangers. Always, we have been one in laughter and tears. But from this minute, it is as if we walk alone.

Now the young people swarm over the fields, shouting words of merriment.

"Flowers for shy Nathalia who will marry Karl Heimer. May they have a dozen and one children!" They laugh and fill their aprons and cossack sashes with bright blossoms, nodding like silly puppets.

Tears, hot as fire, creep down my cheeks. And I vow that no one shall choose a husband for me. No one! Not even my father. No one shall pick flowers for my wedding with silly songs about thirteen children by a man I do not love. I will not stay in this land of serfdom, this Russia. I will not accept the practice of our people. When they left their German Fatherland to live among the Russians they took up the strict custom of having parents choose the mate so that no child of theirs would ever marry a *Russ*.

I think it would have been better if Empress Catherine, who is blood-kin to us Germans, had let my people stay in Germany. But they tell me Germany was land poor — it needed *Lebensraum* — and Frederick the Great, for a few concessions, was glad to grant Catherine her wishes. Catherine needed resourceful Germans to plow her wild steppes, barren except for marauding Tartar bands and the dark-skinned *Kalmucken*, Kalmucks, and yellow *Kirgisen*, Kirghiz, who roamed in from the dry wastes of Asia to graze their herds over these same untamed steppes, from the salt wastes of the Caspian to the shores of the Black Sea.

The bright blowing fields smile on Nathalia and me in vain. Slowly we turn our steps toward the village, where kindly neighbors are preparing the wedding feast. Behind barnyards pigs are being slaughtered, while lambs bleat a sad lament.

Smoke rises from every chimney. The good villagers are baking large loaves of *Roggenbrot*, rye bread, and *Kaffee-Kuchen* topped with watermelon syrup, and buttery *Streusel*. Some are roasting suckling pigs, calves and lambs, ducks and geese, and boiling plump hens in iron caldrons to make noodle soup and *Butter-Knopfe*, dumplings.

The *Hausfrauen* are also dressing out a flock of geese for the Gypsy fiddlers who will play the *Hochzeit Tanz*. These *Zigeuner* bands roam the great steppes, begging or stealing their food. We are wary of these dark and mystic nomads, but they play beautiful music!

3

Some villagers are decorating the church, while still others prepare a smooth place for the dance to be held under the stars.

Poor Nathalia! Never have I seen such an unhappy bride. I cannot bear to look on her face. I look toward the village and see a young man coming out to meet us. It is Karl Heimer, Nathalia's husband-to-be!

I see the radiant light in his face as he comes near her, and I am surprised. He is not bashful, I think, as he is in the village. Quickly he spies the great tears in her eyes and pain wings across his own. He draws near in awe, and with gentle hands he smooths back her golden hair and dries the tears from her cheeks with the back of his hand.

"*Ach, Liebchen*," he says, "it is not good for a maiden to weep on the eve of her wedding." His voice is soft.

Hot shame comes over me at his tender way with her. But Nathalia is not crying now. Her hand in mine no longer trembles. I cannot hold it when it slips away. All at once I know it is true: I walk alone, a separate path. Nathalia has a husband at her side.

I quicken my steps, and it is as if I am both sad and glad. I look at the flowers I hold, and suddenly they look different — so fresh, as though they were still clinging to the mother-root in the cool, black soil.

This night I lie in bed and think about the wedding that will be tomorrow. The thought does not seem so harsh as before. Not every girl is fortunate enough to get a man so close to her own age. Some girls get widowers with many children.

There is still a feeling of wonder in me as I sit in church. Women are crying, wiping their tears on sleeves and skirt hems. But I do not cry. I look closely at Nathalia and see a strange stillness on her beautiful face, and in my own eyes the tears will not come. I can only see a happy ending to something that yesterday looked bitter and cold.

I bow my head in prayer. "Dear God, make all marriages like this one." But a shudder comes over me as I think of my own future. One evening the *Freiers* will come to my father's house to bargain for my hand in marriage. Then, it will be all over for me. Here in church I sit and realize I do not know the way. Blind and frightened I walk the road of life. My stepmother tells me nothing.

I do not sing with the crowd as we wend our way through the streets to the wedding feast. My heart is empty. The rich food does not taste good to me. People swarm around me, eating with their hands from large platters which the women carry through the

4

crowd. The people joke and shout and sing. But I cannot do any of these things.

A man in his coarse way calls to me and slaps me on the back. "Do not be so sad, little filly. Perhaps you will be the bride, next time." He winks at a brash fellow, and this one doubles up at the joke.

"*Ach, net!* Oh, no!" I say, "I will not marry." My voice is hard, for I do not like the insinuating smiles. I try to get away. But Karlotta Dahmer, who is dark and handsome, laughs.

"*Na*, what do you think of our Evaliz?" she asks in a high and lilting voice. "A lamb she is, and suddenly she roars!" The villagers laugh, and Karlotta who knows her power turns smartly and walks away. She has hurt me and she knows it. I cover my eyes in shame. An old woman puts her arms around me to speak comfort.

"They are full of wine," she says lightly, "See how their tongues wag loose on both ends."

Though I should honor her by showing gratitude, I can say nothing. It is as if a stone weighs heavy in my throat.

"*Ach, Kindchen*, grieving the heart does not make for happiness." She presses me tight to her bosom and makes me a promise. "*Liebchen, glaube nur, die Zeit bringt Rosen.* Better that you go now and sing."

Yet her arms are hard around me, and for the first time I feel a measure of strength. So solid and strong this woman of *Russland* stands, she has strength enough for me, also. I feel it come over me. It seems at last my feet are planted with sureness beside these strong women, walking the steep ways of life, so gallant and brave.

The woman's words come back to me. "*Liebchen, die Zeit bringt Rosen!*" Can it really be true? Will time bring me roses?

In the evening, people young and old come crowding out of the houses for the wedding dance. I am with the young. All are loud and happy. The girls smile at the boys and turn up their noses in laughter. The girls get many dances. But Karlotta gets more than any, her full, bright skirts swirling about her dancing feet. Karlotta, so proud and bold! I do not like her handsome eyes, her shimmering black hair, nor her sharp tongue. She is a hellion. I keep away from her, and from those who crowd around her, so that I am not taken for one of them.

Yet for all my shyness one young man then another comes to dance with me. But I do not like their arms so tight around me, nor their eyes looking deep into mine. Such a strange light fills their eyes. I do not know what they think, but it can't be anything good. I dance no more. Instead I sit near the Gypsy fiddlers who play lively music for the *Hochzeit*.

Never have I seen a Gypsy as dark as the oldest man. He is like a grave digger risen from the black, somber earth. But the young Gypsy is handsome and straight and tall. He smiles as he plays the jaunty tunes, his black eyes flashing. *Ach*, such a big man! Never, even among the Russians, have I seen such a tall man, so handsome and standing so straight. His earrings shine like hammered copper swaying in the sun. But there is no sun — only stars and the moon in the sky and the lantern under the eaves of the house. Strange people, these Gypsies! Even their metals glow with brightness when there is no sun!

I see him watching me, searching my face, caressing me with his handsome eyes, eyes like no others I have ever seen. For a moment I lose myself in their dark wonder. Suddenly, a fire runs through me. I look away, but I am forced to look back. I tremble, because his eyes will not leave me. He speaks words I do not understand, soft as the tune he plays. Then, slowly, he says them again. He bends so close, I feel the tantalizing warmth of him on my face, in my veins.

"*Shukar Balan.*"

And I know that he says, "White Lamb."

*Ach!* Never will I forget the brightness of his teeth when he smiles and says these words. My heart pounds inside me. My breath is a bird held captive in my throat, struggling to be free. I fear that the young Gypsy, thinking only of me, will forget what he is playing. But he does not. His winged fingers dance and the bow skips lightly over the strings. The sweet, tender tones he makes caress me.

All at once I am afraid. I want to run from him. Still, I cannot. It is as if he holds me with arms of bronze.

Like a *Sperling's* wings the music soars! It speaks that life for me shall be different! It speaks of a strange world where a woman can make of herself something other than an ox of the field — an ox with empty eyes who works from sun to sun without feeling or pride or spirit. All of a sudden I know I will not always be like this. I will make something of myself. Nothing shall crush my spirit. This I am sure of this very night!

I make a vow as I hear the soft music and strange words this dark nomad speaks. But Karlotta, with her high hair-do and pouting lips, swishes her way to my side. Hands resting on hips, she smiles dourly. I can see she is insanely jealous of me. But before she speaks there is discontent in the young Gypsy's eyes, and his music is at once burning and wild. This is strange. To think that I, Evaliz Haffner, am making Karlotta jealous.

She shouts, "So! A black *Zigeuner* yet, steals her away from her father, even before she is dry behind the ears. *Pfui!* Shame!" The people laugh. But there is a gleam of black fire in the Gypsy's eyes.

I say nothing to Karlotta. Neither can I look at her, for my face burns with shame and tears well in my eyes. Still Karlotta carries on.

"Maybe he says he would like to eat you, Evaliz," she smirks and pokes her finger roughly against the braids across the top of my head. "Maybe he thinks, golden sausages they are, so plump and sleek. *Ja*, good they should be with the apples in your cheeks!" Her laugh is shrill and loud.

I see the strange fire in the Gypsy's eyes as he draws himself up, all his beauty gone from him. The music he plays rises and falls like waves dashing against a cliff. I think he is displeased with Karlotta pressing so close to me. But when I look again I know he does not even see me. His eyes are not of this place, this little peasant village of *Russland*. His eyes speak of a cruel world, of its fierce joy and its depths of despair. They say how the taste of life is both sharp and bitter-sweet.

It is as if the Gypsy has two souls — a bright soul and a dark one, a golden soul and a black one. His music is fiery as the sun and tender as the moon.

When he is finished, the people stop their mad dancing. They throw clinking coins at his feet, shouting and clapping their hands.

"Come, Evaliz," my brother Friederich says, taking me by the arm. "Come, this is enough! Father will be furious when he hears."

I smile and follow. Little does Friederich know that I am, even now, walking to a life that will be different.

Although the night is nearly gone, I have not slept. I lie awake and wonder what life holds for me. It is a great puzzle.

At breakfast my father looks at me and says, "My, so red the cheeks, so bright the eyes, for a little girl who tosses and talks in her sleep all night."

"I did not even sleep!" I say, surprised, my face getting hot.

My father laughs and winks at my older brothers, Wilhelm and Friederich. They smile and I'm afraid of what it is they heard me say.

"*Ja*, Father," Friederich says, "a Gypsy yet makes eyes at her. Big eyes! Better that she stays home and not be stolen."

"*Ach, net.* Oh, no," I say. I cover my blushing face.

But Otto, my younger brother, who is twelve, has the devil in his eyes and a foolish smirk on his face. Before long he will tell it to the village youth. Then I will be ashamed to walk on the streets.

It is different though with Friederich; he is so kind. He leans away from the table and pulls me onto his lap. He tweaks my cheek and smiles. "With cheeks like these, she will get the best man in all *Russland!*" he says and adds with a big voice, "Know ye, that even Gypsies stand still when they see such beauty." Friederich laughs and pushes me off his lap.

My stepmother, a slight, greying woman, her hands folded for prayer, looks at Friederich and smiles. She is a good woman. A widow, with two young children, she took on a large family to raise, when she married my father.

These two, Lydia, eight now, and Jakor, six, sit at the table, heads bowed, too shy to look up. My three older sisters, Katrinliz, Marik and Malia are not at home. They are working in the homes of the rich. But Otto smiles foolishly. My father commands him to wipe the grin from his face and bow his head.

Father opens the Bible, and as he reads there is no other sound throughout the house. When the text is finished we join in the Lord's Prayer.

"Our Father which art in heaven, Hallowed be thy name . . . "

Silently my father closes the book and nods that we should eat. And though I dunk my bread in the sour cream and eat it, my thoughts go to the strange picture world in the Bible: to Abraham, binding his son Isaac, to burn him as a sacrifice to God; to Joseph, thrown into a pit, and later sold to the Ishmaelites by his brothers; to David, whom King Saul sought to kill. There are pictures of palms and doves, of Jesus walking on a stormy sea, of Him feeding the five thousand with but five loaves and two fishes; in one picture Jesus hangs nailed to a cross, while lightning rends earth and sky. *Ach*, great was the pain He bore for our sin.

I sit and listen to the clatter of wooden spoons striking against wooden bowls, as busy hands lift *Gerstenbrei*, barley-meal, to eager mouths. My father speaks.

"Today, Otto, you help Evaliz carry water to the garden,"

By "garden" father means the huge meadow near the dam, where villagers have their individual garden plots. There women and young maidens, wearing full-skirted dresses, with white scarfs on their heads, hoe the rows clean while children carry water in wooden buckets on shoulder-yokes from the dam. It is hard work. The sun is hot and merciless. Yet, day after day, we go from sunrise to sunset. And I like it best when the water splashes cool on my tired and aching feet.

In the evening there is more work bringing in straw for the great cook-oven, built in the wall of the bake-house where we eat. This is work for Otto and me. But tonight he will not help. He has a secret he won't tell until I do all the work.

"I have heard it in the gardens today," he raves. "All the women are talking of this strange thing."

"I heard nothing strange," I say, "only how sick *Grossvater* Fritzler is and how Georg's Marie-liz got another baby so that they now have twenty people in their house."

Otto kicks the soft dirt with his bare foot and says, "When the straw is in, I will tell you. Even if I don't believe it myself."

What can it be? I hurry with the great baskets of straw. I press the straw in hard with my feet, so that I do not have to make too many trips. The loads hurt my shoulder where the yoke has rubbed all day. But I fill the huge box in the kitchen corner and wait for my reward.

Otto does not make me wait. Already he has been kept from play too long.

"Frau Tittle, who lives five barnyards up the street, has a letter from her brother in a land, America, across the sea. But, I have seen the thing and I have too much sense to believe a flimsy paper could have traveled so far without mishap."

"You say America?" I ask Otto, not believing also. "You have seen this letter?"

"*Ja*, sure! I have seen it. Do you think I'd tell a lie?" he says, and I know he speaks the truth.

This night I have no appetite. I barely touch the cabbage soup and chunks of rye bread, sprinkled with salt, which my stepmother has placed on the table. I cannot even sleep. I lie awake all night thinking about America. It lies across a sea, and I have not even seen a sea. It must be very far. I must see this letter, I tell myself all night.

In the morning I do all the housework, even before my stepmother comes in from the bake-house. I sprinkle damp sand onto the dirt floor to keep the dust from rising. The light brown earth is hard and smooth from many scrubbings.

I also make the beds here in the main house. It is a two-room building, with a partial dividing wall about six feet high, which is really a wall oven, on whose broad top the children sleep. In some homes the broad adobe wall serves as the bed of newlyweds, who prefer privacy. A curtain can be rigged up around it.

I use the long handle of the broom to smooth out the beds, for they are large and piled high with feather-ticks. The pillows too are plump, and square, so that one can sleep sitting up in bed. But we do not have enough beds; we have only three, and when all the family is at home, four must sleep together in each bed.

"My, how industrious you are this morning, Evaliz," my stepmother says, when at last she is settled down to her knitting. I think now is the time to ask her if I can go to Frau Tittle's house to see the letter, but I do not know how to begin.

"Always, you are a good girl," she goes on, "not like your sisters who sass me." In and out go her knitting needles, in and out. And here I stand like a *stumm Ochs*, whiling away my opportunity. The minutes go by. If I don't speak now, she will give me an errand.

"*Mutter*," I begin. "Frau Tittle has the twins and the other one is still so young, perhaps I can help her with her morning work. Besides she has a letter from a far land." My face is hot from saying all these words and my knees quake.

My stepmother is quick to answer.

"*Ja*, Evaliz, always fussing they are. Maybe, better you go," she says, smiling, for she knows my scheming. "Frau Tittle will show you the letter gladly. So proud she is with it."

I can go! *Ach*, my breath leaves me. I want to touch my stepmother with loving hands because she is so good, almost as good as my own mother was, but embarrassment holds me back.

Still I do not rush out of the house. I linger awhile, thinking I should do something else for my stepmother. So I go with her out into the bake-house where she kneads down the bread dough, getting ready for the noon-day meal.

When I get to Frau Tittle's house she is only starting her morning work. She is not fast like we are in our house. So I clean her house also.

"My bread comes first, Evaliz, before house or child," she says, her uncombed hair stringing down her face. "See how nice it raises. Soft as a cloud!" Gently she presses her finger down on it and as soon as she lets go it comes right up again. Frau Tittle forgets that we too bake good bread, and without any special fuss.

When I am through cleaning up after the little ones, I make her beds also. Then I ask to see the letter. She brings it quickly from a wooden trunk. And I am like Otto. I cannot believe it has come so far. But Frau Tittle believes. I see the proud look on her face, then I see the tears.

As I hold the slight packet I study the postage. There are three stamps. Each has a picture of the same man. The man has snowy white hair, a round face, and eyes that are far too young for so white a head. Surely, this is a man of another world.

"Will you go to this new land, Frau Tittle?" I ask.

10

Frau Tittle's voice is overly loud when she speaks. "*Ach, nein, mein Kind!* For me it is to stay in *Russland.* My parents have lived and died here. I, too, shall live and die here. This is my home, Evaliz. Our home! Yours and mine and our children's children."

"No!" I say hard. "I will go to this new land. I will not die here."

"*Ach,* Child," she chides. "How foolish you talk. The people will stay. *Ja,* always they will stay. The land binds them."

When I start home, Frau Tittle hands me a large piece of freshly baked *Kaffee-Kuchen.* "For you, Evaliz," she says. "Eat it before you get home, so that you do not share it with the children as always."

"*Ach,* sure, I'll eat," I say. But when I step out of her gate I decide I will not go home yet. I do not eat the bread as I promised. Instead I fold it inside my apron and tuck the ends over my waist band.

I walk straight through the village, out past the dam, past the gardens and out over the wild steppe. I do not bother to look back. Without looking I can see each straw-covered roof and remember how in winters past they have been uncovered, so that the cattle should live, regardless of how much the household had to suffer. The snows in Russia are devastating and the bitter cold months are long.

There are the dooryards with their high willow fences, the stables, hen houses and pig sties all built adjoining each other, under one common roof. The farm people in Russia live in villages, as did their forefathers — a protection against various marauding tribes who resented the white people's intrusion on their age-old grazing ground.

I do not look back, only ahead. All that is back there, I already know. But ahead, I do not know. I walk over one hillock and yet another. I want to know what it is in this land that holds the people, like Frau Tittle says.

The land lies before me in endless waves. It is rich with wild growth, and the winds blow free. Never once am I afraid that a band of Cossacks will come and steal me if I do not go back. There is a dreadful song Karlotta sings about Cossacks who abduct unprotected maidens, but I refuse to think about it.

I hold up the hem of my skirts and climb the swell of the land. Suddenly I stop. I hear bells. They ring soft and faint in the wind. I hurry to the top of the rise and look down into a meadow. I see the blind village cowherd grazing the cattle and sheep homeward. Some of the animals stop eating to look at me. The sheep that are far out from the herd come in close, looking frightened, because of my wide, billowing skirts.

I hurry down and the herd's shaggy dog comes to greet me, wagging his tail. When I come close, Yasha, the herder, knows my voice and asks what brings me.

I look upon the bedraggled youth, barefoot, his cossack blouse open at the throat . . . a forlorn youth, my own age. I see his gentle face, his unseeing eyes — no, they are not unseeing; they are all-seeing.

Suddenly a great compassion comes over me. "This is what brings me, Yasha," I say, remembering I have kept the fresh bread.

I let down my apron and break the delicately crusted piece in two. The sight of it tempts me, for I've had no noon meal. But I see that the reed basket tied to Yasha's sash swings empty. He shares what little he has with his faithful dog. Already the dog is watching me, half-expecting the dainty morsel any moment, drooling and licking his mouth, sitting down and getting up again in nervous succession. In my heart I know I cannot deny his wish.

"Half for you, Yasha. Half for your dog," I say, and give the bread. The dog bolts his portion and looks for more. But Yasha takes his with a slight bow. I see the hungry quiver in his fingers as he holds the bread. He has hunger, but before he eats he asks me again what has brought me.

"Today I seek something in this land that I do not find," I say to him.

Yasha is quick to answer. He knows the restlessness that plagues the young. "Have you looked in your heart, Evaliz?" he asks, his voice full of understanding.

Always I have liked Yasha, but until now I did not know how much. Surely he is wiser in his blindness than many another man who walks by sight and has the world at his feet. He speaks the truth! Have you looked in your heart?

*Ach*, such tenderness comes over me as I look upon this gentle lad. Life holds nothing for him. No promise. Nothing save darkness and endless obstacles to hinder him.

"You are right, Yasha. I am foolish to think only of myself."

Suddenly my soul goes out to him. Here is a man I would consent to marry, should he ask me. I would be willing to lead him through life and never recall the tears of the heart again.

Then I look on his calm face and see that he does not need me. Already God has shown him the way, with the light of understanding. He is content with his assignment as village cowherd.

Through Yasha's wisdom I begin to see what it is that holds the people to this fertile land. It is true. I, too, am of this soil. My yoke is linked to it. I feel its restless will with the growing under my feet, and sense its vitality in the lilting winds that billow my full skirts about me.

I stand and gaze out over the land and recognize it confidently laughing in the sun and I understand something of the power that holds these plain people in awe of its golden promise. They will not leave. They will await the promise. And though they may bend before its icy blast, they will never break.

As the sun dips to the rim of the land, Yasha commands his dog to start the herd homeward and we follow. Yasha is guided by instinct and by the ringing of cowbells.

As we near the village the cattle and sheep increase their speed, lowing and bleating, hurrying to the dam for a drink, as always. But why are there so many villagers at the dam? I wonder. Still others are rushing down the steep incline shouting to each other. Fear grips my heart.

"Someone has drowned," I shout to Yasha, "I'm going down to the dam."

I run as fast as I can to where a group of people are gathered. As I draw near the people look at me in disbelief.

"*Herr Gott im Himmel*, it is Evaliz!" a woman shouts. The shout mounts as it is passed from one to the other. Hands go up in stark relief. All eyes turn to me.

My father hurries up and lays his trembling hand on me. My stepmother falls about my neck and weeps aloud. But of them all, Otto cries the hardest. "They said you came this way to the dam, Evaliz, and no one saw you come back," he says, his teeth chattering as though he has a chill. "We have looked for you a long time. Friederich and Wilhelm are out in a boat with grappling hooks."

"*Ach*, Otto, make no more tears," I say tenderly, wiping his wet cheeks with my apron. "See, here I am, not dead in the water."

But Otto weeps all the harder. Then he runs to call the good news to my brothers. They too are torn by emotion, so that I cannot bear to see the sorrow and joy without weeping myself.

It is not for me to die yet, I say to myself. There is so much in this life I must still do!

# CHAPTER 2

# *The Shadow*

My stepmother and my three sisters are busy making featherbeds for my sisters' dowries. Soon they will be getting married. First Katrinliz with dark laughing eyes, next Marik who brooks no nonsense, then Malia, fair, long limbed, and swift as a gazelle. I think a man will have it hard to keep up with her.

My sisters are not pleased with having a stepmother in the house; they do not care how soon they marry.

During the winter months they hire out to the rich estates. They do housework, but also, when the need arises they must help the men servants haul manure from the large stables. For this menial labor they receive six kopeks per load. All the monies go to my father to be used for the common cause, and rightly so. Times are hard and taxes are high.

It takes much to keep a large family going, to say nothing of the livestock. Without my three grown sisters there are eight at table. They are my father and stepmother; her two young children, Lydia and Jakor, by a previous marriage; my older brothers, Wilhelm and Friederich; Otto and I.

The rich people for whom my sisters work have many servants and it is no disgrace for a girl to work in the stable. In fact, the young people, both boys and girls, vie for the work. They have a lark singing and shouting and racing their teams, seeing who can haul the most. There is much nonsense, too. Many a maiden standing on the shaft, outside the cart, is forced to sit down in the muck as some brash young fellow races past and clouts her horse with a stick.

The manure is hauled outside the village and placed on a smooth plot of ground. Here it lies to rot in sun, wind, rain and snow. When it is thoroughly fermented it is spread out, mixed with straw and water, then smoothed out to dry in the sun. But before the mixture dries too hard, it is cut into blocks to be used as fuel in the great cooking ovens that are built in the dividing walls of houses. This is the common fuel for rich and poor alike. I have often helped my father make this kind of fuel for our own use. It has tremendous heat and the coals are long lasting.

I do not mind that my sisters leave me to do this menial task at home, without pay, for they bring me the cast-off clothing from their mistress' growing girls. So pretty and bright-colored the dresses are, with fancy needlework and ruffles.

I can hardly wait until the supper dishes are done, when I have a few minutes before the evening work of weaving and knitting begins, to try on these clothes. I smooth them down over my body with loving hands. I think no one is taking notice, but Otto, peeking into the room, says something smart and runs before I can grab him by the arm and shush him up. I do not want my older brothers and my father to hear his foolish remark.

What he says is true. Already I am formed like a woman. Soon, I too will be old enough to marry.

"*Ach, net.* Oh, no." A sickness fills me. I will not think of it. I go quickly to my private corner to change into my old dress that is loose and ill-fitting. After this I think twice before I put on these dresses again.

I will not marry so young and spoil all my chances, I tell myself. I will not live in a household where there are perhaps four or more bosses. It happens. In some homes the *Grossmutter* still lives. She is head supreme over women and children. Next in line is the mother-in-law, then may follow two or three daughters-in-law, each lording it over the other. All live under one roof, as one family, regardless of number, and one must wash clothes, weave, and do field work as dictated often 'till one's fingers are worn to the bone.

"No," I say, and I say it again. "No, I will not marry before I see the outside world."

My sisters are satisfied. They marry into large families. They do not mind the back-breaking work of washing clothes down on the dam in summer and winter. Neither do they mind the field work, sick or well. And soon their families will be bigger. Babies are born close together.

The people are overjoyed when it is a boy-child, for then another *dessjatin** is added to their fields. There is little praise for a girl-child if the man of the house prefers land to a daughter. Then the mother must hang her head, treasuring the joy only in her heart.

Months have gone by since Nathalia's wedding. My eldest brother Wilhelm also has married and has brought Anna, his bride, home to live with us. It is fortunate for them that our three sisters married beforehand, so that they have a bridal bed, though it is in the same room, behind a drawn curtain. They are luckier than most couples. Some have to put their featherbed on the floor, or on the wide shelf above the wall oven overlooking both rooms, the sleeping room on one side, the eating and weaving room on the other. The people who have a bake-house take their meals there, at least in the summer months. In the winter the bake-house can be reached only by tunneling under perhaps twelve to sixteen feet of snow.

With more marriageable sons in the house, our family is destined to grow. And if they should have sons our fields will grow also.

The Fausts who live four door-yards down the street have twenty-eight souls, counting both young and old. Their fields are great and far away from the village. *Grosser* Hans we call him, because he is also a man of great build. But he was not good to his wife who, during the last harvest, bore him a girl-child. He is not kind like my father or my brothers; he has the black heart of a demon.

I still get chills when I recall how that gentle woman gave birth to her baby. The story is all over the village that even on the last day when she should have been home preparing her sick bed, Hans made her work with him in the field. Awkward and heavy she gathered the grain behind him and tied it into bundles while he cut the length of the field again and again. Toward the last her pain was great. Her face, dripping wet, was streaked with dirt.

"Hans," she pleaded, "my time has come. The pain is unbearable."

*Dessjatin* — a Russian measure of land, approximately 2.7 acres.

But Hans, the story goes, only grunted. He hardly looked her way and worked faster than before. When she lagged behind, he called over his shoulder, "*Na, Donner Wetter*, can you think of nothing but your pains. Work! When we are through you can rest."

When, at last, they came back to the place where their wagon stood she is supposed to have said: "Hans. *In Gottes Namen!* It is time. Take me home." Those who witnessed it said her voice was shrill with fright and there was the sweat of agony on her face.

Hans was enraged, they say. He strode to the wagon and hitched up the horses, while she climbed in. But before he was ready the baby was being born. It was a girl-child. A girl had no value for him, when in his mind's eye he had already added another *dessjatin* to his fields.

"*Na, Kissel Feuer!*" he swore.

Then, as they tell it, big Hans stood in the lumbering wagon where the shrieking woman lay. He swung the loose reins upon the unsuspecting horses' rumps, shouting fiendishly. The startled horses leaped forward, running wildly over the clump-grass steppe. But instead of taking the nearest road into the village, Hans circled to the north and came down the main street, lashing the horses and shouting, "Veal for sale! Veal for sale!"

This is the part I saw myself. Those of us who had remained in the village that day were shocked at the vicious disregard for the woman giving birth to a child. We all ran from our door-yards and followed down the street. Lamenting mothers for once left their crying children behind. Dogs barked. Youngsters of all ages came running from everywhere.

Big Hans stopped the horses at his gate. His wife, her skirts horribly soiled with blood, climbed out over the wheel of the wagon and walked into her house, holding her wailing baby in her arms. The child's life had not yet been cut from hers!

The ugliness of the event made me sick all over. Oh, God! Let nothing like this ever happen to me. Never will I marry such a cruel man. Never!

It is the beginning of another summer. I have forgotten about the Gypsy, but I do not stop dreaming.

There are strange tales underfoot, tales of emigration to America. True, our people have been leaving Russia since 1876 when Czar Alexander II revoked the century-old promise of freedom from military conscription. But that *ukase* was expected and many people have willingly given their young men to serve in the armed forces. Their new fear is that their judicial rights will now be revoked also. The village talk is that more and more people are leaving Russia to make lives for themselves elsewhere.

"*Ja*," say the emissaries returning from North and South America, "The climate is good for agriculture. Land and work is plentiful! Rail beds are being laid everywhere."

Not only are emissaries exciting the people, but foreign representatives arriving in larger villages are actually encouraging people to go, promising to help them make all arrangements for safe transportation once they get outside the Russian border.

And I know of people myself, who are packing up to go. Like the Mennonites from South Russia before them, they take with them Turkey Red seed-wheat to plant into American soil. The report is that this wheat produces abundantly, but millers of flour are complaining that the hard kernels are breaking their mills. Still, in the long run, it is the wheat that does not yield to black rust, a disease capable of laying waste entire fields.

Nights, when visitors come to our house, I sit and listen as they talk about this land of milk and honey, like in the Bible. And inside of me, I am bursting with joy. "I'll go. I'll go." My heart pulses the words through my being. "I'll go. I'll go." My knitting needles click, as I fashion a woolen sock. Still, I tell no one for fear they will ask laughingly:

"How will you go? Swim?"

But how can they know what hope is in my heart? I will not always be of this land, *Russland*. My life shall be different.

In the morning I sing as I carry buckets of water from the dam. The shoulder yoke weighs heavily and my legs must strain on the upgrade, but I fill the caldron in the bake-house even before my stepmother asks me. There are only two wells in our village. They belong to two rich land-owners. Other people must get their water from the dam. It is fortunate for us that the dam is large, with a separate cove where the cattle may wade and take a drink, and an out-of-the-way place where women do the family wash, scrubbing the clothes with strong straw ash, then trampling them with bare feet on wooden planks. After this the clothes are boiled in caldrons, rinsed, and spread out on the grass to dry. Here, at our dam, pocketed between two grassy draws which gather the winter snows and summer rains, the villagers also come to bathe or to watch sail boats ride the waves.

I skip as I bring in the straw to feed the fire in the bake-house where we take our summer meals. The small adobe structure stands only a few yards away from the main house, and oftentimes in the winter we go back and forth through a snow tunnel. In any case, the straw box is always empty.

"*Schnell! Mach's schnell!* Go, quickly, Evaliz," my stepmother calls. "The bread must bake."

For baking bread, we prefer a straw fire to that of the dried-out manure blocks. The fire must be fed several hours. I must twist more and more straw to produce the right heat. When the temperature seems to be exactly right, I quickly pull out all the ash and embers and wipe the inside clean. Next I sprinkle crushed wheat in the bottom and carefully place the delicate loaves in to bake. Our oven holds twelve very large, round loaves at one baking. It takes much bread to feed our *Familie.*

I have no more than taken the brown loaves from the oven when Otto comes in from play. He snatches a crust of hot bread. "Ah-ha," he says, and dares me to take it from him. "Today I heard something about you." His voice is filled with taunts and there is a gleam of the devil in his eyes. "But it is far from me to tell you, Evaliz," he laughs.

I cannot bribe Otto. Already he has a larger piece of bread than he should have. Our stepmother would be furious, I know. She is good to us children, but she has no room for foolishness. I look up and there she stands in the doorway.

"What is this, Evaliz?" she asks sternly, looking at Otto's hand.

"He says he hears something about me out on the street." There is a shakiness in my voice and I think I cannot tell her that Otto stole the crust. Neither can I tell her that I gave it to him. *Ach,* never have I lied to this woman.

But she does not compel me to lie. She only says, "So then, he can tell his father at supper." She urges me to hurry.

The meal is a sad one. My father asks the blessing and for once I think it will never end. What is it Otto knows? My heart pounds inside my still body until I think everyone will hear. Far better that I lie to my stepmother, I think, than that they should all laugh at me at the table. My brothers, Friederich and Wilhelm, are so good natured, but also so teasing.

When the blessing is finished and we have all begun eating, my stepmother speaks to my father. "Otto knows something concerning Evaliz that is being talked about on the street."

"What talk is this?" My father's voice is severe as he turns to Otto. His eyes are stern. "*Na,* speak up, lad!"

The smartness drains from Otto's face immediately. The gossip he knows must come to light. "That awful blacksmith, Fritz Geist, will marry our Evaliz."

"What?" My breath catches in my throat and nearly chokes me.

Friederich's fingers twitch so violently, he spills tea all over his plate. Wilhelm and the others jerk to attention.

"Who says this?" my father thunders.

Otto is afraid to speak. His eyes stare at the bowl in front of him. Finally he finds his tongue.

"Herr Lunden and Herr Rohr say it. They have been drinking *Schnaps* at the blacksmith all day and shouting to everyone that they will come to our house tonight to ask for Evaliz's hand."

"*Ach, Gott,* no!" my heart stops cold. These are the same two fools who fixed Nathalia's wedding, and my father knows them well.

No one can eat, nor can anyone speak. My brother Friederich puts his hands on the table and clenches them tight. Through my tears I see his strong, brown fists swell before my eyes. With such fists, hard as stone, he could kill a man. Then the round tears fall from my eyes and I see his knotted hands grow again, bigger than before. The thought comes to me that perhaps Friederich can save me from this brutal man, Fritz Geist. But what can Friederich do? It is my father's word that counts.

Long after the supper hour, when it is night, we are all gathered in the room busy with our evening tasks. My father is sitting at his work bench braiding newly tanned leather, which he has first rubbed with *Pech*, cobbler's wax. Friederich is busy mending boots. My older brother Wilhelm is stationed at the weaving loom. Otto is fashioning a wooden shuttle with his knife. My stepmother is knitting, the same as I am. The rest are here, too.

Then, all of a sudden, there comes a loud clatter at the door. They have come!

"Let us in, Herr Haffner!" The door strains at the hinges. "We have come for your daughter's hand in marriage." Their voices are thick with drunkenness.

My father opens the door. His hand outstretched, he bids them enter. And as always the good host, he seats them in the lamplight.

From my out-of-the-way place I dare to look at their moist red lips, set in heavily bearded faces. In turn I see their glistening eyes penetrating my dark corner, as though trying to draw me out into revealing light. *Ach,* the sight of them makes my stomach retch.

Herr Rohr is too drunk to talk, but Herr Lunden runs glib words off his tongue as always. He can make the rottenest man sound good without any effort. Fritz, the blacksmith, did not come with them. But Herr Lunden does not need him. He can get brides easily for men who cannot speak for themselves, as well as for those who speak too well. He doesn't even need Herr Rohr who sits on the bench half asleep, drooling in his beard. His long arms hang down, the hairy fingers curled inward, looking like *semljanken** spiders.

*Semljanken* — earthen dens used as living quarters, oftentimes infested by spiders and tarantulas.

21

Lunden tips the stone jug he has brought and pours the Russian liquor down his throat. It makes him shudder but he smacks his lips and beams. "*Ja*, my friend," he says nodding at my father. "Fritz has the strong back. The iron arms! A good husband he will make for your Evaliz."

At his words my throat locks tight with terrible pain and my eyes dim with tears so that I cannot see the stocking I am knitting. And even though I can perform the stitch without looking, my fingers tremble so that I cannot go on. I sit thinking bitter thoughts: a woman's life is nothing without love. Her lot then becomes worse than an animal's whose sole function is to bear the fruit of its kind.

My father doesn't drink. Lunden cannot make him believe there is none better than Fritz for a husband. "Alex Lunden, make done with the talk!" my father says, sternly. "A girl with rosy cheeks like my Evaliz does not marry that big blacksmith."

But Lunden does not take no for an answer. He laughs in his drunken swagger, hooking his thumbs in the red cossack belt around his fat middle.

"Seventeen, she is! Old enough for the braids on top of her head, and the strong back for hard work. Think it over, Haffner."

Herr Lunden's calculating eyes see how I stiffen my shoulders, and he smiles at the prospect of the blacksmith's taming me. "Haw!" he snorts, throwing back his head to show moist, fat lips under the shaggy roof of a stained moustache. "Like Big Hans cowers his woman into a dutiful wife, so will Fritz —"

At this, my father holds up his hand and demands fiercely that he stop such talk.

Terrified I think how my life with Fritz Geist would be a hell on earth like Big Hans' woman's is. *Ach!* When I recall how that gentle woman bore her child, a blinding pain comes over me so that I throw my hands over my eyes.

"Oh, God!" I breathe. "Help me, let not my life come to this. Never. Never!"

Great and startling tears come into Otto's eyes, and Lydia, my little stepsister, starts crying out loud.

"*Ruhig, nur ruhig*," my stepmother soothes. She lays the grey woolen stocking she is knitting in her lap and draws the young girl to her.

Wilhelm who is taking his ire out on the weaving loom, suddenly stops and stares before him, like a mad man.

I have in mind to go outside, so that I do not hear this talk. But to do so I would have to walk in front of my father and his unworthy guests, and that I cannot do. It is raining outside, but even a soaking rain would be better than this.

Friederich, mending his boots by candlelight, jabs the sharp awl through the leather. He twists the instrument cruelly about and draws it out. Then with unsteady fingers he threads two waxed leather strips, one facing the other through the wide hole and pulls them tight. Too tight. One breaks and I hear him swear under his breath. Friederich is angry enough to kill. But this man is drunk.

Anna, Wilhelm's wife, lies across the bed, face down, and I think she is asleep through all this talk. But I see her body stiffen when Lunden says this about Fritz Geist, and I know she is not asleep.

"This has gone far enough!" my father thunders. His face is red with terrible anger, and he calls my stepmother to speak her piece.

She steps forward quickly, holding the door wide. "Herr Lunden," she says, firmly, "our Evaliz does not marry. Go now. Go! Do not come back until you are sane."

At her words, the two *Freiers* get to their feet, sputtering at the insult, and step out into the damp, black night.

There is a singing inside of me when they are gone. My stepmother is a good woman. She has saved me from a bad marriage and I love her very much.

# CHAPTER 3

## Wings of Hope

I think now that Wilhelm's wife Anna is with us I can go to
school to learn to read and write — to make something of
myself other than an ox of the field.

But for once, my father puts his foot down. "You are
too old for school. School is for children who are too young to
work." My father's voice is gentle, but firm. "Already you have
learned the Ten Commandments, the Bible verses and songs,
Evaliz. You are old enough for field work. I need you now that your
sisters are married and gone."

Scalding tears well in my eyes and I let them fall, and with their
falling all hope lies shattered at my feet.

"Your father is right," my stepmother says, shaking her head.
"No girl nearing the marriage age goes to school. For what man can
afford a wife who has not learned to work? Come, I will teach you to
sew a fine seam. You will know more than any girl in the village.
More than Karlotta, even."

"Karlotta, bah!" I say angrily, but I let my stepmother teach me
anyhow.

In and out goes my needle, but my mind is not on my work. It is
on the school that my *Vetter* Dietz, the *Bürgermeister*, has
provided. Preschin is a fortunate village to have a school since

25

teachers are not always easy to come by. School will be held in the church. I only wish I could attend! I am so busy daydreaming that I stick my finger, and my stepmother gets upset with me.

When next I see Karlotta she is all excited. "Evaliz, wait!" she calls as she runs out of her house and confronts me on the street. "Just think, he has arrived!"

"Who has arrived?" I ask, noting her black flashing eyes. It must be someone very special, I think, hating her a little for latching onto every newsy tidbit first.

"David Becker, the *Schulmeister*, our new teacher, you *Dummkopf*. Who else? *Ach, du lieber!*" She hugs her arms about herself and casts her eyes to the heavens. "You should see how tall and young and blond he is — a sergeant in the czar's army!"

Karlotta can hardly contain herself. Her words topple one over the other.

"My, how straight and fine he walks. Like this," she says, throwing back her shoulders until her young breasts stand out firm and sharp. "I'll bet few village girls can come up to his standard."

Karlotta stops babbling long enough to glance down her nose at me. The glance in brief says, "Evaliz is a nothing."

All of a sudden a crazy pain stirs in my heart. I have never been jealous, but all at once I do not like that Karlotta has set her cap for him.

I wish I could see this young man. He must be very special, I think, to be teaching both German and Russian, but I reconcile myself. If schooling is not for me, then, perhaps, someday I can give it to my children. Like me they shall never be. I swear it.

All the while I'm trying to think, Karlotta keeps up her excited chatter.

"I'm going to school, Evaliz," she announces. "My father may whip me and shout no, but it will not stop me. He may drag me to the fields, but I will run away."

Karlotta's laugh is high and taunting as she looks at me. With feet planted far apart and arms akimbo, she says "A *stoffle-Ochs*, like you, Evaliz, I will not be. I may even become the schoolmaster's wife, who knows."

Smart-like she draws herself up tall like a fine lady.

And now the pain that is in me is worse than before. I detest her flashing eyes, her loose talk. And all at once I have a will of my own. I will have him for myself!

On Sunday, when I go to church I see him. He is seated up front to be announced before the congregation.

Karlotta is right: he is handsome. Shy and with trembling I study his strong physique, his light hair, his blue eyes and his sun-tanned complexion. They go well with the straight, broad shoulders! His eyes roam over the congregation lightly. Then they meet mine; they flicker, stand still, and hold fast.

A warmness rushes over my face and burns fire in my cheeks. It races the blood hot in my veins, and I cast my eyes down. But I must look again. I am compelled by a power too strong to resist. *Ach*, such painful joy has never been mine!

A strangeness comes over me here in church where I should be listening to the sermon. I know I should be ashamed. But, for once, I am not ashamed. Instead, I vow that Karlotta shall not have him!

May God forgive me and grant me strength. I am so shy. I cannot speak for myself.

Almost a month has gone by and I have not seen the *Schulmeister* again. I am with my family camped at the edge of our harvest field, far away from the village. We are not alone. Other villagers are camped nearby. Here we live like Gypsies, eating and sleeping under the open sky, until the work is done. All our provisions are here, our milch cows and chickens. The chickens are housed under harrows set at an angle and covered over with quilts or tufts of grass.

On Sunday afternoons when Karlotta comes bustling into camp, along with others, she talks of nothing but the schoolmaster, and how close she is to him every day. She laughs and jeers at me, until I can feel nothing but hate for her. When she finally leaves, I get all clumsy and my mind is in a whirl.

My duty in the field is to lead the yoke of oxen while Wilhelm loads sheaves of wheat into the wagon. It is hard to walk all day and half into the night, barefoot, through cruelly sharp stubble. The uneven stems scratch my legs every step I take. Some even break the skin, causing trickles of blood, which draw the flies. Usually the flies will annoy only the livestock, but now they swarm about my legs stinging me, nearly driving me crazy.

*Ach*, I get so weary of it all! But what can I do? I cannot run away from the field, like Karlotta. For me it is to obey.

And because I am so upset, I stand too close to the lead ox. Obstinate as he is, he stamps his hoof down on my bare foot. I cry out in pain and pound him with my fists, but he will not move. I cry aloud with terrible pain, again and again, flailing him hard. And it is as nothing to him. Even my brother Wilhelm cannot make him move. Wilhelm shouts harsh words. He strikes the ox about the ears with the pitchfork handle. Finally he uses the prongs on the tough fore-shoulder so that the blood oozes out. Still the ox will not move his foot. The pain is so great that I can hardly bear it. Wilhelm must try something else.

"*Gee!Gee!*" Wilhelm commands. He grabs hold of the animal's tail and twists it again and again. Hard! Without mercy, he turns it into a knot, until I hear the tail bone crack.

When, at last, my foot is free, the pain is no better than before. So Wilhelm takes me home to the village. There Anna, Wilhelm's wife, who is great with child, puts my foot in warm salt water, then wraps it tight.

I feel shame that I have brought the injury on myself because now Anna must take my place in the fields. All are working, my stepmother, Otto, Lydia and Jakor. The last two should be in school, but they, too, are needed.

When I think of Lydia who is nine years old, I feel very badly. I recall how tired she looked whenever we met, gleaning the field. I can still see the perspiration streaking down her thin face. *Ach!* She is so sweet, so quiet, and her large, blue eyes are so quick to brim with tears. When I think of the plight of children in this land, I make a promise to myself: if ever I have children they will not work like this. But how can I be sure?

I am beginning to put weight on my foot. It is important that I walk again soon, for Anna's days are drawing near and she is still working in the field.

Now is the time the people over-exert themselves. When the moon is bright, they will even work all night. The reaping and threshing of grain must be done while the weather holds, and while they and their work animals can still ford the streams, for cold weather follows the harvest all too soon in this wide open land.

Then when the ice is thick and there is snow on the ground, the grain is hauled in from field granaries by wagon sleighs. It is then taken to the mill and ground into flour, or sold.

My hands are busy while my foot is healing. I knit woolen stockings for the entire family, against the time when Siberian winds will turn our land into ice and snow. Mountains of snow! But before that happens, Anna and Wilhelm's child will be born.

On a day when a rainy spell has driven the harvesters out of the field, back to the village, Otto comes running to me, shouting, "Evaliz, I have news. Nathalia, your friend, has a son!"

"*Ei*, it is good," I say, because now Nathalia can rest her fears, lest it be a girl. Having a son will add land to Karl's family holdings.

This, we hope, will also be the case in our family. For Anna's baby is due any day now.

Anna is tired and soaked with rain when she returns to the village. And in the morning when the family returns to the field again, she is left behind. Already, pains are running through her body. It is decided that I stay with her while our stepmother goes.

Once they are gone, I am sick with fright. I know nothing of childbirth, except hearing women scream. I am ashamed to look at Anna. And Anna seems uneasy to have a younger girl attend her. We hardly speak. I keep the water hot like my stepmother said, and wait. I wring my hands. Anna walks the floor.

Anna cannot go to bed. No woman goes to bed at a time like this. Bedding is too rare to be soiled with such a mess. She must kneel at a chair.

*Ach!* The pain must be terrible. Deep moans escape through tightly clamped teeth. She clenches her fists and presses her eyes shut, but still the tears stream down her face.

"*Gott im Himmel,* help us," I pray.

Again Anna walks the floor. She doubles up and stumbles along in terrible pain. Then she no longer holds back her cries.

I cannot stand it! I think I must go outside. But I cannot go outside. I must stay with Anna.

"She will die!" my heart cries inside of me. Then I am reminded of Big Hans' wife, how she bore her child in a jolting wagon, and I know that Anna will not die. But how can I be sure?

Anna kneels at the chair and screams, shrill as a slaughter animal, with the knife at its throat. Tears stream down my own cheeks and I renew my vow: never shall my life be like this!

Anna exerts pressure on the chair, so that the hard earth under it crumbles to bits. She clamps her arms around the back of the chair, and strains her body with iron strength. Still, nothing.

She screams, loudly, "Go, Evaliz. Get someone, or I'll die."

I turn to run, but before I can get to the door, the new-born babe drops to the earthen floor. It cries lustily and it is all speckled with sand. But to me it is beautiful. The terrible ordeal is over.

"*Gott sei Dank!* God be praised!" I say. I shout it. And, for once, my voice is free. I feel no more shame.

I lift the baby from the floor and do as Anna directs me. I cut the umbilical cord and tie the knot. Then I wash the baby clean and wrap it tight inside a cloth, to make it feel secure.

Too bad it's a girl, I say to myself. A son would have warranted the household a *dessjatin* of land. What will my father say when he comes home? Will Wilhelm sulk and be angry? I glance at Anna cleaning herself up and I feel sorry for her.

The day the family returns from the field, Anna is out in the yard standing over the caldron boiling clothes. Her eyes momentarily sweep over Wilhelm, but it is my father she hurries to. She holds out her hand and he enfolds it with both of his. "No son, for you, Father Haffner," she says, her eyes brimming with tears.

From where I am, sweeping the dooryard, I look at my father all grizzled and dust-stained from a week of field labor and wonder what his reply will be. It could be harsh, since his shoulders droop with weariness. But when my father speaks, his voice is all kindness.

"*Ach*, Anna, Anna, wipe the tears," he says. "Am I a werewolf that you should be afraid of me? Daughters we must have also. They will mother a thousand sons yet to come."

Truly, my father is a man of wisdom. There is peace in our house. And there is joy in my heart because Wilhelm has made me a promise.

"For all this, Evaliz, you shall see a city," he says, happily holding out his little finger for the baby to clasp onto. "The next time I go to the great market place, I will take you with me."

I can hardly believe it. I, Evaliz, who have not been anywhere, will see a city! It does not matter that I have to wait for winter. "I must tell Karlotta," I fairly shout, running out of the house and out the gate.

"Do not disturb the class," Wilhelm shouts after me, but I keep right on going. I can't wait to see Karlotta's face, when I tell her. She will die of envy.

I hurry down the rutted street toward the church where David Becker, the schoolmaster, teaches school. When I get there the class is in session. I hear the soft murmuring of voices through the open window. The lesson goes on and on, and presently I think I cannot wait any longer.

I stretch my height and peer over the window ledge. I see the schoolmaster only a few feet away and my heart flutters up a storm inside of me. Luckily his back is turned to me and the students are intent on their lesson. My aim is to catch Karlotta's eye and coax her outside, but where is she?

I raise up on tiptoes and place my arms on the window sill, careful not to make any noise. Still, no Karlotta. I try it again. I lean this way and that way. It is a good thing the window is to the back of the room, or the class would surely see me. The schoolmaster is close enough to touch. He is bending over a tousle-haired lad helping him with the alphabet.

30

"*Nein, Johannes*," he corrects, fitting his hand over that of the boy's. "Write the letter this way." The slate pencil screeches as it moves across the slate.

I draw myself up even higher. This time I see Karlotta. She too, is writing. How elegant she looks in her red dress. Her raven-black hair is piled high, away from her shell-pink ear with the large, gold earring. How comely she must be in the eyes of a man, I think. With Karlotta I have no chance whatsoever with the schoolmaster. Suddenly, I am stirred with rage, so that I lose my grip on the window.

The schoolmaster turns and looks at me, surprised. Then he beckons me to come inside. Now I must do as he bids. I cannot say no. My knees quiver as I go toward the door. My legs feel like they will go out from under me as I mount the three steps. I think, how can I bear to look into his face? How can I bear to have Karlotta laugh at me? But when I get to the door only he is waiting.

His blue eyes smile a welcome. Even so, I am too ashamed to look into them. A wave of misery wells up inside of me and washes hot over my face. Quickly, I turn to run. But he reaches out and takes my hand, holding it gently, and I have no desire to take it away.

"Come, *Fraulein*," he begs kindly. "*Ach*, do not tremble. It is good to have a visitor."

He leads me down the church aisle to introduce me to the hushed children, who have turned about, wide-eyed, to see what is going on. I feel Karlotta trying to stare me down, but I ignore her. The church is a holy place, not meant for petty quarrels, but for learning. I see the books spread out on the laps of the children, their fingers poised on the lesson. I see the large slate covered with handwriting. And I long to read and write.

Suddenly, I am no longer shy of this man, this schoolmaster, David Becker. In him I have found a friend. Nor do I care that Karlotta thinks me a dumb-ox for walking into the classroom. Already, out of the corner of my eye, I can see her smirking, trying to draw my attention. But I refuse to look.

When I tell David I have a message for Karlotta, he bids her to go outside with me. The minute we are alone, I tell her about Wilhelm's promise to me.

Karlotta cannot stand anyone's having fun.

"*Bist du ein Narr?* Are you a fool?" she storms. "It is not smart for a know-nothing, like you, Evaliz, to go to a city. Bad places they are. My, such heathens!" Karlotta shakes her head and clucks her tongue. Yet all the while, I can see the hot glow of envy fuming in her eyes. Karlotta cannot hide everything behind a sharp tongue.

31

I do not like it when Karlotta belittles me. But I cannot get a word in edgewise. She raves on and on about the wickedness of the city and its cruel people.

"Just remember, Evaliz, what old Adamka, the village storyteller, always tells about the city," Karlotta warns me. "A werewolf will seduce you, and we will never see or hear from you again."

"*Pfui* on Adamka!" I say with venom. "He is a windbag, like Herr Lunden, the marriage-fixer."

"A windbag, or not, still it's your neck, not his, if it happens. Think of that," Karlotta says in a sugary tone. "*Ja*, Evaliz, you had better not get caught in a blizzard and have to stay at a devil station overnight. Adamka says they are 'murder camps' run by robbers. In the center of the room there is a large, wooden shaft, reaching from floor to ceiling. Straw is piled around it for a bed. But the catch is this. Travelers must lie with their heads toward the shaft. Then when they all are asleep a circular block is released from the ceiling to crush their heads. Their possessions are confiscated and their naked bodies tossed out on the frozen snow for wolves to devour.

"But, best of all," Karlotta needles further, "they keep the beautiful women for their private use. Especially, tender ones, like you, Evaliz. Ha! Ha!" Karlotta laughs a high-pitched laugh when the tale is finished.

"*Ach, Gott,* I do not believe you," I say angrily. But inside of me my blood runs cold. Karlotta has a hard heart. She never leaves me any pleasure. But, maybe she is telling the truth.

Even though Karlotta's loose tongue irritates me, I am compelled by curiosity to listen to more of her prattle.

"If you think the innkeepers are cruel, you should hear what they say about Empress Anna of Russia who ruled the land before our German people came. When one of her lovers married a beautiful Italian woman, the Empress became so angry, she broke up the marriage, then ordered him married to the ugliest woman in all Russia.

"The spiteful Anna built him a palace made of ice and commanded all freaks to come to the wedding. The freaks entered the ice palace, seated on goats and swine as ugly as they were. After the wedding, the handsome slave and his ugly bride were sealed in a bedroom of ice."

It delights Karlotta that I look startled at such a preposterous story. "*Ja*, it is true, Evaliz. Every word of it," she whispers slyly, a naughty gleam lighting her eyes. "How else then could they have had twins? Boys, born on the very day the dreadful Empress died."

32

"*Ach, net!*" I say. "You soil your tongue with such rotten lies." I set my lips tight and turn to go back home.

But Karlotta storms after me, screaming, "You do not believe it, Evaliz. But it is true! Not only does Adamka say it, but my father, also. They say other things, and all of them are true. All! You go to your city," she yells. "And may the werewolf get you!"

When I ask my father about the truth of it all, he says, "*Ja*, what Karlotta said about the Empress Anna is true. About the other things, you let your brother Wilhelm take care of that."

What my father says I believe. Karlotta does not know everything. I will show her.

Even while I speak and dream about the city, Nizhni Novgorod, the season is changing. The blustering screeching winds pouring out of Siberia foretell the approaching winter. Winters in Russia are very grim. The meager fires of straw and homemade manure blocks, burning in earthen ovens, built into the dividing walls of two rooms, are not sufficient to hold the bitter cold out. No matter that the clay-and-straw made brick of the houses are two feet thick.

People wrap themselves in woolen shawls and wear heavy high felt boots on their feet. Where there is a surplus of straw — there seldom is — it is spread out on the dirt floor for added warmth. The days are spent tanning leather, mending harness, weaving, knitting, baking, singing, reading the Bible, and tending stock.

Then, one day, the snowbirds wheel in the face of storm clouds and the next morning, and all week through, there is no sun. Even the snowbirds are gone. Heavy snow is falling, falling everywhere, covering the world with a mantle of white.

Many heavy snows fall after this. Then a still, deadly freeze follows. The sun drains off its sunset fire and the whole world becomes a land of glazed ice, a place of bleak desolation that is like the world's beginning and its end, around the edge of which swarms the vehement pack of howling wolves.

In making a trip one must take advantage of the lull in quiet weather.

Wilhelm and I prepare to go quickly. So do a great many other villagers. The trip may last several weeks. Our neighbors have asked Wilhelm to bring them various supplies; David, the schoolmaster, wants books, slates, and slate pencils.

Wilhelm packs the bottom of our sleigh with straw. The sleigh is very simple; it has only a plain board laid across for a seat. Next he places a *bunshak*, a heavy felt quilt, over the straw for me to sit on. He also puts in provisions: sausages, bread and cheese for us to eat,

33

then grain and hay for our horses. Next, with the help of Otto, he brings sacks of heated sand from the house and places them where our feet will be.

On the top of all this he throws two more heavy quilts, to cover up with. My stepmother is there to supervise, saying, "Do it this way and that way."

Wilhelm only smiles and follows her orders. While he is doing this, my father and brother Friederich are hitching three fast horses to the sleigh. Over the shoulder of the middle horse stands the troika, a wooden bow, to which a bell is fastened.

"Hurry, Evaliz!" Wilhelm calls, *"Mach's schnell!"*

I dress hurriedly. On my feet I have two pair of woolen stockings. Over these go my high, knee-length felt boots. I put on my heavy woolen dress, with its tight jacket. Over this go two large shawls, for I have no coat. No woman in our family has a coat. The men have coats made either of sheepskin *Pelz*, or camel-hair,* but they have none to spare.

"Quick, Evaliz!"

My stepmother brings her great shawl from the trundle bed where she keeps it, and draws it tight over my forehead, then folds it so that it comes down over my cheeks.

"See, how pretty she looks," my stepmother says to Anna and my brother Otto who are standing by. "Just like a Catholic nun. And as sweet." They all smile.

*"Ach, net,"* I say embarrassed. "I am Lutheran."

Laughingly my stepmother fastens the shawl under my chin with a large bar pin. Next I put on a pair of mittens. I am ready!

"You are a roly-poly," Otto taunts me, grinning from ear to ear. "Look at her. Now if a *Russ* wants her, she will roll right into his arms. But he must be a big one. Ha-ha!"

Once outside the house, frost nips my nose, and the bright glitter of snow nearly blinds me. Although I am round as a stuffed pillow in my clothes, my brother Friederich, so tall and handsome, picks me up bodily. He laughs and rubs his whiskers against my face.

"Ah-h-h," he muses. "This is how it shall be when you find your Prince Charming, in a far-away place."

*"Ach, net,"* I say, boxing him with my mittened fists.

Amid gay laughter, he puts me down in the softness of the sleigh and tucks the quilt around me.

---

*Camels were secured in Russia from Tartar bands traversing the country, but their use eventually died out because oxen were better suited to the severe climate.

Then follows a solemn moment when my father folds his hands. It is a signal that we all do likewise, while he asks God's blessing for a safe journey.

Wilhelm is on the seat, ready.

But, suddenly, there is a great commotion behind us. We all turn to look. The Johann Mauers, our neighbors, are shouting and rushing toward us. Minna is carrying her baby bundled in a great shawl, floundering in the deep snow and stepping on the corners of her own shawl. Johann grabs hold of her arm and drags her along. Finally they make it.

"*Bitte!* Take us! Our baby is so sick," Minna cries. "The scabs in its throat are so thick. We must see a doctor. *Bitte!*"

And though my father rants that they are placing the child's life in jeopardy by going, my brother Wilhelm cannot turn them down. He makes room for them in the sleigh. Minna sits with me amid the straw and quilts, holding her baby. Johann shares the seat with Wilhelm, the two sitting inside another quilt, the corners of which are folded snug about their feet and legs. Their fur collars stand high around their faces, halfway covering their fur caps. In their great hulk, they remind me of ferocious looking Tartars I have seen riding past our village.

Because of the severe cold I see very little on the trip. Mostly I keep my head under the covers holding tight to the edge of the quilt to keep the prevailing winds from billowing it out, or tearing it completely from my grasp. I only hear the wild ringing of the troika bell and the screeching of sleigh runners skimming over the icy snow, or the clear cracking of the *plotka*, the braided leather whip, as other drivers catch up with us or pass us. The Mauer baby, muffled inside its tight bundle, moans softly. It is too sick, I think, to cry.

Only at the end of the day, when we stop for a night's lodging, can I look around. It is in a plain village, no different from ours. Not at all like the devil stations Karlotta has forewarned me about. Karlotta is a windbag! I will tell her so, when next I see her!

The next day is even colder. Wilhelm has great concern for his horses. He stops often along the way to remove the ever growing ice-needles forming on the hairs around the horses' nostrils. Even so, the dangling ice-prisms become stained with blood. And soon they are a deep scarlet.

*Ach*, I do not like to think about it. Our poor horses! A constant fog of freezing breath has bristled their shaggy pelts with ice.

Then on another day, coming through the deep pine forests we see the gilded domes of cathedrals and the old turreted  kremlin gleaming on the horizon, the bell towers of the churches guiding our way.

Now I can no longer keep my head under the covers. I must look. "What will it be like?" I ask Wilhelm, all excited.

"You will see soon enough," he laughs, the wind taking away his words. Then reaching a high knoll he shouts, "Look!"

Before us lies a Mongolian encampment. An archery contest is clearly in progress. Wilhelm stops our horses and we watch the event, spellbound.

Fierce looking Mongols dressed in sheepskin, mounted on hardy steppe-bred ponies and armed with crossbows are stationed at one end of the field. The targets are in place, the spectators standing in two lines. The horsemen, their eyes gleaming in their yellow faces, are chattering and making wagers among themselves.

Never have I dreamt that I would see anything like this! At first they shoot standing still, and the sound of the arrows landing on the target clouts is like the rattle of hail on a wooden roof.

This phase of the contest finished, the wagers settled in a loud and harsh manner, they begin to ride down a line at right angles to the targets discharging their arrows while going at top speed. Surprisingly, many arrows hit their mark.

*Ach*, never have I experienced such excitement. Each rider, in turn, wheels his mount with a wild shout of "*Nada Uk!*" and comes pounding over the hard snow, a volley of frozen clods spraying out in all direction from the flying hoofs.

When the shot is straight there is a shout of approval. If it misses the lively spectators jeer in jovial derision, even as we do on the sideline.

After this come the wrestling matches. The mountainous fellows strip down to their girdles and do not seem to mind the cold at all.

"The bouts are conducted according to a set rule," Wilhelm explains, knowing something about them, his face aglow with his former youth.

The thick torsoed and short, bow-legged rivals face each other, now advancing and now retreating, stamping their feet to a steady chant of "*Nige! Hoir! Gorba!* One! Two! Three!"

At each repetition of "*Gorba*" they lunge forward in an effort to catch the other off guard. The arms of the wrestlers become locked in battle and a struggle ensues. Each man heaves and pushes, letting out loud grunts and bellows of rage. The end comes only when one lies unconscious on the snow.

While the struggle continues, the Mongols on the sideline look on with a fierce lustiness, twisting about in their saddles and crying, "*Chisu! Chisu!* Blood! Blood!"

Strange people, these Mongolians, and I cannot help being somewhat afraid of them. For I am reminded of the age-old stories told of them by our villagers on winter nights. They say that Mongols suffocated Christians in felt cloth because the steppe-dwellers did not wish to have a brave man lose his blood. They wanted him to serve them, intact, in another life.

And I recall our people telling about the hardiness of the Mongol messenger of long ago riding between military out-posts. At times he came galloping in with a cloud of dust behind him, his body bound tight with leather bands, his greased face half covered. The bells at his saddle marked him as a courier of the Khakhan, and a fast horse would be waiting for him when he pulled up. The post roads spread over the old silk route and across mountain ranges where the gorges and rivers had not been bridged before.

Wilhelm turns the sleigh and we move on. The city lies before us.

Nizhni-Novgorod! Once an ancient Russian out-post, and now, for centuries past, the place of world fairs where all caravan roads meet. It is a place of many faces, of people I did not even know existed. I look and stare. The upper town with its walled kremlin sits on hills of alabaster white, sparkling in the afternoon sun! What beauty the city has with its cathedral domes, its ancient palace, its monasteries and its great halls of learning. There are great houses. So rich! I can hardly believe it. But there is also the lower town lying drab on the banks of the Volga and Oka rivers, and here we stop in front of tall gates intricately contrived of copper and opening on a wide street.

Here are the shops where burly, and heavy-whiskered merchants sell the winter catch of furs — marmot, sable, miniver, black and silver fox, and beaver from the north as well as hides, tallow, and many oils.

Other shops have iron fire-strikers, laquerwork boxes and chests, weapons of forged iron: lances, long swords and hand axes. There are lariats made from hemp or horse hair for the hunter. I see drinking cups made from the horns of mountain sheep — cups of such amazing size it is hard to lift one of them with two hands.

There are shops with kettles, spice boxes, and other utensils. There are grains, barley and millet. Sunflower oil. Teas. Dried fruit. *Tabak*. Parchment and slates. Woven rugs. Sickles.

There is carved ivory in every form imaginable, gold clasps in shapes of animals, great lengths of silken brocade "from Cathay," the slight merchant with piercing black eyes says. What a place this is. Never have I seen so many different wares. Linens. Incense. Saddles and bits decked with silverwork. Harnesses caparisoned in leather or iron links.

There are the flour mills and the breweries, the shipbuilding works. To one side are the now empty corrals for animals — sheep, camels, horses.

I look about me in awe. All is so strange. But stranger than all are the women. They are so haughty and chic. They wear fur coats with bright sashes about their waists, and fur caps. On their feet are trim leather boots, banded on top with red.

I eye them with curiosity and think about what Karlotta has said. Maybe they are heathens, so fancy, so proud, so bold! They do not cast their eyes down when a stranger looks at them. Sure, they are not humble like our women. Karlotta is right.

Nor are the men like ours. Many are dark-skinned with fearsome eyes. Kalmucks, Tartars, Kirghiz, Mongols, Russians, Gypsies. So straight-shouldered Cossack militia men ride down the street on spirited mounts, decked in beautiful uniforms and pleated leather boots.

Two brash young officers come into the store where Wilhelm has left me, sitting on a bundle of feed. They spy me immediately. The tall, black-moustached Cossack says something and laughs between white teeth. He winks at me and makes a motion that I should go with him, and my heart stops cold. He waits for me to decide, while the other stands straddle-legged, drumming his fingers against the broad belt at his waist, a devilish grin on his face.

When I refuse in stony silence, the tall one strides in front of me and scans me from head to foot. His eyes are like livid fire, searching, burning. And though I am dressed three deep in clothing, I feel naked before him. In shame and terror I draw my eyes away, praying God to save me from this evil man.

Then, almost at once, the bold Cossack clicks his heels smartly, throws back his head and laughs loud. The rude episode is over. He leaves me alone. It seems I do not breathe again until they are both outside the door and out of sight. The fat, bushy-haired storekeeper in whose care Wilhelm has left me while he finds us lodging has paid no attention. He is busy counting on his fingers and marking sums in a ledger. Later he offers me a piece of black bread made from meal and flavored with dog flesh. *Ach, Gott!* I take it not to hurt his feelings. But, how can I pretend to eat it?

Minna and Johann have gone to find an *Arzt*, a doctor, for their baby.

More strange men come in the store, bringing with them the sour smell of strong drink. They too gaze on me. I do not understand the jests that pass between them, but I know it would be simple to say that I am a round *Kartoffel*, a potato. I look at my clothes and am ashamed to stay in their presence, but where can I go? Outside would be no better. I must stay and wait for Wilhelm.

Never did I think my happiness would turn to shame. Karlotta is right. I am not so smart. I am a *Dummkopf!* A nobody! A tear nearly boiling hot spills over and courses down my cheek.

I am convinced, a city is not so much. So far it has been nothing but a place of brash people and foul smells: *Tabak*, fish oils, and dark *Pech* to smear on harness, newly tanned hides stinking to high heaven, foodstuffs rotting on grimy tables. *Ach*, such squalor. Such filth!

Sure, I do not like all the city, only the beautiful that is not meant for me. Even our city lodging is something I want to forget. My bed is a narrow wooden shelf in a crude peasant hut. There are cockroaches with legs blacker than the night walking over my face. And in the morning the burly, tattered peasant says jokingly, "I raise them large enough to pull a plow."

"*Gott!*" I say under my breath, wiping an arm across my face. "He can have his bragging."

I am happy to be going home, but I will not tell Karlotta everything, only that which will turn her eyes green with envy.

When all things are in readiness and the quilts are drawn tight around our shoulders, Wilhelm takes up the reins and shouts, "Homeward, Ho!"

The response is immediate. The troika bell, sensing the eagerness of the center horse, begins to clang in glad anticipation. The three-horse team leaps into motion. The sleigh runners, idle overnight, jerk loose from their ice-bound mooring. Our heads snap back, then forward. Presently, all runs smoothly. We are on our long way home. The two sleighs of villagers who accompanied us to market are following behind. I take one last look and see the city gliding away, backward, fading into nothingness.

In front of us again lies the wide expanse of snow. The great sky, as on those other days, is a bowl of glittering blue and silver. The quiet stillness of winter-cold has not altered. Only the sound of horses' hoofs and the singing of sleigh-runners gliding over frozen snow can be heard, blended with the sweet ringing of the troika bell as we wend our homeward way.

We count ourselves fortunate that the weather holds. Our nights' lodgings are spent in small hamlets half-buried under snow, with genial hosts, one whose only threat was that he had five tartarish-rough-and-tumble boys. Karlotta will have to be disappointed that I have not been caught in a devil's camp in a blizzard, as she predicted.

"So far, so good," Wilhelm says, scanning the open sky. "Not a sign of a storm brewing."

"*Ja*, good weather," Johann snorts. "But —" Johann breaks off the sentence to let his nervous eyes search the bleak snowfield for yet another kind of danger. "Don't forget, a hard freeze brings on the marauding wolves." His voice is high pitched, and his constant fidgeting keeps loosening the protecting quilt about them.

I glance from under my warm covers in the back of the sleigh and see that Wilhelm has a hard time calming Johann and changing the subject.

"Poor Wilhelm," I think. His face is purple from the cold, and his moustache and beard are bristling with ice. The responsibility of getting us home safe is enough, without having to bother with a coward.

Sure, it is pathetic to see a grown man like Johann so afraid. All day he fidgets, sitting on the seat beside Wilhelm, his fearful eyes searching, searching, as though "willing" a wolf-pack to come.

Minna, on the other hand, in her drab silence, has hardly spoken a word. She sits dry-eyed beside me, hunched under our quilt, holding her lifeless bundle, moaning softly. The baby died soon after sun up.

Late afternoon of another day finds us within five versts of home. Soon we will be with our people and all will be happy. All, that is, except Minna and Johann, who must somehow find a burial plot under house-deep snow for their baby.

The anxiety of getting back home is in man and beast alike. Our horses run freely, without a hint of the whip. I peek out to see if the other two sleighs are still following us. They are. They look like black shadows skimming over the white plains. Each driver chooses his own route, since there are no roads on the wide expanse of wind-swept snow.

Suddenly there is a faltering in our smooth flight. The steady pace of our horses is broken. They are filled with alarm. The loud shouts of Wilhelm and Johann drown out the silver clamor of the troika bell. I push away the covers and look out over the desolate snow and see nothing. But Wilhelm understands the danger.

"Snow wolves! Flanking our left," he cries, ordering Johann to sit down and keep his head. "We'll outrun them. Hoi! Hoi!" he shouts, getting to his feet also and applying the braided *plotka*, the whip, to the horses' rumps for the first time.

But ordering Johann to do something is like talking to the wind. Half-crazed he struggles with Wilhelm to get hold of the reins, confounding the already frantic horses. Once as a boy he had an encounter with wolves, and he has not forgotten.

"In the name of God, sit down!" Wilhelm thunders. Wilhelm forces his elbow into Johann's chest and compels him to sit down, but only for a moment. Then Johann is up again more bothersome than before. Our horses cannot keep their heads, with Wilhelm and Johann fighting over the reins.

"Throw out everything but the quilts," Wilhelm commands.

Minna lays aside her still bundle and together we struggle to get the heavy barrels of oil overboard, next the sacks of heated sand, then everything Wilhelm has bought, the bolts of bright fabric, metal chests of *Tabak* and tea, cones of wax, the China doll for Lydia, the schoolmaster's books and slates. Out they go! It makes me sick to see them spill over the snow.

"Johann!" Wilhelm shouts, "Throw out the seat!"

But Johann is beyond comprehension; he neither sees nor hears. Crazy gibberish escapes his throat. So I must do this also, adding to the pain I feel in my chest.

My lungs are screaming for breath. It is impossible to breathe deeply in this cold. Before I can get enough air into my lungs the moistness inside my nose causes my nostrils to freeze shut. The thin web of ice melts again as I let out a short, hot breath. To breathe through my teeth is excruciatingly painful.

So far, our three-horse team has not laid eyes on the wolves. Wilhelm has been able to keep them slightly ahead of the seething pack. But there is no mistaking, they have caught the scent that rides the wind, and Wilhelm's soothing words have little effect on them. He stands terrible as a hussar, his feet planted far apart, his deep fur collar turned up to protect his face from the cold, his moustache and beard a sheath of ice.

Then suddenly, over the white crest of snow on Johann's side come the snarling wolves! They come on in droves, their fangs bared. Closer and closer they come, and once more Wilhelm tries to out-circle them. But our horses panic. They will not settle to their harness.

"Oh God," I pray, "save us from a terrible death."

Absolute chaos reigns inside our sleigh. Johann demands that Minna throw the body of the child to the wolves. "Throw it out," he shouts. "Throw it out, to save us from those fangs!" He takes hold of the bundle, pulling hard.

But Minna resists him, her cries agonizing and terrible, while she clings to the still form with arms strong as iron.

"No, Johann! No! God help me, I cannot!"

The struggle goes on between them. Wilhelm takes no part in it.

Wilhelm has been busy getting control of the horses again. He stands in the sleigh, driving them ever faster, postponing the attack only by minutes. He swings the long, leather-thonged whip over his head and cracks it over the menacing, yelping pack. His voice is shrill. Sure, our fate lies in his hands. The horses are running wildly. The wolves are closing in.

I look back to see if the other two sleighs are coming to our rescue. Far from it. Instead, they are circling wide, away from the attack. The drivers are standing, lashing their horses. They are not going to help us. True they could not if they tried. It is better that they survive and bring us help; otherwise we are all lost.

Wilhelm loops the reins around his neck and tries to wrap the thick quilt around him to protect himself against the onslaught.

"Do likewise," he shouts to me, "protect yourself."

The wind tears the quilt from his grasp, so I help him, tying it around his middle with a halter rope that I find in the straw. Then I draw another quilt tight around me, keeping away from the husband-and-wife battle that is still going on. The sleigh is very shallow.

"Give it," Johann shouts, his eyes filled with blue-white fire. "What good is it now? What good I ask you? Let go! Minna, let go!" He grabs hold of the wrapping and tears it away.

"No!" Minna wails. "It is my heart — my breath — my entire being! *Ach, Gott!* No!" Her bloodcurdling cry is loud enough to wake the dead.

Johann is a demon. With brutal force he wrests the body away from Minna, then uttering an oath he throws it to the oncoming wolves.

It is a pitifully small bundle, bouncing crazily in a spray of snow.

Minna grips the side of the sleigh with iron fingers, screaming her heart out.

"*Lieber Heiland!* Dear Lord!" I wail at the awfulness, and my heart breaks with hers.

The ferocious beasts snatch up the tiny token, tearing at it, but not all of them are satisfied with so small a morsel. Only a few stay behind to devour it. Then suddenly, there is more offered them. Minna lets out an ungodly cry and throws herself from the sleigh. A grey wave swarms over her body, yapping greedily. But less than a score of wolves stay behind to worry with the paltry heap that was once a woman. There was much more to be had.

Now with the smell of blood in their nostrils the remaining wolves come on with even greater lust. Then we are speeding erratically within the swarming mass. Some of the wolves leap high against our squealing, ranting horses, aiming for their throats. Wilhelm tries desperately to drive them off. Shouting terrible shouts, he swings the whip hard over the lean, muscular bodies of the yelping wolves. Some of them tumble over the snow, howling in pain. Yet they rise again and come after us with added fury.

I crouch at Wilhelm's feet and hold my quilt down tight. But Johann, completely demented, stands in the back of the sleigh cursing and laughing and shaking his fist. Then, as it is bound to happen, two snarling beasts leap high and snatch him to the snow. The wild scramble stays behind, diminishing swiftly, like a dark object falling down a well. A shrill scream splits the air. Then I hear his voice no more.

Now there are only my brother Wilhelm and me. How long can we last?

"Oh God, our heavenly Father, look down upon us in mercy and help us!" I pray aloud. I lift up my head, imploring God. But Wilhelm puts pressure on me with his knee.

"Keep your head down!" he shouts. "Can't you see I have my hands full?"

So far, Wilhelm has been protected by the heavy quilt and the whip he swings, but the assault is now directly on our horses. Some of the wolves lunge to tear at the horses' hoofs only to get trampled under foot, while still others leap for the throat with tenacious holds. The frenzied horses squeal and rear in their harness.

Then, suddenly, all is confusion. Our horses go down in a swirl of snow, a mass of snarling beasts riding their manes. The air is filled with the wild scream of crazed horses, the lusty snarls of ravenous wolves jostling each other, and with the creak of taut harness ripping asunder. Out of the holocaust, billowing with vapor, comes the sickening sweet odor of warm blood and hot entrails.

Immediately after the horses go down, Wilhelm kicks a piece of board loose from the sleigh. "Here," he shouts, handing it to me, "defend us while I turn the sleigh upside down to cover us."

We leap out into the snow. Wilhelm struggles to tilt the heavy box-sleigh on its side, and immediately we are set upon by a lunging beast. Miraculously I beat it down with the club, only to be faced with still another. It seems when one pair of yellow-green eyes and drooling fangs have been warded off, another is at hand. The sound of crushing bone is in my ears.

"Oh, God, help us! Hurry Wilhelm; I am sick." I think I will vomit.

"Hold on," Wilhelm shouts, "I am almost finished." The sleigh goes over with a bang. "Here," he commands, "crawl underneath, while I lift it. Then see if you can help me."

Quickly, I scramble in on hands and knees. I arch my back to help hold the sleigh up for Wilhelm. The wolves tear at his high, knee-length felt boots, but their sharp fangs fail to penetrate. Crouching down, he rests the edge of the heavy sleigh on his shoulder, and with the help of strong arms squirms underneath, to safety.

He takes my hand and holds it tight. After seemingly endless struggle it is hard to believe that we are still alive. Our horses are dead by now, their insides strung out over the snow.

Through a crack in the boards, Wilhelm and I see the wolves devour our horses. They growl and menace each other as they tear at the bloody carcasses, some dragging away choice morsels, staining the white snow with scarlet, feasting in tight knots, bristling with animal dissension.

Long afterwards, when the wolves are gone and the night cold has driven into our bones, there comes the clamor of men and sleighs to the rescue. Those who witnessed the attack have summoned help.

*"Gott sei Dank!"* Wilhelm cries, rising up and lifting the sleigh, toppling it right side up again. Together we scan the rim of the semi-light snowland. And presently there blaze a row of fiery fagots.

"They're coming. They're coming."

Wilhelm picks me up and holds me, his arms trembling mightily. Then he runs, stumbling, toward the oncoming sleighs.

Riding in the first sleigh is my brother Friederich, two years younger than Wilhelm and single. With him is David Becker, the schoolmaster. David jumps out even before Friederich can stop his skittish team and comes running to us.

There is deep pain in his eyes as he looks at me. Then reaching out, he takes me in his arms and carries me to the sleigh. And it is only now, in the shelter of his embrace, that I feel like swooning. All around me, in the intermittent glare of weaving fagots, swirl a company of familiar faces emitting glad shouts. Friederich's face goes by with anxiety and joy mixed together. But here in the schoolmaster's arms the world is solid and safe. He presses his cheek to mine.

I feel the coolness of his cheek, then, the living warmth, the tenderness. The unbearable joy of it makes my head reel. *Ach*, how can this be so? An hour ago I feared death by freezing. Now this!

*"Liebchen! Liebchen!"* he murmurs into my ear. "So cold, so cold."

Then I am not sure if he said it at all. It is what I wish him to say. Sure, I must be dreaming.

Later on in the week, when I meet David quite unexpectedly at a neighbor's house, I am too shy to look into his eyes. I feel embarrassed, not because of David, but because everyone is teasing me, saying he is my *hospodar*, who rescued me, held me in his arms and kissed me for all to see. And so, I do not let on that I even notice him. Yet, I am aware of an eagerness. His eyes plead when at times I steal a look at him and find him looking too. And now, I am sure that he said the words. They are mirrored in his eyes.

And though I have a terrible urge to rush to him and put my hands on his face in love, I act foolish instead and add torment by ignoring him, turning my back to him, helping the good *Hausfrau* with the baking of bread.

In the meantime, Karlotta is burning with rage. She cannot accept the fact that I should be the one to get all the praise, to be talked about as the most beautiful, the most courageous maiden throughout all Volgaland. The mere mention of the schoolmaster carrying me in his arms sets her to ranting and pouting in turns.

It is better this way, I think. Because now I can be truthful about the uneventful part of my trip to the city. For no matter what I say, good or bad, she will not believe me anyway. Poor, jealous Karlotta!

"Always, you are the one that gets everything," she storms at me. "Everything, Evaliz! The city! The villagers at your feet! The schoolmaster eating out of your trembling hands! *Ach*, I hate you! I hate you!" she wails, not knowing when to be still. "But wait," she taunts, "it will not always be so. You cannot hold him. Your hands are not strong, like mine. Quick, he will slip through your quavering fingers. See," she points, "how they tremble, even now."

Karlotta talks so fast. She is mad. Her voice is so shrill. And I know this is only the beginning of what Karlotta can do.

# CHAPTER 4

# The Ancestors

I t is cold December. Wilhelm's wife, Anna, and I, along with other women of the village have taken our laundry to the frozen dam. Even Karlotta is here. Usually she is spared the ordeal, or plain refuses. She is so spoiled. All of us are wearing high felt boots, full woolen dresses, with long-sleeved, tight-fitting bodices, and over our heads and shoulders are wrapped great shawls. Every woman is getting ready for *Das Heilige Weihnachtsfest*, Christmas, the day of our Lord Jesus' birth.

But today Karlotta does not torment me with her chatter about winning over the schoolmaster. It is far too cold here on the wind-swept ice. There is the constant swirl of needle-sharp snow sweeping across the ice and stinging our faces, blowing under our full billowing skirts, chilling us to the marrow of our bones. No one voices foolish words on a day like this, not even Karlotta. We all hurry to do our washing before we freeze.

First we have boiled the clothes at home in snow water, using straw ashes for soap. And now we have brought the wash in wide baskets down to the dam to be washed clean. Using hammer and wedge we break holes in the ice. Piece by piece we take the clothes, already frozen hard, and plunge them in the water; then we lift them out and trample them with our heavy boots. This we do as often as twenty times to get all the grey ash out so every piece is clean and bright. So proud we village women are of our white clothes that every wash-day becomes a contest. Anna and I would not shame our *Familie* with a dingy wash.

But we must work fast. There is no time for gossip or self-pity. The stabbing pain in wrists and near-frozen fingers must be endured.

Even so, I lament and weep inwardly — as surely every woman here must be doing — while frigid winds spray water against my skirts causing them to stand out stiff with ice, making them heavy and ungainly so that the soles of my feet smart when a gust of wind throws me off balance. And my fingers? They sting so, it is like fire burning under my finger nails. Yet it is better that I keep them in the water, otherwise they would surely freeze.

*Ach*, such torture! A man would not treat his work beasts this way! I wonder, how will I ever stand it? Not only today, but on all those other wash days throughout my life. How?

Quickly I wring out each piece, but before I am finished it is frozen brittle, so that it is almost impossible to get all the wash back into the baskets. Then, fast and clumsy, Anna and I hurry back to the warmth of our house, for even our felt boots are frozen chunks of ice.

Once inside, the torture in my bruised hands and wrists becomes even greater. I clasp my hands together, not knowing where to put them, and walk the floor. Anna is no better off; she, too, paces here and there.

"Come, Evaliz," my stepmother says pityingly, "I will massage them." So quickly she brings out her soft woolen shawl and folds my hands inside. And it is not surprising that when she takes it away, it is streaked with scarlet.

To dry the clothes we hang them on everything available, wall pegs, table top and benches. In the summer time it is much easier, we simply spread out the wash on pasture grass, dozens and dozens of women laying out a carpet of wash over meadow and hillock, reaching almost all the way from dam to village. On days such as this there is laughter and singing, and a good round of bathing for every woman and child. The men keep out of sight.

I myself know of only three flat irons in all the village. They are something new to our Volga-German people, brought all the way from Moscow. The irons belong to the rich lady my sister Katrinliz worked for before she got married. To heat them, the irons are buried in red hot ashes, then a wooden handle with an iron tip is fastened on top.

But we peasants have it much easier. We simply fold our clothes, brushing them smooth with our hands. And after each piece is folded it is sat on for added finish. For our best linens there is a board that is made in alternate ridges and grooves, which has a separate roller. The sheet or table cloth is folded twice the long way, then rolled onto the roller, beginning on one end. Then holding it tight, we roll it back and forth over the ribbed board. Our holiday cloths with deep knitted lace are treasures we are proud to spread on our festive tables.

Christmas Eve is a night when all Volga-German children are filled with mystic joy, and great fear! They feel joy, because of the Christ Child's birth, the singing, and the festive programs. And they fear *Belz-Nickel*, the Kriss-Kringle, who will surely come, not to bear gifts, but to slap the open palm with a broad stick if one does not know a given Bible verse. The one who plays the part of *Belz-Nickel* is usually a man like Alexus Lunden, the marriage-fixing sot. Decked out in a long fur coat and *Schilfgras\** tail he comes banging on the door after dark, scaring children half out of their wits.

"Do you know your verse?" he roars, confronting them in his awful costume.

If the child has forgotten, or is too frightened to open his mouth, he gets a slap on the hand and the promise that Old Kriss-Kringle will be back again next Christmas.

"And beware that you know your verse then!" With that he stumps off into the winter night to call on another home. And there is much laughter and fun-making among the grown-ups. But I never laugh. Never will I do that to my children, when I have them, I promise myself.

And yet the people are sincere about Christmas. We have two Christmas days, the 24th and 25th, and we keep them holy by family devotion and going to church. In our village we do not have a regular minister, but must depend on those who make the rounds to perform marriages, baptism, burials, and confirmation. Often the sermon is given by a dedicated man in our *Dorf*. To my amazement that man, this Christmas season, is David Becker, the schoolmaster.

Then Christmas is gone, and time seemingly stands still. The winter storms howl and rage. Windows and doors rattle. The village livestock, in an atmosphere of utter dejection, huddle inside straw-thatched barns. The fowl, heads smothered under snow-decked wings, wait out the days in bleak misery, while vagrant winds pile in more and more ice particles. And the people sit in

*Schilf* — (German) reed, or sedge grass.

their houses, or in the house of their neighbor, and tell the old, old tales — tales they heard from their fathers and mothers, whose fathers and mothers in turn had told them and whose elders, before them, had seen and lived the strange events.

And while the people talk in their gloomy houses, the men mending harness and boots, the women, knitting, weaving and baking, the lugubrious plaints of snow wolves ride the howling winds and confirm the trueness of the tales.

Here, sitting astride his cobbler's bench is my father. Seated at his right is Johann-Henerich Berger who is dressing out a slender strip of leather for a boot lace by drawing it through *Pech*, cobbler's wax, held in the palm of his hand, his arm swinging wide to accommodate the length. Next to him, sitting circle-wise, facing my father, are Metzler's Jakor, Haffner's Georg, and Kindsvater's Salmo. And back of them, toward one corner of the room sit my brothers, Wilhelm, Friederich and Otto, each in his place, for this is my father's house. Otto is carving a wooden spoon to go with the bowl he has made. We women are busy with our own work, my stepmother with the baking of bread, Anna, Wilhelm's wife, at the loom weaving *Sarpinka**, gingham, and I, when I am not twisting straw for the fire, am knitting woolen stockings. My stepsister Lydia, and stepbrother Jakor, are studying Luther's Catechism. Anna's baby, Marikchen, lies happily in her trundle bed, kicking and waving her fists and cooing.

I listen as the men relate the story of a bright light appearing on the wild steppes in our ancestors' time. The depression in the earth is still there. I have seen it often. But it is not nearly so deep as it once was since grasses have grown over it. And though I've heard the story dozens of time, I listen carefully again.

"*Ja,*" booms the voice of Johann-Henerich, the story-teller, as he extends his arm and brings it close again to draw the leather strip through the *Pech*. "It was such a light as has not been seen or heard of since. It rose from the earth, the color of burning sulphur, round as the moon! It marked a Mongolian treasure, it was supposed, hidden from the time of the terrible Khan, Batu, whose golden city lay on the Volga.

"*Ja,* the ancestors were afraid to go near it at first." Johann-Henerich goes on with the story. "But the light appeared night after night and some of the braver ones were irresistibly

*According to Jacob Volz (*Festschrift der Balzerer*, York, Nebraska, 1938), Casper Volz, a Volga-German, learned the *Sarpinka* trade in Sarepta, near Astrakhan. He introduced it to Balzer, a prominent village in the Volga-German region. Balzer alone produced over five million meters of *Sarpinka* for domestic and foreign markets. The Balzer *Sarpinka* mill, among others, was seized and destroyed during the Bolshevik Revolution in 1917.

lured to it. Then, as they drew near, the light blinked out, leaving for their inspection the same wild growth as was everywhere on the wide open steppes. And no matter how many times it happened, they never could see where the light came from or where it went.

" *'Gott im Himmel!* It is hexed!' some exclaimed, drawing away in fright. *'Jawohl,'* others concurred, 'the devil, himself, has decreed that it shall be a warning to all meddlers!' After that, whenever the light appeared, the people locked their houses. And their children grew more and more afraid.

"Then one night, Christian Prabbler, a young man of that time, had a dream. The dream was that he should go to a stream nearby and select two of the most supple and finest willow branches he could find. He was to fashion a cross of the wood and lay it on a Bible. Then, holding the Bible in front of him, he was to walk toward the light, quoting Scripture all the way. And even though the light went out, he was to keep on quoting from the Bible and never stop. The cross then would turn and point to the very spot. 'Here, you will dig,' the dream said, 'and you will find such things as you have never seen before.

" 'But, beware! Not a word other than the Scriptures shall you utter. Not one single word!'

"And so Christian did what his dream had told him. He made the cross of choice willow wood and while he whittled he told the villagers around him about his dream.

"*Ach*, they could hardly believe such strangeness! They stood with mouths agape, shaking their heads. 'He is addle-brained,' some said and looked on him sadly.

" *'Nein.* He is very holy!' said the others and looked on him in awe."

Johann-Henerich, his brown eyes bright with the joy of holding a listening audience, stops the story long enough to glance around the room, to see if there are any doubters as to the veracity of Christian's good character among us. And while he pauses, the moaning winds tear at our meager roof, showering us with bits of straw. We, the listeners, brush the straw away, stifling a sudden stir of laughter, half-embarrassed for the interruption. But Johann-Henerich is so engrossed in getting on with the story, he's not aware that a bright yellow shaft stands upright from his black wavy hair, where it glows like a candle.

The sight of it evokes foolish snickers inside of me and I swallow hard to keep them down. "Evaliz," I say to myself, "you wouldn't dare!"

So quick, I cast my eyes down, putting speed to my knitting needles. Even so, Otto's sly glance comes through to me to tell me that he, too, has noticed. Uncontrollable mirth already has him in spasms. He sits on a bench behind my father, bobbling like a steam-filled samovar ready to blast its lid.

"*Ach, net!*" I groan, clacking my needles even faster, hoping the outburst will never come. But Otto cannot contain himself. He startles everyone with a loud hick, and immediately my father turns about and subdues him with a stern look.

Johann-Henerich takes no offense. The story continues:

"But, no matter what the people said, Christian saw his dream before him. He whittled on and finished the cross. Then, when night came, six of the strongest men took their spades and went with him.

"And it happened just as in the dream. They found the place and started digging, mumbling the Scriptures. At first there was nothing but grass and earth, like everywhere else. Then their spades hit upon something strange, a web of branches laid as a covering. Then they found the skeleton of a man. Two gold-encrusted sabres lay criss-cross over it. And deeper down under the tangle of branches rested a copper kettle with trinkets of jade and emeralds. The copper kettle was blemished with age. It was buried long ago. The men dug on. Finally their spades struck against an even greater object, a casket, encased in iron grill-work. It was the unknown treasure!

"The six helpers stared in awe. '*Himmel, thu' dich auf!* Heaven, open up! Now we will solve the mystery,' one of them shouted, forgetting that no other word but the Scriptures should be spoken.

" '*Ei, Ei.* You *Dummkopf!*' Christian scolded.

"Then, suddenly, there followed a mighty sound, like the crackling of lightning and the rumble of thunder out of a starry night. And just as suddenly, the large casket sank down into the earth. Sumf-ff-f . . . down, down, almost dragging Christian with it. He was saved only by the tangle of branches. And that is it!" Johann-Henerich, the story-teller, exclaims, taking up the work at hand.

"Whew," I let out my pent-up breath, for I am tense with excitement, the way it always is when I hear the old tale retold. Otto's eyes are bulging out, bright as stars in the black of night. My young stepsister and stepbrother are clinging to their mother's skirt. Such excitement in our house today! I wish they would go on and on with their story telling.

When someone questions Johann Henerich if the story is really true, he says:

"*Jawohl!* The copper kettle was set aside before the crash came. And to this day my own *Grossmutter* Prabbler wears two copper bracelets made from it. You have seen them yourselves!" he says, brushing aside his long moustache with the back side of his broad hands, revealing shockingly red lips under the long hairs. He eyes each of us in turn and settles back his shoulders as if the whole thing is finished. But it isn't just yet.

"She wears them," he adds, "one on her wrist and one on her ankle, for the *Gliederschmerz*, the rheumatism in her joints. By two notches cut out on each end they clamp together and hold. So." He nods his head and slaps his knees with his fat hands to emphasize the truth.

I know of what he speaks. I have often seen these copper bracelets on the old lady's bony wrist and ankle. Some days they are a murky green and on other days they are bright as the sun, depending on how she feels, the old *Grossmutter* explains.

The trinkets in the copper kettle were sold on the age-old world market, at Nizhni-Novgorod. Some were stolen by roving Gypsies, Johann-Henerich tells us.

The men who sit in our house relate yet another story: The story of why we Germans live in Russia. It all began, they say, when Catherine the Great, herself a German, became Empress of Russia soon after the death of her husband, Peter III.

She was dissatisfied with the sloven Russian peasant and wanted some of the resourceful, hard-working Germans to cultivate the black loam of her vast Volgaland. With this in mind she made concession with Frederick II — Frederick the Great — for German colonists. She sent Cossack generals, with light cavalry, to bring the first great throngs of Germans through the waist-deep vegetation of these endless steppes. Other stories say that they came by ship through the Baltic, then by land.

The Germans came in wagons and ox-carts linked together, and they came on foot, with songs on their lips, filled with the spark of adventure, eager to turn the new soil of this great "promised land," Russia.

"*Ja*, a promised land, like no German had ever seen, or ever will," relates Georg Haffner, another guest in my father's house. Georg continues, "Though in truth, the Fatherland's bosom was rich as mother's milk. Was this disrespect, to forsake the Fatherland?" he asks and gives the answer. "*Nein!* What did the Fatherland care? Did it bring the colonists back into the fatherly fold when reverses came and Russia broke her promise? I tell you, no! The people were promised military freedom for all time. But Russia broke that promise after the first hundred years." Georg becomes heated over the matter and my father quiets him down. But Georg cannot contain himself.

"A hundred years is but a sigh in the infinite breath of life. For who is there that does not know that life eats life, as surely as day follows night?"

Georg stops his indignation long enough to fashion the toe of a shoe he is making. Gently, and quite apart from the wrath he has displayed, he taps the leather with a light mallet until it fits the form. Then he resumes the harangue.

"But perhaps, the Fatherland was glad to weed out the unwanted, the over-many who trounced, trampled, and suckled out the life sap from her aching breast? It is no secret that Germany was torn by war. The people had unpleasant memories of militarism, and the poor were barely a step above bondage. Some even gleaned the fields of the rich, as the poor did in Biblical times.

"In this new 'home land' they were promised livable houses, pastoral lands and rich black loam that ripened into golden grain — land such as no other world has known!

"But as our forefathers continued the trek they detected something was wrong. Where was this promised garden spot? Bewilderment laid hold on them. Deeper and deeper the now silent, home-sick, weary-of-heart human chain waded into the never-ending swaying grasses, like wading into a boundless, enveloping sea.

"Day after day, they marched into a solitude so vast that whoever knows nothing of real solitude knows nothing of unending vastness. And as they marched onward, the great wheel of the seasons marched with them; flowering fields and lush green grasses turned to brown wastes that tumbled before the winds. The summer gaiety of the bird throng was no more as they lifted their wings and wedged their way through the endless sky into nothingness. And all about the people rasped the constant dry whisper of infinite loneliness and the coming of winter winds.

"And, then, one day, before it was time to lodge for the night, they stopped and the Cossack general spoke:

" 'This is it!'

" 'Is what?' they laughed, trying to make light of the unexpected jesting of their Cossack leader. They did not know what he meant.

" 'This is what the *Kaiserine* Catherine has given you. You poor *duraks*, fools, that you are! All that your eyes can see — all the wild steppe from one heaven to the other — she gives to you gladly.' And he laughed at them with strange nomadic eyes, and his long moustache parted and showed gleaming white teeth. He waved his arm about him, taking in all the land to the endless horizon. 'Free Germans you are now. Who knows, how many years? Then, saddled Russians!' Again the Cossack general laughed. Then with a sharp command he turned his cavalry men about.

" 'But there are no houses!' the people shouted. 'No stables. No nothing! And it is September. Soon the Siberian winds and ice and snow will be upon us. Where are the house builders she has promised us?'

"There was much wailing and crying among the women, I can tell you," Georg continues with the story, while we who listen wait with bated breath.

"Some of the women threw themselves on the ground and wailed aloud, and their children screamed in fright when they saw this. And there was loud, unholy swearing among the men. 'Teufel! Teufel! We will not stay!'

"But the Cossack general called his troop and rode a circle around them. There was nothing left for them but, to stay. The promise that they could return to their Fatherland if they did not like it in Russia meant nothing. Later on a stockade was built, open to the sky above. Its only door was the body of an escapee, for those who tried to escape were caught and brought back and lashed to within an inch of their lives — some were even whipped to death.

"And so that their lives be spared from the cruel Russian winter, the people dug holes in the ground along the hillsides. With their wagon-beds, they made doors. The gloomy windows were made of pig bladders, stretched tight. And the smoke from their damp, meager fires ate their lungs out. That they should not die, they sang songs, putting into words the deep sorrow they felt in their souls:

1

*Ach, wie bin ich so verlassen*
*Und veracht' von Jedermann.*
*Freund und Feinde tun mich hassen,*
*Niemand nimmt sich meiner an.*

2

*Ist denn Liebe ein Verbrechen,*
*Kann ich denn nicht glücklich sein,*
*Und mit meinem Liebchen sprechen*
*Und mich seiner Liebe freu'n?*

3

*Und so reuet mich das Leben,*
*So beklag ich die Natur,*
*Möchte ich mich doch ergeben*
*Auf der weiten Gottesflur.*

*Ach, wie dunkel sind die Mauren,*
*Ach, wie sind die Ketten schwer,*
*Ach, wie lange wird's noch dauren,*
*Ist denn keine Rettung mehr?* *

"Even though the words were sad, still, they were songs," Georg Haffner says, finishing the story. "And this is how we German people came to be in Russia."

*Ach*, this is the story I will never forget. I look at our snow-blown windows and think how glad I am that I live in our time where houses have glass windows, heavy doors, and thick, earthen walls, with sod or straw-covered roofs. Here in closed comfort, while the winter winds wail and moan in the chimney-top, my father and his friends sit and retell the old story.

They also tell stories about Catherine the Great. They say Catherine was a wanton woman who married the Arch-Duke Peter of Russia. It was told that he was an imbecile and that she later helped to do away with him.

"*Ja*, sure, the crazy czar was murdered," these bearded men, sitting by my father's fire, whisper, even as their parents, and again their parents before them whispered it. Peasants, as of old, are not entitled to personal opinions; they receive no thanks for words of wisdom. So, even now, they converse in hushed voices whenever they speak of the empress's guilt in Peter's death.

The story has it that Peter III was crazy even in childhood, that he slobbered his food. When he was a boy he was oftentimes punished by not being allowed to eat for days. When food was finally set before him, he snatched it up greedily and swallowed it, for fear it would be taken away. On days when food was denied him, he was set up against the wall facing a princely table decked with roasted fowl, fruit, and wine, and made to watch the royal courtiers, almost as ill-mannered as he, tear the baked birds limb from limb, eating and smearing grease from ear to ear until it dripped off their chins.

They tell of Emelyan Ivanovich Pugachev, the bloody robber who made an uprising, claiming he was the murdered czar. All who did not believe or bow down before him were hanged to the gallows which had been built by the people themselves, under whip lash.

Helped by the enemies of Catherine, Pugachev sacked and burned towns and villages, and murdered men, women and children. He came to the Province of Saratov where the German colonists lived and their losses were great.

*Old German folk song. A song traditionally sung by Volga-Germans.

"That is true," says Jakob Diener sitting here in the room with us. "That is how Johann-Peter Kratzke and Grellman's Heinerich, my uncle's great grandfather, lost his life."

"*Ja, ganz gewiss!*" puts in Jakor Kindsvater. "My old *Grossmutter* used to tell us stories that were handed down through the family. She said that even our neighboring villages, Mueller, Franzosen, Husaren, Rothammel and Grimm, as well as Kratzke felt the plague. Later the imposter was captured in a bloody battle. He was hung to the gallows on the *Roten Platz*, Red Square, inside the Kremlin, in Moscow."

And so the story telling goes on throughout the long winter, while shrill winds bring icy blasts, the wolves howl, and snow covers all the houses. One neighbor must liberate the other from his oftentimes not-so-cozy prison by digging a tunnel up to and opening a snow-bound door.

The young people, too, gather in each other's houses. For refreshments they bake squashes within the hot ashes of their large wall ovens. These are evenings of entertainment and work, mostly work. The young men bring their wood carving of household accessories, and leather and harness making. The young maidens have their knitting and hand sewing. Large families require many pairs of woolen stockings, and every girl must do her share of the work. There is much singing and merrymaking at a gathering such as this. Everyone chimes in, for what generation has not learned the words to

> *Du, du liegst mir im Herzen,*
> *Du, du liegst mir im Sinn;*
> *Du, du machst mir viel Schmerzen,*
> *Weisst nicht, wie gut ich dir bin!*
> *Ja, ja, ja, ja,*
> *Weisst nicht, wie gut ich dir bin!*

As soon as the song is finished, they sing another. The boys sing the first part and the girls join in the chorus. One favorite is the Huntsman Song, "*Der Jägersmann*":

> *Im Wald und auf der Heide,*
> *Da such' ich meine Freude,*
> *Ich bin ein Jägersmann!*
> *Die Forsten treu zu pflegen,*
> *Das Waldpret zu erlegen,*
> *Mein' Lust hab' ich daran.*

> 2

> *Das Huhn im schnellen Fluge,*
> *Die Schnepf' im Zickzackzuge*

*Treff' ich mit Sicherheit!*
*Die Sauen, Reh' und Hirsche,*
*Erleg, ich auf der Pirsche,*
*Der Fuchs lässt mir sein Kleid.*
*Halli, hallo, halli, hallo,*
*Der Fuchs lässt mir sein Kleid.* \*

The girl whose work is most admired, whose work outshines the others, is the one each boy tries to walk home later. They all know that a woman who sews and knits well will also make a good wife. A man in *Russland* looks for this sign first, it seems, before anything else.

It is a great pleasure to have the schoolmaster, David Becker, join us. The girls look at him with wonderment and longing in their hearts. The boys look to him for worldly knowledge. Whenever he speaks of America, I cling to every word he utters. What a good place it must be! Such mountains and prairies and crystal clear waters. What opportunities for all men! And what is even better, he says he will go there some day. "This is my greatest wish," he tells us.

There is a mixed feeling of pain and joy inside of me when I hear him say it, for it is my greatest wish, also. But I keep the thought to myself. It would be the worst thing to let Karlotta know what I am thinking. That black-haired vixen can spoil everything.

In secret, waking or sleeping, I plan how I will go with him. How it will be done, I do not know. I only know that I love him, and I must go.

David is capable of many things, so why not this? He can give the sermon when there is no minister; he can calculate the hardest arithmetic and reason weighty problems with the best of our village officials. Before coming to us he helped survey some of the outer terrain where the Trans-Siberian Railroad is being built now.

I lie in bed at night and think that he is already mine, that we will go to America together. But in the morning I am not so sure. *Ach*, what if Karlotta Dahmer should get him, like she says she will?

Karlotta prides herself with her sewing and with the many going-home dates she gets. She is so boastful the girls all hate her. She looks down her nose at us in her smart way. Once, even David walked her home, and I did not sleep that night. I thought I would die with jealous pain.

\**Sammlung Deutscher Volkslieder,* Bismarck, N.D.

Better that you improve your stitches, I told myself, so that Karlotta will not have her way. *Ach*, never! She thinks she can out-do me. But, I will show her.

Then, one winter's night, a month later, when the young people are gathered at Anliz Shuster's house, Karlotta swaggers up to me.

"Hello-oo, Evaliz," she says smart-like. "Who will walk you home tonight?" She tilts her head to one side and her mocking eyes go from me to David across the room, who is busy laying pleats in the shank of a leather boot. "It won't be him, I can tell you that," she laughs.

Her remark sets some of the girls to snickering, and I am so mad I want to stamp on her foot and tear her sewing all to pieces. But, instead, I set my lips tight and keep on with the wide lace I am knitting.

Karlotta hasn't the grace to let me be. "I will tell you, Evaliz, who will take you home — no one! No one, ever takes you home." Her mouth draws up into a smirk.

*"Herr Je'!"* I almost swear under my breath. This is all I can take from her, yet I control myself. At last, she goes to sit down. She makes me so mad I could scratch her eyes out and grind her smirking face into the dust. But my father would not like to have me be like that. "Always, a lady, Evaliz," he has warned.

Karlotta cannot sit still for long. She flounces over to where the schoolmaster is pleating leather and proudly shows him her needlework.

"Ah! It is very fine," he says, looking it over. "Tell me, how can you make such tiny stitches?"

"That I will tell you," she says, tossing her head like a sassy colt, "when you take me home tonight, David."

Ach, Gott, I think, now it is David, instead of Herr Becker.

"Did you hear that?" one boy shouts, and immediately there is laughter and joking throughout the room.

"Be careful, schoolmaster," another exclaims, "or she will have your heart in stitches."

The boys all laugh. But for us girls the whole evening is spoiled. Or is it? All of a sudden I am determined that someone must stop Karlotta from having her way before it is too late. That someone has got to be me. A strange, bold feeling comes over me. If she thinks she can outdo me, then she has another think coming, for I, too, have done my very best.

*Ach*, never do I show off, but my heart is set on David, also. I will show Karlotta. Right now! And suddenly, there is no shame in

59

me. Feeling very proud and bold, I let out the neat roll of knitted lace I have made. It is so clean, so smooth, and the pattern is so intricately designed.

Right away Karlotta makes out she does not see it, but the other girls crowd around me, oh-ing and ah-ing, until the boys come to see for themselves.

"*Ja*, that is the very best!" they say, jovially. "Evaliz shall be my girl tonight."

"No, no, she shall be mine." All are shouting and pulling at my arms this way and that way in fun. But it doesn't last.

Karlotta, her black eyes flashing fire, pushes her way through to me and slaps me full in the face.

"Evaliz, you are the mean one," she shouts. "Your father will whip you for being so fresh." But before she can strike me again, David has pinned her arm to her side. There is no kindness in his eyes. Neither is there any laughter left in the room.

David lets go of her arm. The fun is over. Everyone gets ready to go home. Not one boy has had an opportunity to pick his favorite girl. I reach for my shawl, place it over my head, and pin it tight beneath my chin. The other girls do likewise.

Then, all of a sudden, the boys remember that they have not picked their dates. A great commotion follows and once again there is hilarity and laughter. But before the boys can decide, the girls throw open the door, and all rush out onto the high drifts of hard snow, laughing and scampering every which way.

I run fast, for I do not want to kiss the boy who catches me. He will snatch my knitting and will not give it back until I kiss him roundly, and to his liking.

*Ach*, I have never been caught. Always my legs have carried me fast enough. Maybe I can get home before one reaches me. I hold my knitting tight in one hand, so that I do not lose the needles; with the other I lift my skirts high from the snow. I hear running footsteps behind me. I try very hard to get away, for I do not know who it is. *Ach*, I must get away. Perhaps it is Peter Auslander, the one with the bright eyes, and the fat lips.

I am almost home. Maybe I can make it. Then, an arm reaches out and I am caught. It is David! A tremble goes through me at his touch. He gathers me in his strong arms and lifts me up and swings me round and round, laughing gaily.

"At last, I have you," he says, smiling in my face, holding me tight in his arms and kissing me. "Umm mmm — so."

Suddenly, he isn't teasing anymore. He stops swinging. He stands, quietly looking on my face. He holds me so close that I can feel his heart pounding in his throat. His warm breath is on my cheek. Then, as if he cannot wait any longer his lips are on mine, tender, yet so firm.

"Evaliz, I love you. I love you," he whispers, his voice heavy, like I have never known it to be.

"*Ach*, yes, yes," I breathe, dizzy with the joy of it. I taste the salt on his lips and I am surprised that a man's kiss is salty. I hear his words and I cannot believe them. There cannot be so much happiness for me, I think. There cannot be so much happiness in all the wide world!

While he holds me like this and says these sweet words, I can do nothing. I cannot fight back. Even my knitting slips from my hands, and for once I do not care if the needles fall out of the stitches. I only know that I love him. I love David Becker, the schoolmaster.

When he puts me down on my feet I feel as if I am filled with wine. My legs will hardly hold me. All my strength is in him. I know I must have him. Without him I am nothing.

Then winter is gone again. It went as quickly as it came! In the stillness of the night there comes the sudden crash of breaking ice, like a thousand hammers striking together on the shores of the frozen river. Then follows a distant murmur which rises to an even higher pitch.

"The ice is breaking!" The villagers dash from their beds in dread apprehension.

I run outside, through the melting snow, to a hillock away from the yard, and I see a dull half-light that is the river. Soon it will be foaming and roaring, escaping its winter bondage in overwhelming madness. The resurrection of spring! Spring has come to Russia! Anxiety runs wild. Sleep is forgotten. Doors are thrown wide. Good neighbors get together to watch throughout the night. Everywhere, by fluttering candlelight, I can see silent prayer in fear-filled eyes, prayers which ask that the river stay in its banks.

In the morning the sun comes up and washes the whole melting world with pink-golden light. And with it comes the warm breath of the west wind!

Swirling waters from the melting snows roar down the jagged gullies and overflow the dam. The dam holds, the river holds! The whole land is drenched with melting snow. Pools, mirroring velvety green carpets, stand everywhere. All means of travel are at a standstill. Man and beast must wade in mud, almost knee deep.

And then, the great Russian steppes are in flower again. *Ach*, such beauty! The air is so fresh and clear. The sky so blue, and the clouds so white in the reflection of the huge dam. For once I can see beauty in this land. The boundaries of my heart have stretched and I have filled my lungs with the thrilling breath of life.

Now is the time for every father and son to ready the plow shares, hammering them sharp on the anvils while red hot sparks fly about them, their cossack blouses open to hairy, heaving chests, their sleeves turned back to sinewy, winter-bleached arms, and their voices pitched above the hissing of the bellows. All through the village there is the reverberating sound of hammer blows, like a throbbing heart pumping life again through wistful veins.

The people of our German villages, here on Russian soil, are no longer heavy with winter weariness. The sap is rising in their limbs, giving a new zest for living, and raising song to their lips calling the yet tender grasslands, the bird throng, the moon and stars on high to witness the awakening joy.

God has been good to our peasants in the Volgaland. Summer has come again. Crops will grow. Arms link themselves in arms, the brawny arms of men and the softer veined arms of the women, and they dance for the joy of being among the living. Youth eyes the fairness of young womanhood, and being noticed, young maidens' cheeks burst into flower while their tender lips fill with a red like wine.

*Ach*, the summers of Russia can be beautiful, now that my eyes are open. I take time out from my gardening to walk the open steppes alone, and I stand on a hillock surveying all. Above me an unbroken blue floods the sky a hundred versts around. A lone wandering cloudlet lies upon it, half floating, half fading away. There is windlessness; there is a warmth, and air like mellowed wine!

Before me roll the vast steppes, like green-golden oceans, swaying in meads of lavender, corn-flower blue, and in all the shades of red and amber. There is a multitude of bird-throng: field larks thrilling their silver tones, pouter pigeons cooing, and a flock of wild geese skimming down from the sky, like a fast moving cloud. Noiselessly the swallows dart to and fro. Silver-breasted gulls bathe leisurely in blue nothingness, while down under, wild ducks, grebes and teals wing swiftly over the overflowing dam, screaming a warning over the backs of oxen wading in shallow pools on the far rim.

Goshawks on steady wings remain motionless in the sky, their keen eyes fixed on the earth. Falcons, sparrowhawks, and terns trace circles in the thin air, eyeing their prey, reptiles and field mice; crows, rooks, magpies. . . .

Below the village flaxen haired children in homespun ginghams tumble over the velvet green grasses of the ravines, barking dogs nipping playfully at their heels. Horses neigh. Oxen bawl. Cattle and sheep browse on the distant fields; the cowherd and his dog recline in the grass. On the path from dam to village young women with strong arms carry large buckets of water, spilling long glistening sheets at first. Then there is only a silvery calmness on the brim, full to over-flowing.

To one side of me runs a ravine, clear as the sky above, with slim rainbow-colored snakes darting across the shallow waters. Frogs croak in the reeds. In the distance, on the line where sky meets the plains stands a Kirghiz covered wagon. A sprinkling of horses, cattle and sheep are grazing on the steppe nearby. All of a sudden, I think I love it all. It is all new to me, now that my eyes are open.

For the moment I am content. I know all this is beautiful only because of David Becker, who loves me. Without him it is nothing.

And, then, though I hardly know how it has come about, David has found me out here on the open steppe. I sense his presence and hear the swish of eager feet coming through the wild growth. I turn and see his smiling face, his white cossack blouse open at the throat, his arms stretched out to me.

"David," I cry, running toward him. "David!"

My heart leaps inside of me as he folds me in his arms, his lips searching mine with ardent longing.

Then, silent, we stand hand in hand and gaze out over the land. Before us roll the vast unending steppes. What do they hold for us? I wonder.

David, too, must be pondering the same question. He is so quiet. Presently, he stoops down and selects five slender blades of grass. "To braid you a ring," he says.

I watch as he folds one supple blade at a time over and under the other, alternating again and again. His fingers are so deft. In everything he is so artistic. He has so much earthly knowledge. I cannot praise him enough.

"It is but a simple thing," he insists, giving me a wink. "See?" He bends one delicate blade. "There is nothing to it."

The happy glint in his eyes strikes a foolish notion in me. "Tell me a tale out of your book learning," I say, teasing — for once not the least bit shy.

"What would you hear?" he asks, eagerly.

As I look at him a puff of vagrant wind fans a spray of hair soft across his forehead and tugs at the neck of his open cossack blouse.

"Tell me a tale about the wisdom of the wind," I decide, quickly.

David is surprised and amused by my request. But before he speaks he bounces a playful fist off the tip of my nose. "Woman is the wind," he informs me. "She is strong as the wind, as untouchable as the wind, as beautiful as the wind."

"*Ach, net,*" I chide, laughing. "What really is the wind?"

David stops braiding for the moment. He puts his arm around me and hugs me close. "If you must know," he says, "the wind is a grey-blue vulture who comes out of the nowhere to blow out our fires with its raucous laughter and then fans the cold smoke into our eyes. It rustles the leaves on the ground and bends the stoutest oak. Now, do you know?"

"Yes. Tell me another," I beg.

For the moment there is no response from David. The grass ring he has made is ready, a fragile thing, and he puts it on my finger. His hands are gentle. Still there are no words between us. To me the ring is of priceless gold. No, it is not gold, it is more than that. It is green — the very color of the mystical renaissance of spring!

"What story shall I tell?" he asks tenderly, holding my hands, looking deep into my eyes.

And because I see the soulful longing I say quickly, lest courage fail me, "Tell me a story of Gypsy love."

It takes a while for David to compose an answer.

I wonder, have I asked it because I remember the alluring Gypsy fiddler who belongs to the wilderness that lies before us? Perhaps. For, who, having once seen him could ever get him out of mind?

David's gaze goes far off into the distance and lingers on the deep ravines, sprinkled with enticing shadowy-green forests, as though the story of his dream lay out there, somewhere. And while I wait for him to speak, I long to see it too. To live it, as he is seeing it now. I get a glimpse of it almost instantly. David, beside me, is drawing a word picture that is meant for me alone.

"If only we were Gypsies, like in your love story," he speaks, in a voice barely audible. "We would stroll out into that heavenly realm and lose ourselves in time and place. We are young, and strong, and we could stand the rigour."

With that his arms go around me and he holds me oh, so tight.

"*Ach!*" my voice catches in my throat. It is all I can say, but the memory of his dream will stay with me, forever.

Spring is the time of the year when the village milch cows and sheep are again taken out to the green meadows. Before sun-up each morning Yasha, the blind cowherd, comes to drive them through the streets, gathering them from the individual barnyards. And, woe to the young peasant maiden who oversleeps and hasn't finished her milking when he blows the horn. For she must later drive her milch cows out of the village to join the herd, while villagers, young and old, lean on their yard gates and laugh and shout. The next morning she is sure to be on time.

Karlotta, always so proud and bold, is such a sleepyhead. It happens to her the very first morning. My, the smart remarks she gets. Such teasing! Karlotta can't stand it. She weeps and sasses back, but it does her no good.

For once, Karlotta is getting what she deserves, I think. Then instantly I am sorry, for who knows, it may be I who oversleep the next time. And the song they are now chanting up and down the street will be for me.

*Heute raum vor deiner Tür,*
*Faules Gretchen treib dein Vieh.* *

It is also the day when the village fathers begin the field work. Their plow shares and wagons and ox-teams are ready and waiting, while every man, his wife and children go to church to ask God's blessing. The roadway to the Lord's house is crowded. The people are dressed in their Sunday best: the women and girls with embroidered waists and bright full skirts, the men and boys in equally bright embroidered cossack blouses with their trouser legs tucked in knee length boots with vamps of colored leather.

Our German people offer solemn prayer and thanks to the Lord that summer has come again; crops, God willing, will come once more. When the services are over they rush home to change their clothes. They climb into their wagons waiting in the door-yards. And, quickly, with *"Hulla Hoi!"* they pick up the reins and, whipping their oxen and horse teams lightly, they are off in a cloud of dust, their yapping dogs following after them. Every man tries to beat his neighbor to the adjoining fields lying far out of the village, and there is great fun throughout the region.

Everywhere, peasants are plowing with yokes of oxen and frisky horse teams, turning the fresh, black loam to sun and sky, harrowing, sowing, the seed flowing in an arc from agile hands from dawn to dusk. *Ei!* He who has not walked barefoot in new-turned earth in the spring, knows not what peace and healing the earth can bring!

On Sunday, after church, when the noon meal is over, the young people roam out over the flowering fields. David Becker, the schoolmaster joins them. Merriment and laughter are everywhere. And in my heart there is a joy too sweet to bear. The girls deck their hair with blossoms and the boys wear them in their bright sashes.

*Take heed lest you shirk your own work, or tomorrow you may have to drive your own herd.

Here are tulips and there are tulips. They are everywhere. The eye can hardly believe such beauty! Each year the people dig tulip bulbs and eat them. But always there are as many as before. Blooming in the first part of the season are the dark red ones, then the rust-red, and following soon after, the sulphur-yellows, all basking in golden sunlight, and nodding to the beck and call of lilting winds. And everywhere the meadowlarks lift their wings into the blue heavens.

The young people swarm over the field. Each boy finds his favorite girl and presents her with a bouquet. Very often he steals a kiss, and if the kiss is good, then two. Some couples walk hand in hand, unmindful of the others. David walks at my side, and Karlotta pouts. She is the only one who has no fun. David picks prime blossoms and sprays of ferny leaves and he braids a wreath while he talks of a princess who should wear a crown of jewels in her hair, instead of flowers. I am confounded with the nearness of him, the sound of his voice, the knowing way of his fingers braiding a garland of flowers.

Then, when David and I are alone for a moment, the same deep look comes into his eyes. He stands before me and places the wreath of flowers on my hair. There is a gentleness in his hands and in his voice, also, as he whispers:

"It is you, I want, Evaliz. You are the wine and the bread of life! Will you marry me, Evaliz?"

*Ach*, I am so happy, I do not know what to say. My heart is bursting, my tongue will not move. I can only stand and look at him and nod my head, yes, yes, while tears fill my eyes.

A tremor passes through me when he takes me in his arms, crushing me to him, kissing me. "David. David," I call him by his name. "*Ach*. David, my love."

After this, Karlotta looks on me with hate, and I do not mind.

# CHAPTER 5

# *The Windows of Russia*

*E*i, night and day, there are rumors! The people are saying there will be war. Russian muzhiks traveling the rutted, dusty road past our village by foot, or by the familiar horse-drawn droshky, leave conflicting reports. Rumors of the same sort also come by the waterways of the mighty Volga. It is difficult to determine what is rumor and what is fact. But with each report fear beds itself ever deeper in the eyes of our villagers.

What will become of us, if war comes? Will it be here, or elsewhere? What of David? He is a soldier. Will he have to go? The thought of his leaving nearly stops my heart. Whenever I am near him, I watch for the least sign of worry, or of what he may know. But I detect nothing.

If there is going to be war, he would know, I tell myself, going about my work, twisting more and more straw to heat the wall oven. When, at last, the oven is hot enough to bake bread, I scrape out all the ashes and slide in the loaves. My stepmother has given all the family baking over to me.

Persistent rumors say that Russia and Japan are engaged in a heated argument over their rights in Manchuria and over the seaport of Port Arthur on the mainland of China. Our Volga-German people know little of the goings-on in greater Russia. Outside of passersby bringing news there is no communication. In the meantime we watch the war clouds gather and only hope that the storm will never break.

Russia is a nation of many people. Its inhabitants are a jumble of creed, color, and races from fair, white-skinned people to the darkest of dark nomads who roam the boundless steppes and who bow down before various idols. They hold many stations in life. Grand Dukes. Princes. Noblemen. Land-Owners. Atamans, and bourgeois. *Hospodors. Bürgermeisters.* Kulaks and muzhiks sweating over plots of land, being taxed and re-taxed. Gypsies. Poles. Germans. Jews. Turks. Kirghiz. Cossacks, both Don and Kuban. Mongols. Tartars. Vagabonds. Vassals. Hirelings. Thieves. Harlots and trollops of all tribes and ages. These and many others are Russia's varied children. Good people and bad people. Some live in great houses. Others live in huts and hovels filthier than pig sties. Still others live in *semljankens,* dugouts, infested by fleas and huge spiders and tarantulas.

"Maybe this trouble will blow over," say some of our village fathers. "*Ja,* maybe, it is only a storm cloud. Always before, Russia has had quarrels with her neighbors over a water route that will not freeze. It is nothing to get excited about."

"Sure. *Ja,* sure."

Even though the rumors subside for a while, others raise their heads to shrill in our ears. These refuse to lie down. They defy the sane reasoning of our elders. They shout that Russia is seething with unrest. Riots in the cities! Dissension against the czar, Nicholas II, whose ultra-conservative policy decrees that agitators as well as political assassins be ruthlessly punished. Rumors say that savage hate has been brewing for years among the down trodden, that, now, the suppressed peoples are rising in revolt. The word "Revolt!" seems to be on the lips of everyone, elsewhere. And the humble German in our Volgaland must cast his eyes down and hunch his shoulders in shame, and dread, and fear.

Every day one hears of far away atrocities. Crimes. Burnings. One hears of peasants and Jews clashing in market places. Pogroms, bloody and terrible. One hears of babies, held tight to the bosoms of lamenting mothers, being torn limb from limb. One hears of peasants revolting against the rich who own the land, the forests, the rivers, and the plains alike. The rich and mighty live in cities, yet their long, iron-clawed fingers reach out and wrest the very breath from the peasants, leaving them not even a handful of grain to soothe their gnawing hunger.

Here among our Volga-German people, living on our open steppes, it is hard to believe that peasants are so oppressed by the great and noble landowners of the cities, though, in truth, we, in

68

our villages, are taxed and double taxed. Yet we live by reason of our diligent labors, rarely complaining.

The picture that is set before our eyes is a picture of Russia gone completely mad. Ripe for revolt! Russian peasants elsewhere are striving to secure more land, more freedom; merchants and industrialists are ready to help in the revolution. Factory workers and students favoring strikes give flaming orations in front of shop doors and street corners. The Revolutionists' armoured cry is: "Crush the czar, the dukes, the princes! Crush the police and all masters of power, then we can open to you and the millions like you the whole world and all her great wonders."

Here, in our Volgaland, our village fathers stand long hours, in ever growing throngs, in front of market places and marvel, and speculate on these strange tidings from the lips of strangers passing through our village.

"*Ja*, it is true," says a merchantman who has traveled to our village from a Volga steamer. "Even students in the great northern cities help in the general revolt by demonstrations and open speeches. Even now, railroads and factories are given over to strikes and riots. Sure. Soon there will be violent bloodshed in the great cities that can't be stopped and Russia's fast strangle-hold on her peasants will be forever broken. Like this — " he demonstrates with his hands and ends the matter with a spirited laugh.

*Ach!* What a terrible gleam is in his fanatic eyes. I look at him and I am afraid. These are things I know nothing about, things I cannot even understand, and I flee from the market place to shut the stark picture out of my mind. But it searches me out wherever I go. Still, I refuse to believe it. And I say to my eldest brother Wilhelm what I wouldn't dare say to my father:

"We Germans, here on the steppe, are not so suppressed that our lives are despaired of. Will we have to join the revolt, and the war?"

"*Kind, Kind.* Child, Child," Wilhelm says, his face clouded with worry. "The war-dogs are straining at their leashes, and not even the hot blood of Beelzebub will sate their hunger. All, yes, even we, will have to suffer when that time comes." Wilhelm shrugs his shoulders and turns from me.

Is there no peace for us? I think. How can I know? In my anxiety I decide to ask David. But David first of all is a soldier. He will not make any comment. Yet I can see that his face belies his inner feelings. Two weeks later he tells my uncle, the *Bürgermeister*, that the school session may have to cease.

"If war breaks out, I will have to return to my post," he says.

*Ach*, I think my heart will break. I cannot find solace anywhere.

As the days go by, anxiety in our Volgaland is rising to a higher pitch. Who can rightly tell what is happening in the north? It seems the free and quiet days are gone forever. Even the slow-wandering travelers of the dusty roads have stepped up their pace. Uncertainty and fearfulness hangs as a dark cloud over our heads.

And, now, a new rumor that bureaucracy is fast losing its hold on Russia excites our learned people. War with Japan is almost a reality! General unrest is growing in extent and bitterness! Strikes! Riots monopolize the gendarmes and make room for robbers everywhere, singly and in bands. I am glad it has not reached our Saratov Province.

Bewilderment fills our people. Among our Germans there has been no great lack of comfort though meals are often frugal. Nor has there been great hatred or contempt for bureaucracy. Our people, here in Russia, are for the most part humble in their lot, demurring seldom, holding fast in their minds the memories of their forbears who struggled to establish this land for them.

The rumors coming on swift wings have disturbed our peace forever. War with Japan! Revolt in greater Russia! Where will it end? Mothers everywhere are concerned about their sons being taken. Don Cossack military troops have long passed through our village and are passing still, silver cartridge bands gleaming across their breasts, tall caracul hats smartly set — rows upon rows of Cossacks in blue coats with silver-encrusted daggers and swords glittering in the sun. First come two officers, then fifty-some Cossacks four in a row, each with a spare horse at his side, followed by a line of long carts loaded with boxes and chests.

Then, suddenly, through my uncle Dietz, the *Bürgermeister*, an army post is set up in our village and the command for instant mobilization follows. Panic is in our midst. No one is sure what it is all about. The army officials waste few words in explanation. Every order is pushed with haste and precision. The question in every household: "Are Russia and Japan warring? Who can be sure? Japan is so far away . . . "

Only one thing is certain, our village is fast being drained of its strong, young men. It is a breach of the promise of freedom from military conscription our people were given so long ago by the Empress Catherine.

Strange things are beginning to happen, here and there, among bewildered people. Young men who have a dread of war are inflicting injuries on themselves in hopes of being rejected by the army. Some inflict injuries to eye, ear, finger, or limb which cause them great suffering, but they know in the end, that they will be well again and free men. Often, however, the deformities intended to be temporary prove incurable, so that there are many young men blind in one eye, or hard of hearing, or lame.

This practice is common among the most frightened but many of our people are true soldiers, having served their four years of compulsory service, subject to further call. David is a true soldier. He has served more than his four years. He has trained in Rostov and Odessa under strict military rule.

Then comes word that David is numbered among the ones to go. I can neither eat nor sleep. *Ach,* God, he cannot go. I have only found him, I say to myself, over and over again. He cannot go.

But all the while I know the Don Cossack militia is riding toward our village to take him. Even now, all our villagers are waiting in the market place in apprehension, awaiting their arrival. The sun is glaring down out of a cloudless sky and the air is close and stifling. David and the other young men are inside the army headquarters across the way, busy with last details. Mothers are bewailing the loss of their sons, while fathers stand silently by, their heads bent in sorrow. Young maidens sob quietly, in the background, weeping for the departure of a loved one.

"Here they come! Here they come!" shouts my brother, Otto. He and the other village youth are running toward the people gathered in the street. A score of barking dogs are following at their heels, adding to the noise. "The Cossacks are coming to pick up the men! They are down the lane leading into town. *Hulla Hoi!* Hear the loud crack of their *nagaikas.* * *Ei,* see them come!"

The utterly unhappy people bestir themselves and move out of the street to make room for the brigade.

Everyone stands in stony silence as the riders approach. The young boys stop their shouting and look in awe. The barking dogs, fearful now of the crack of the whip, hump their backs and slink away.

The Cossacks are only a stone's throw away, and David has not come out yet. I fear there will be no time for farewell. I tear my eyes away from the door and look at the mounted patrol so nattily dressed in blue coats and tall, caracul hats, swords at their sides and rifles in holders of shaggy kid skin on their backs. Each has a spare horse at his side.

Usually these warriors are brash and foul-mouthed when they ride through the village and a young girl wouldn't think of being caught on the street, but today they are all *Soldat,* soldier. They

*Nagaika* (Russian) — a short horse whip, used in place of spurs. It has short leather thongs.

71

come riding down the street in precise formation, four abreast, their harness trappings jingling, the hoofs of their prancing horses beating a rhythmic tune: clippity, clip, clap. The cadence says they have come to take my love away. I cover my face and weep.

Then, all of a sudden, our young men leave headquarters and are given over to the Cossack command. *Ach!* It is true, there is no time for secret words and fond farewells in all this excitement and hurry. Even the highly trained horses are impatient to be on their way.

Somehow I spy David and I wave to him. He is so handsome, so straight and so tall. He is no longer the schoolmaster but the soldier. So quickly he comes through the crowd. He takes my tear-stained hands and presses them to his lips. "Wait for me," he whispers. His voice is heavy. Then, comes the hetman's command to mount and David swings into the saddle. He is leaving me, riding through my heart and out of my life.

"Good-bye, Evaliz. I'll write," he calls back.

"I cannot read," I cry.

"I will write to Karlotta. She will read for you. Good-bye." Then he is off in a cloud of dust, lost among the fast moving Cossack cavalry.

"No, no. Not Karlotta," I cry after him, but it is of no avail. He does not hear me.

But Karlotta, the vixen, is by my side. She smiles at me with her bright diabolic eyes. "Come Evaliz," she says, "let us be friends. You will need me now."

*"Ach,"* I say, "I hate you!" But Karlotta only laughs.

Weeks go by, and life doesn't seem the same anymore. There is no joy. The sun shines, and wind lilts, but to no avail. Meadowlarks lift lazy wings over flowering fields and shrill their songs in vain. I look with eagerness on Karlotta's face whenever I see her. But, as always, I see nothing there. David has not written to her, I decide. But I cannot be sure. Karlotta might keep it a secret, and first make me suffer. David does not know this, and I cannot blame him. He had not planned it this way, I know. It just happened in the press of things.

Otto, who is not old enough for the service, is possessed with the idea. He wants to be a Cossack general, he thinks. On the sly, when my father is away, he takes my father's best team outside the village. There he tries out all the intricate maneuvers David has shown him, trotting, leading the spare horse at his side.

Even in such a short time he can change from his mount to the spare horse at full trot. He is so good that even my father will have to marvel at his accomplishment. But he is too reckless, I think.

Without a thought for his life he gallops down the field. Then, without a sign or warning, he slides out of the saddle down underneath his horse and holds there between the pummeling hoofs. My heart rises in my throat and I cover my eyes in fright. But there is no need to worry. When I look again he is standing on the saddle at full gallop, making believe he is shooting a rifle. *Ach*, such a boy! He cannot wait until he can be a soldier. He says he will be a great *Kapitän*, a *Hauptmann* like the Cossack general we saw. But right now Otto is only a rascal, still yanking the girls' hair braids.

A month goes by and I have no word from David. Very few letters come to our village. When they do the matter is posted on a slate in the *Bürgermeister's* office. But I am too shy to see for myself or ask my uncle Dietz if I have a letter. I will rely on Karlotta, instead. She is one who could not keep her mouth shut forever on such a matter.

When, at last, a message is posted it is something entirely different. It excites all the people and there is great jubilation throughout the village. There is no war, the bulletin says. It was only a quick mobilization to test the strength of the country, a special act of preparedness, shrouded in a veil of secrecy.

Our villagers are deeply concerned. Everyone is asking each other, "What is really happening? Is there no truth to what we have heard? Well, no matter what it is, it can't be good," they all conclude.

"If we are not at war with Japan, maybe the whole thing will blow over," I try to reason with my brother, Friederich, who is next in line to go.

"No," he says firmly. "The flame is lit. It will not soon go out. Russia, at last, will have her way at a seaport. She will hang on. You wait." *Ach*, maybe Friederich is right. But I pray that he is wrong, and that David will be home soon.

This noon when I come home from the village garden where I have been hoeing all morning, I see Karlotta running down the street toward our house.

"Evaliz, Evaliz," she calls. "Guess what has happened."

"What?" I shout, and run to meet her. But she offers no more. She is the sly one. I see the cunning look in her black eyes and I know I must beg for what is rightly mine. "Do you have a letter?" I ask, the pain in my heart nearly killing me.

"Yes, I have a letter," she says, giving me an impish smirk. She brings the letter from the fold of her skirt. "See, Evaliz, he has thought of me," she moons, pressing it deep into the intimate softness of her full bosom. One cannot stop Karlotta once she is possessed.

"His words would turn your eyes green," she says, coyly. "Here, read it," she laughs, and hands me the letter. "Go on, read it," she mocks. "You should read as well as I. You are as old, and as smart, I think."

I look at the paper trembling violently in my hand and I see his dear writing. The words are mine. But without reading I cannot claim them. I am dependent on Karlotta. I hate myself for being so dumb. And I'm ashamed and mad, too. Still, she has let me touch it; maybe that is enough.

Karlotta, so dark of hair, and so pink of cheek, delights in the tremble of my hands. Finally, when she has enough, I swallow my pride. "Does he say anything about me?" I ask, my voice quavering out of control.

"That I will not tell you. I'm no *stoffel-Ochs*, Evaliz." She laughs, and throws her head high like a sassy colt, her long mane flying. "I will say only one thing: maybe he will be home soon."

*Ach,* my heart skips a beat. It is all I need to know. Maybe David will be home soon! I leave the letter with Karlotta and run through the courtyard gate and into the house.

The grain has ripened in the field and still there is no David. Karlotta does not hear from him again and she looks miffed. I leave her alone.

It is harvest time and I am with the reapers out in the breast-deep golden wheat. Karlotta hardly ever comes; she hates to work. The wind sighs and the yellow grain bends and rises, running laughing ripples across the field. One wave chases the other, rising and rippling again. Peasant backs bend roundly, arms extended as swishing scythes rise and fall and leave broad swaths of gold on the ground. We women, young and old, the hems of our full skirts lifted and tucked in at our waist bands, follow in our bare feet to glean and bind into sheaves what falls behind the men.

Suddenly, there are singing voices coming from afar. The swish of falling wheat ceases. Surprised men and women unbend their backs and look toward the village.

The singing comes closer. *"Heilli, heillo, bei uns geht's immer . . ."*

"Look!" the reapers shout to one another. "Marching men. Our boys are back!"

All of us run to meet them. Is David among them? I ask myself, my heart pounding as I run. There should be twenty. But where is David? David. . . . Then I see him. He is smiling and singing and marching with the others.

74

Mothers throw their arms around their sons and kiss them; fathers stand silently by, tears glistening in their eyes. But there is no father or mother to greet blond, sun-tanned David. His parents live in the village of Tscherbakowka.

"Ho!" a sweat-stained fellow shouts. "Is there no one to kiss the schoolmaster?" He casts his glee-filled eyes over the young girls present and clacks his tongue for shame. "Come! Do not make him wait."

Everyone laughs in fun, even we embarrassed girls, a little.

"Where's Karlotta?" A brash-voiced woman raises her voice above the crowd. "She would not make him wait, I can tell you."

Again a shout goes up. "Let it be Evaliz, then." And I feel myself being pushed forward. Shame burns on my face. This is not the way I have dreamed of his homecoming. I would have had just the two of us.

Then, David is standing in front of me, waiting. He is so straight and handsome, like the soldier he is, all brown from the wind and sun. A glad smile is on his face and his blue eyes are looking warm and searching into mine, forgetting the crowd. He reaches out and takes me into his arms and my heart thumps with the nearness of him.

"David," I whisper, putting my lips to his, also forgetting the crowd. His arms are around me like bands of iron and I am in heaven.

I hear teasing laughter and I break away and hide myself in the happy crowd, glad that Karlotta isn't around to make matters worse. She must really be sick to stay away from an occasion like this, I think.

Before long David is back to his job teaching school. And it would take wild horses to keep Karlotta away. She mocks me at every turn and is plainly amused when she knifes me with what she and David said or did. I know that she lies. She is the wicked one. She will not obey her father. Her mother can do nothing with her. She is in school all day just to be near David, hanging onto his every word, saying, "How do you do this, David?" or "How do you do that? *Ach,* you are so clever. When will I know as much as you, David?"

*Pfui!* She makes me sick. How I hate her. Sometimes I am afraid to go and work in the field for fear she will win him away from me. I lie awake nights thinking about it. Yet, I know, I must do all I can for my father. It will take money for my dowry if, and when, I get married. My father could not, and would not, hire a man to take my place.

So I go with my *Familie* to our faraway fields to help thresh the grain. It is hard work and there is much haste for soon the season will be changing. The threshing floor, or *Denner*, is made much like those in Bible days. First the grass is scraped from a flat unplowed piece of ground. The place is made round then wet down with water brought from a nearby stream. Next straw is added and pressed down hard by driving ox-teams and wagons over it. It is left to dry. When the ground is hard the straw is swept off. It is remarkable how firm and smooth the place is when finished. The sheaves of wheat are placed on the *Denner* and the grain is ridden out with ox and horse teams pulling the threshing stones. When all the grain is trounced from the chaff the straw is raked away and the grain winnowed. The golden kernels are dipped up in shallow pans held high in the wind, and poured out again so that the chaff is carried away in puffs of golden clouds.

The hours are long and grueling. The barbs blow into our clothes and scratch us unmercifully. All day our backs are bent, our throats parched, and our legs weak and quaking with fatigue. My father sees how I am suffering. "Child, take a handful of grain and chew it for strength," he urges.

I scoop up a handful of the hard wheat kernels and cup them in my hand, trickling them from hand to hand, blowing away the sharp barbs and soil. I chew the grain as everyone else is doing, and it gives strength to my flagging body. Here in Russia everyone in the family works as one, young and old alike. Old women, weather-beaten and brittle as locusts, are sweeping and guarding the stray kernels back into captivity allowing not a single one to escape — for this is the staff of life. Everything depends on it.

In the shade of our wagons hang *curdukes*, goat and lamb skin bags, filled with sour clabber milk. We drink this like water to quench our thirst. We learned this from the yellow-skinned Kirghiz who roam the steppes with their grazing herds. Milk is their main staff of life here in this wide open land. Mare's milk, they claim, is far the best.

I am glad when the threshing is done. Now I can hire out, like my sisters, Katrinliz, Marik, and Malia did. I plan to make money for the things I need for my home, if I should get one. I will need linens and a change of clothes, some shoes — if money permits. I have never had a pair of leather shoes. I have always had to wear heavy felt boots in winter. In the summer I go barefoot.

There is one consolation and I keep it locked in my heart. If David keeps on teaching, I will not have to live in my husband's household. Some families consist of twenty or more members, men, women and children. If it is a peace-loving family well and good. But, if they are quarrelsome life can be hectic, especially with a collection of frisky children.

All is in vain. I find no work. All the places in rich homes are taken. There is nothing left but to haul manure. This is done by young men and oftentimes by girls, too. In fact the job of cleaning out the barns and corrals of the rich people and hauling the manure out onto the fields is greatly sought after by some for the fun it affords. It is no great shame in our village to do this work and I accept it gladly.

My father furnishes me with a team of horses and a wagon and I go to the great barns of Herr Lichtenwald. There in all the muck and stench I load my wagon and haul it out to the field where the *brigoshig*, the land supervisor, has shown me. Others are doing it too, and the piles of manure become large and many. Here it must stay and winter and ferment.

I work hard. My feet and clothes are stained with the stuff. My throat and eyes burn from the stench. I cannot sit down because the wagon has no seat, nor would I sit down on the high-piled load. But I stand on a board fastened on the wagon right behind the horses' tails. This is fine until some fellow comes racing past me and whacks the rump of my horses and I am pitched backward into the mess, stained to the skin. I laugh, for, what else can I do? It happens to all the rest of them. The boys think it a great sport.

It could never happen to Karlotta. No, not Karlotta. She is much too fine a lady, she thinks. She would never come near the place. If she were asked to go, she would lie on the floor and rant and rave, like a spoiled child. She would even swoon to prevent her father from asking her. She is content to let her father worry about her dowry. Yet, what makes me so angry is that she is so pretty, though worthless, and all the village dandies cast their mooning eyes on her.

All the manure is not used on the field. It is far too precious for that. The people must have fuel for the long winters. What we have hauled now will not be ready until next year. First it has to take the summer heat, wind, and winter snows wetting it down, so it will heat and ferment.

When it is well rotted in the spring, the huge piles are pulled apart and spread out. Each villager takes charge of his own store of manure. Straw is hauled onto the fermented layer and water added. Men and boys use wooden sleighs to haul barrels of water up from the dam to pour on. Then children astride oxen and horses ride through it. Some villagers even go in it with bare feet. Round and round they go mixing in the straw and water. More straw and water is added, if needed. Then, when it is all mixed, it is smoothed out to the depth of a spade blade and left to dry.

When the manure mixture is dry enough to cut, the men bring spades, sharpened in their blacksmith shops, and cut the mixture into squares. When the blocks are at least half dry, women and children go out and turn them over so they finish drying in the sun. When completely dry, the fuel is hauled home to the courtyard and made into stacks, to be used in the large baking ovens built in the dividing walls of their houses. These ovens open on two rooms and can be fired from both sides. And the top provides a flat surface for a nice warm bed.

The people learned long ago that the firm, almost stone-hard blocks of fuel give a long lasting heat that is much better than a fire fed by twisted bundles of straw or grass. And, when properly cured, the manure blocks give off no smell and can be stacked in the house beside the oven.

My pay is only twenty kopeks a day, but I take it gladly.

# CHAPTER 6

# The Road Of Life

We are all busy, my stepmother, aunts, and my sisters, stripping goose-down from the very smallest feathers, for my dowry. We have shut ourselves in the bake-house so that we will not be disturbed. The door must be kept shut or the down will lift up out of the tubs over which we are working. Even with our breathing alone the soft stuff floats everywhere, tickling our noses, settling thick on our heads and making us all look like white-haired women.

When all the work is finished my pillows are soft and downy. They are square, so light and full that one can almost sleep sitting up. Both my featherbeds, one to sleep on and the other to cover up with, are equally full and thick. My linens are very special because my brother Friederich helped weave them.

I look about myself and realize how rich I am. This is mine, and that is mine. Never, in all my life, have I owned so much. I take the hem of my apron and wipe away the tears.

My stepmother is fitting my wedding dress made of wine-colored wool. David bought the material from a Gypsy band traveling through our village. They told him it came from the royal mills in

Kiev. Karlotta mocks the idea and says Gypsies are such liars. I ignore her and listen only to David. "Wine color, Evaliz, like the ruby you are," he says, putting his arm around me.

Karlotta seeing him storms out of the house, slamming the door so hard that a wisp of straw floats down from the thatched roof and settles in my hair.

David is impressed by it and pleased. "Ah," he says, "a golden crown on golden blonde hair. A good omen."

We both laugh. But when it is over I feel just a bit sorry for Karlotta. She has so much. But a wine-colored wedding dress she does not have.

My dress is very beautiful, the frills around the neck are soft. The bodice is high and full, the waist slender. The narrow gores of the full-flowing skirt begin at the waistline and widen out toward the hemline which is finished with a wide band of ruffles which nearly brush the floor. I feel like dancing in the long, ruffled skirt.

"Stand still," my stepmother scolds, smiling, "or I can't finish this."

"*Ja*, sure," I say. Everyone looks at me with sparkling, loving eyes. For once I am completely happy.

But, more than this, my brother Wilhelm is making me a pair of leather shoes from the leather my father has tanned with such care. He looks up from his work to give me a wink and a smile. "Our little Evaliz can't marry without shoes," he says.

The remark isn't lost on my stepmother, neither is the wink. "*Na, aller Zeit,*" she puts in. "Then she will really float, right out of this world. See how giddy she is already."

"So, let her float on her angel wings," my brother Wilhelm chides playfully. He lifts me up with his strong arms and kisses my cheek. "The moon and stars will be her habitation." Wilhelm lets me down and all that are in the house laugh. I laugh with them, remembering what the old lady said to me at Nathalia's wedding, "*Liebchen, die Zeit bringt Rosen*...Darling, time will bring roses."

When at last Wilhelm is finished with my shoes I cannot believe how light they are. Not klunky like my boots. It seems I can hardly stay on the ground. Wilhelm is right! Maybe they will take me to the moon and the stars — or even to *Amerika?*

I have a lace shawl, soft and white as angel mist to set on my hair for a bridal veil. My father bought it from wandering Gypsies along with gold-spangled earrings. I look into the mirror my sister Marik brought from Frau Lichtenwald's house and I can hardly believe I am seeing myself.

*"Ei,"* my stepmother exclaims, "wait until David sees those apple cheeks, the stars in your eyes, those teeth, so pearly white. *Ach!* And those lips, so soft and full like a Gypsy maiden's." She turns me around and around like angel chimes spinning from the heat of candles atop a *Christbaum,* a Christmas tree. All that is lacking is the jingling music, but I have that in my heart.

My stepmother smiles and nods, satisfied with the way my outfit looks. Out of the corner of my eye I see Otto spying around the door. By the look on his face, I know what he is thinking, "Can our Evaliz really look like that?" He is such a tease. Yet he is touched, I can tell that.

Later when he comes strutting into the room, he sinks his hands deep into his pockets and says boldly, "You don't look like so much, Evaliz." But I catch a note of sadness in his voice.

I have no wedding bouquet like Nathalia because it is long past the season for prairie flowers. I remember the wreath of flowers David braided and placed in my flaxen hair when he asked me to marry him, and it is enough. I do not need them now.

Together, David and I walk down the church aisle where the sunlight comes streaming in. He is holding my arm, keeping time with my step. He is handsome in his new cossack blouse, cinched in at the waist by a silver filigree sash he has made himself. The church is filled to overflowing. Pastor Hahn, looking massive in his black robe, is waiting for us at the altar rail, Bible in hand.

Once there, he extends his hand and we make our pledge to God. The text Pastor Hahn has chosen is Isaiah Chapter 64, verse 8: "But now, O Lord, thou art our father; we are the clay, and thou our potter; and we all are the work of thy hand."

I am quivering all over and I feel a warm glow flooding my face. I think I will sink to the floor, but David steadies me with his arm. David is strong and sure in his ways. I count myself fortunate that I have found him to help me walk the steep road of life.

Two months have gone by. David and I live in the back room of the church where he also teaches school. The winter is severe and there is only enough fuel to have one fire. This makes it very crowded. The children sit in deep straw spread out on the dirt floor around the fire. I sit further back with my knitting, stockings for David, and a large, heavy shawl for me. I have no coat.

As I work, I listen to the children read, and I am fascinated by the things words can unleash. Here is knowledge for the taking, but it is not as easy as all that. The children must work very hard;

teaching is no play with David. They must learn a great deal by heart: the Ten Commandments and their explanation as set forth in Luther's Catechism, the Creeds, the Lord's Prayer, as well as Bible verses, and many, many hymns — some with twelve verses. There are problems in arithmetic to be reckoned on an abacus or on slates, and history and geography.

While I am busy knitting I learn many hymns and Bible verses by heart. But reading is another matter. I cannot get myself to try. I would feel shame before these young children. David begs me, "Come, sit with them and learn."

But I say the knitting comes first just to get out of it. Sometimes it's the bread baking, sometimes the washing or the folding of clothes. To get the clothes smooth I fold them carefully and then sit on them, pressing them down. I will sit on six or eight pieces at a time, or until the pile gets too high, then I remove the bottom pieces and keep on folding others. This does a good job getting the wrinkles out.

It is strange being a *Schulmeister's* wife. I have so little to do on these dark winter days. "The work is like child's play," I told my old neighbor. Everyone calls her *Grossmutter* Volz. She is withered and dry of bone as a crow. But that wizened old woman answered with a high-pitched and knowing laugh out of her toothless mouth:

"*Ach, glaube nur*, believe, it will not always be so. Even the smallest pebble cast into the sea of life strikes a three-fold ripple. *Ja*, many are the pitfalls to be met later." I know that her grown children, one by one, have left her and gone to *Amerika*, forsaking her in her old age. But, for once, I refuse to believe her words of wisdom. Surely, for me, there can be nothing but happiness, I reason.

Today as I sit in my corner, away from the reading school children, my knitting in hand, I think back on the words *Grossmutter* Volz spoke, and I see how right she is. Life does not stay the same. The young must strain to learn, some more than others. Nothing comes easy.

Suddenly, a thought comes to me. It is only a wee thought, but it pierces through all the noise the children are making. I recall I had a headache this morning when I got up. I had one the morning before, also. *Ach*, maybe things are different with me. How can I be sure?

I decide I will go to *Grossmutter* Volz and ask her about it. She will know. I roll up my knitting and go out the door. The wind howls and shrieks and clatters the door and windows. I draw my shawl tight around me and stumble over the high drifts, the wind stinging my face with swirling bits of snow. I grope my way to her door and

82

bang hard on it. She lets me in in a gust of wind and it raises a vapor in her house so thick that I can hardly see her. Nor can she see who has entered.

Finally when the fog clears I see the withered, impatient woman before me. *"Herr Je', Herr Je',"* she screeches, bouncing up and down. "Only a fool would come out in weather like this. Sit down!"

When I loosen the shawl about my face, she says, "Oh, it is you." All at once she is gentle. She is a strange creature, hard one moment, soft the next. Her thin hair has the whiteness of winter snows over the dry, parched land that is her face.

"Is there something, Evaliz?" she queries, her bright all-knowing eyes seeing right through me.

"I don't rightly know," I answer, and I think she is not listening, because she is busy stirring up an herb tea. I watch the copper bracelet she wears on her dry, bony arm for the *Gliederschmerz*, the rheumatism in her joints, go jangling to and fro. They seemingly can't find a place to land. Finally, she is finished.

"Here, drink this," she commands, handing me the bowl with the steaming brew.

I taste the stuff. *"Ach*, it makes me sick to my stomach."

"You are with child, Evaliz," she says simply. And it is as if she had said: "Today I saw a sprout of wheat. Tomorrow you will knead it into bread," or "The meadows are greening. Tomorrow it is summer."

I will have a son for David! My heart sings inside of me. "A son for David but not for Russia," I say with sureness to the *Grossmutter.* "Maybe, now, David will take me to *Amerika."*

*"Amerika, wah!"* the *Grossmutter* shrieks like a witch; her face darkens. Her withered hands, hard, and skinny as the claws of a bird, grip the back of a wicker chair. And the copper bracelet slips down over her hand and clamps over her bony fingers.*"Wah*, it is a wicked land. It robs an old woman of her own flesh and blood." Her voice breaks. She becomes something sad and helpless. A lone tear, large and glistening, washes down a deep gully, where many have washed before.

A tenderness and pity wells up in me. It does no good to argue with this old woman about the goodness of *Amerika.* But it must be fine, for all that her children do not bother to write to her. "So, so, *Grossmütterchen."* I sit her down on the chair and soothe her trembling hands. "I will take your children's place," I promise.

She smiles softly on me like a wounded child when comfort has finally come. She surely has lived a hard life in this burdened land. No bright promise lies before her, as it does for me; only God's acre is her lasting hope.

After this I finish the knitting I have started and begin making things for the baby. I keep it a secret from David because I cannot get myself to say it, just yet.

The winter is almost past when David notices my condition. *"Liebchen,* why did you not tell me?" he asks, and I see the gladness on his face. "Now I must make other plans, maybe get some land. Teaching alone will not keep a family. These people are so poor."

*"Ach, net,"* I protest. There is a feeling of dread inside of me. If David binds himself to this land then he will always stay. His yoke will be linked to this soil. I have seen it happen to many people. The earth has a way with man.

"Maybe, we can go to *Amerika?"* It is the first time I speak up for myself. "There it will be different." Now that I say it, it sounds foolish and I cannot be sure that it would work.

A twinkle comes into David's eyes, then he laughs out loud and pulls me down on a bench with him. "Look, *Liebchen,* it takes money to wander so far. We will not think about that for a long time."

Now that my golden dream has shattered, I bury my head in his loving arms and cry great tears. David lets me cry. *"Ach, Liebchen, Liebchen,"* he reasons. "It is one flight to the house top; it is the leap of the soul to the sunrise. *Amerika* is far away."

It is summer again. The wind has turned overnight. An almost forgotten mildness is in the air. "Hosanna in the highest," the tender breezes whisper. "The winter has passed." It is as if unkind winter had never been. Strong and relentless the sap is rising from the soft, moist earth, filling the veins of every man, woman, and child. Everywhere there is summer gaiety and laughter and joyfulness. And my son is born.

I suffer a painful childbirth, like Anna, my brother Wilhelm's wife. And though I say I will not scream as she did, I do anyway. *Grossmutter* Volz has come to help me; she sends a neighbor's child to bring David from where he is working in the village store Saturdays. *"Geb' Acht Madel.* Beware, girl, that you do not stop to play," she warns.

My stepmother and sisters cannot help me because they are out in the field, as is every other adult. It is good that I have the *Grossmutter.* She brings a folded towel, where I am kneeling by a chair. "Bite into it, *Liebchen.* Bury your teeth into it; it will make your burden lighter," she says.

I do as she says, but it doesn't help much. My body is torn with pain. David! When will he come? When? My fingernails break as I grip the chair where I am kneeling. The neighbor child has stopped to play. David doesn't come. I think I am lost. In my suffering I become confused about the *Grossmutter*. At brief intervals I think what a strange old lady to have at a time like this. The old and the very young so close together! My mind conjures strange thoughts: She is the dry husk. The child-to-be is the seed. The plowing must be done; the wheat must sprout; I must knead it into bread. How long? How long? This is *Amerika's* child. *Ach*, no, it belongs to Russia. When will David come?

At last, I am in my bed and the *Grossmutter* brings me my son. He is so tiny and lovely. I call him Theodore because it means the gift of God. I am proud that I can give sons to my husband. "David will think he is an angel," I smile and say to the old woman.

"*Ja*, sure!" she replies. "An angel to pull the heartstrings." She nods her head and her thoughts wander off to who knows where.

Suddenly a fear comes over me. Is she thinking my son will die? I must ask.

"*Grossmutter*, will my son grow big and strong?"

She laughs a good laugh and reaches down to pick up one tiny hand. She rubs her hard, dry fingers over the wee fingertips and her bright eyes twinkle.

"*Na*, sure, he will be a fine *Landsmann*. Even with fragile hands like these he will feel the rough, dry clods of a stubborn earth." She puts back the wee hand and gently draws the covers close to him. As she does so, I see a change come over her face and the light in her eyes seems to go out.

I have a foreboding and fear grips my heart. How can anyone know what this woman is thinking? She can see into the future, I know. But what? My mind recalls the pending war with Japan, the riots in the far cities. Will war come? What will become of us? Who knows?

Presently in my new-found happiness, I push all this out of my mind. But, still, I cannot forget that David is a soldier of the czar.

Here in the room, the *Grossmutter* goes about her work, mumbling to herself. I catch only a sentence: "Perhaps, far better the cool peace of God's acre." I cannot understand what she means by that. But before I can ask her, David comes bounding in.

"*Evaliz! Grossmutter!*" he shouts. He catches the old woman in his arms and swings her around. She protests loud and shrieking, but with gaiety. "I heard it on the way," he says, and there is such a gladness on his face.

Then he is by my side and there is a gentle healing in his cool hand as he lays it on my forehead. It is enough. I need no other assurance, only to have David near.

I watch my baby day and night. He is growing some, but he is so very quiet. He doesn't cry or fuss like other babies do. The day fades into night and still, he hardly makes a sound. But, a sweetness plays on his face. He is an angel, sure!

The *Grossmutter* comes to look at him and clucks her tongue. More and more she talks of God's acre. She is failing fast these days, I think.

I lie awake at night thinking of the strange words she utters: "Perhaps, far better God's acre."

"*Ach, net,*" I sob. "My son shall live. He shall be big and strong!" What does an old lady know? But I am so troubled that I have a terrifying dream. I dream that I am standing out in the yard, looking up into the star-filled sky. There I see a pure white steed, in ornamental harness of shimmering gems, racing across the sky, his arched neck flung high, running swiftly, riderless and wild. His wind-blown mane is a silver blur against the veil of night.

"*Ach!*" I catch my breath. I stand in awe, as he comes down the windy lane his hoofs leaving sparks of star-dust behind. Down, down he comes. "*Ach, liebe Welt!*" Such wonder lies in the rippling muscles. Such majestic beauty! Such grandeur!

I am so enthralled by his splendid beauty that I forget about the wooden bowl of leavening dough I have brought outdoors with me. I have placed the dough on the ground, by my feet. The dough is my very best. It has raised so high, so light, so round. It glows white in the night.

The pure white horse comes nearer and nearer. The thunder of his wild hoofs is in my ears. His fiery breath is on my face. "*Ach, Gott,*" I cry out, remembering my dough. But it is too late. The riderless horse is right in front of me. He lunges in fright when he sees me and rises high on his hind legs, churning the cold night air into my face. I cannot move. Then, down come his mighty hoofs to crush my bread dough to the very bottom of the bowl. And there is no more life left in it.

Two days later we laid our baby, Theodore, in the cool, peaceful earth of God's acre. And the *Grossmutter* went to rest next to him on the same day, under her cool blanket of earth. Content, at last. Side by side, the seed of life and the ripened fruit.

1

*Hear ye the troika bell a-ringing*
*And see the peasant driver there?*

Hear ye the mournful song he's singing,
Like distant tolling through the air?

2

O eyes, blue eyes, to me so lonely,
O eyes — alas! — ye give me pain;
O eyes, that once looked at me only,
I ne'er shall see your likes again.

3

Farewell, my darling, now in heaven,
And still the heaven of my soul;
Farewell, thou father town, O Moscow,
Where I have left my life, my all!

4

And ever at the rein still straining,
One backward glance the driver gave;
Sees but once more a green low hillock,
Sees but once more his loved one's grave.*

*"The Troika": Old Russian Gypsy folk song.

# CHAPTER 7

# *The War Dogs*

Sure, things are different now that I am married. Six years have gone by since our Theodore died. David and I have three other children, all girls: Elizabeth, four and one half, Nathalia, three, and Leah, one.

My father and stepmother are getting old. My stepsister, Lydia, and stepbrother, Jakor, are obedient children and fine workers in the field. Lydia has thick golden braids and soft blue eyes. Jakor has a curly head, and gay laughter on his lips.

My three older sisters, Katrinliz, Marik, and Malia are all married and have large families. They live with their husbands' families. In Russia the families get large depending on how many sons there are; each son brings his bride home to live in his father's house. This makes many hands to work the great fields outside the village.

My brother Friederich is also married. His beautiful wife, Gredel, and he have three sons. Friederich is determined to take his family to *Amerika*.

Karlotta Dahmer, the smart *lusha*, is also married. Everyone was surprised when she married Fritz Geist, the big blacksmith, whom Herr Lunden and Herr Rohr, the marriage brokers, had offered me as a husband. *Gott!* She can have him.

Karlotta has not changed. She is as fiery as ever. Even Fritz is not as good as they put him up to be at taming her. His iron muscles and thick back count him nothing, when it comes to her. She has him dancing on her fingertips while she lashes him with her fiery tongue. *Ach*, such living! I want none of it.

My brother Otto is still thinking of joining the regiment when he is of age, which will be soon. Now that he is grown he has no time for girls, though the soulful eyes of shy Mariesophie Maier follow him wherever he goes. All that matters to him is that he become a great *Kapitän*, a mighty *Hauptmann!*

Otto is of fine build, hard of muscle, and very handsome. His black hair and dark eyes have the girls swooning. But he thinks of nothing but riding and grooming the spirited horses of the great landowners. Father's horses already are not good enough for him.

The whole village marvels at his accomplishments. He is very near a soldier, though he has had no official training. The open field outside the village has been his practice ground. Here his comrades join him on a Sunday afternoon for the clean fun of riding, jumping, and marksmanship. Otto's trainers have been young men who concluded their four-year conscription and who have returned home to live and work and be in active reserve for the following four years. These men execute outstanding tricks on horseback. But it is not long before Otto can do as well. He can saddle and unsaddle his horse with lightning speed.

The riding tricks he could do at thirteen, he can do even better now. He stands on the saddle at galloping speed, aiming his rifle, and hits the target true and straight. Then, coming back at full speed, he hits it again. But this time he is hanging on the side of his horse, left foot in the right stirrup, left hand gripping the saddle horn, right hand and arm bracing the rifle. The villagers shout him on as down the field he comes.

Young maidens with stars in their eyes elbow each other to be out in front of the crowd, the better to be seen. But Otto has no time for them. His eyes are to the future, dreaming that some day he will be a fine colonel.

"So now, it is a colonel," my father says. Sadly, he shakes his head and leaves the field.

The next exhibition Otto performs is a Don Cossack maneuver, that of plunging a short dagger into a target and withdrawing it at neckbreaking speed.

This time the young girls really push out front, cheering and yelling, all but shy Mariesophie; she alone holds back, fearing for his safety. She is surrounded by a group of teasing, thoughtless children.

90

"Look. O look, Mariesophie. Here he comes! Maybe his horse will fall — and he will break his neck. O-oo-o, look!"

Again she is forced to look as down the field he comes at a wild gallop. he performs the trick in great style. His next trick is to ride blindfolded without bridle and saddle. A man stands by and whacks the horse with a wooden paddle. This time, I think, he will surely be killed. I cannot bear to look, but I must. The people yell; the men wave their caps, the women their babushkas, adding to the confusion as the horse comes bearing down on them. Mariesophie throws her hands to her face and holds her breath. And for once the pestering children forget to notice her. But even in this stunt Otto excels. He rides the frantic horse to a finish.

When the race is run and his horse fastened, Otto comes bounding through the cheering crowd to the water barrel. The children are at it again, taunting Mariesophie. They chant, "Mariesophie loves Otto . . ."

"Hello! What is this?" Otto asks, looking surprised and somewhat angry. He catches one tousle-haired rascal by the collar and holds him up at arm's length, kicking and squirming. Otto stands there dark-skinned, his cossack blouse open at the neck, looking like a Don cavalier.

"Now, what is this?" he demands. He sets the boy free.

"Ah, she loves you — so, she weeps," explains a bold, freckle-faced lad pulling Mariesophie's tear-stained fingers from her face.

The pretty girl tries to flee, but Otto reaches out to stop her. He turns her about and his gaze is gentle now. The children hush, but he has already forgotten about them. Sweet, loyal Mariesophie whom Otto has teased since childhood, jerking her braids, and laughing at her tears.

Now she stands before him, full grown, trembling, and he looks closely at her sweet, uplifted face, wet with tears.

I can only guess that he is filled with wonderment at what he sees, her full red lips, her lovely cheeks, her misty hair, all gold and soft like tassled corn silk.

He bends nearer and his hand moves hesitatingly over her golden hair. *"Liebchen,"* he says, "do not mind them. They are only teasing."

Then, as suddenly, he seems to remember that he must be a great colonel and he breaks away from her, speaking harshly to the children. "Run, now, and play elsewhere."

Sure, I cannot figure him out. Has he already forgotten her, or has he done her a favor, by getting the children to go? Otto can be unthinking and without feeling sometimes.

A man traveling from Tsaritsyn, the army headquarters, has brought David some leaflets concerning Russia's position in a possible war. David reads and re-reads every detail and I can see that he is becoming more and more worried. Finally, he becomes vocal on the subject. "I tell you, Evaliz, Russia is sticking her neck out this time." He rattles the papers in his hand.

"What is it?" I ask, fear striking my heart. "Explain it to me."

"It is this way," he says, clearly. "Russia and Japan have conflicting interests on the mainland of Asia. In other words Manchuria and Korea. Both Russia and Japan are trying to get control of this rich, strategically located region. Russia, so far, has the upper hand. She not only refuses to withdraw from Manchuria, but is penetrating ever deeper into Korea. My guess is that Japan will make a stop to it." Perplexed, David shakes his head and walks the floor.

I cannot understand the issue, but I know that it isn't good, and my heart grows heavier and heavier. I let David talk.

"Russia is determined to have a naval base in warm waters," he says, by way of explanation. "She has built more than 4,000 miles of the Trans-Siberian Railroad, linking Russia to the Pacific Ocean. The railroad runs east through Omsk and Irkutsk, crosses Manchuria, and re-enters Russian territory to end at Vladivostok. See, Evaliz, here is the diagram." He shows me the map.

I know a little something about the Trans-Siberian Railroad. Before I knew David he had helped survey some of the terrain for that purpose. My mind lingers a while on the subject, but David talks on.

"Russia has built a naval base at Port Arthur, at the tip of the Liaotung Peninsula which she has leased from China. I tell you, Evaliz, Russia will go to war to keep all this."

"Sh-h sh-h," I say, afraid that someone will hear his peasant talk. But David cannot be stopped. To him, war is certain.

"Then, you will have to go, David," I cry, unable to hold back the tears.

"Yes, it is very likely," he says evenly, like a man who has had time to think it over. "But, perhaps because of the children, I will not be taken right away. Maybe, not at all." He comes to me and takes hold of my arms, shaking me a little. "*Ach, Liebchen*, wipe the tears. I only tell you this so that you will be prepared. It is better that you know. Many women will not know." He walks to the window and stands looking far into the distance, and to me it seems that he is gone already.

"*Ach*, yes," I say to myself and my lips feel numb. I think it would be better if David didn't read the pamphlets. But, what would that help? War would still come, and I would have no hope. It is right David should tell me.

At army headquarters, in Tsaritsyn, our young men are being signed up for training. David's papers are on file there, perhaps to be called later. A sickness fills me when I think of it, and in the night I cry softly to myself. I believe David. If mobilization comes, it will be for keeps this time.

Now, maybe, my brother Otto will be the hussar he has dreamed of being. Foolish youth, with only two stout legs to stand on! What is that before snarling war-dogs with the smell of blood burning in their nostrils? I fold my hands to pray: "*Lieber Gott*, let there be no more wars." But even as I pray, I know there will be wars and rumors of war until the end of time. I remember my father reading it to us from the Bible.

Then, spring is on the land again and Otto is old enough to go. Wild horses can not hold him. It is on the same day that Mariesophie is visiting me. She has just offered to bring me a bucket of water from the dam when Otto comes bounding in with the news.

"Evaliz, I'll be gone in a week," he shouts, not realizing she is here. He stops short and comes face to face with her and, for once, he has nothing to say. Always before it was a cheery slap on the back or a merry "Hello, Ma-riz." But, today, not a sound.

I think up to now he has not even seen her. He stands and looks at her, a flick of light in his eyes, and I know he has been thinking about her a lot. Then, I see the hungry look that passes between them and quickly I turn my back, busy with bread kneading. Even though my back is turned, I sense all that is happening between them. Otto draws her into his arms and crushes her to him. I hear his kiss, not once, but twice. And I hear soft murmurings as he whispers his love for her. Surely, I think, he can find no one better to love than sweet Mariesophie.

Then, for my benefit, and as a clue for me to turn around, Otto says, "Come, Ma-riz, I will help you bring the water."

"Oh no, you strong dolt," I say happily, handing him another bucket. "You bring me two." And they are off, his fingers entwined in hers.

It is also the week that my brother Friederich and his wife Gredel take their three small sons and leave for *Amerika*. "Promise me," I say to him, "that you will send me the money, so I can go too."

"I promise," he says, smiling, hugging me tight, "they say money drops from trees in *Amerika*."

*Ach!* I think I cannot stand the sorrow with both Friederich and Otto gone.

Because David cannot find any land to work along with his part-time teaching, he travels from village to village to find a better paying job. He goes to Kamischin, to Tombovckoi, to Kindsvater Kutter in the Don Artchada. Here, at last, David finds work teaching the Russian language. To teach is a family calling. His father and grandfather are known throughout the Volgaland as *Der Meister 1*, and *Der Meister 2*, and now David will be *Der Meister 3*. I am very proud of him. His father and grandfather taught in Tscherbakowka, Saratov, Potschinaja, and Avilawa.

Besides teaching in Kindsvater Kutter, David will also be the *brigoshig*, land supervisor, for Herr Seewalt, a rich landowner who farms a thousand *dessjatin* of land. His fields are so far from the village that David will be given a fine team of horses to use in his work as overseer. I am so excited. Now, maybe, we can make something of ourselves.

We waste no time moving. David borrows a wagon and a pair of oxen from my father and my brother Wilhelm. We load in our small belongings and our three little girls, and are on our way.

When we arrive, the rich lady gives us lodging in the servant's quarters. We are grateful, but the place is so crowded. There is no privacy among these strange people. Their combined children number eighteen, all under ten years of age. Some squall the livelong day, and when they are not squalling they pinch my children, or pull their braids, and when they are not doing that, they rub mud into their hair until I want to take a stick to them. Sometimes I think I cannot stand it, especially now that I am expecting again.

Then, sooner than we thought, there is a brighter outlook. We are given permission to build a house on Herr Seewalt's land, right here on the edge of the village. It will be a two room house with a *bage*, or *bagega*, a low, handmade oven built in as a dividing wall to keep both rooms warm. Better yet, the shoulder-high wall is wide enough to make a bed for my children. It will be ideal in winter. This our people have done ever since they came into cold Russia.

There is no lumber to build a wooden house. We have enough only for the window and door frames and the low sloping roof that will be covered with straw and sod. David and I mix and form our own clay blocks that will make the walls.

Because David is gone so much of the time, and because I am overly anxious to have a home, I haul most of the clay by myself, with my little ones with me. With an ox-team and wagon we drive out to the high banks along the stream, and while my children play nearby, I load the wagon high. Going back I walk alongside of the wagon while my children sit on top, their bare feet and legs buried deep in the soft, moist earth, molding red-brown cakes with little stained hands. For them it is great fun.

When I get back I spread the clay alongside other loads David and I have brought. The smooth mixing ground is near where the house is to stand. When finally we have enough clay, David hauls water on a flat, wooden sleigh. Herr Seewalt has ordered one of his laborers to provide the straw for the bricks. Then, on a beautiful starlit evening the rich man sends all his help out to mix the clay. Such fun. It is like having a party, playing in the mud. Men, women, children, and dogs help. There is singing and laughing and barking, as straw and water is added to the clay.

Five ox-teams are brought out to be driven round and round through the oozing mixture. Everyone gets in, boys and girls in bare legs; men, their pant legs rolled up; women, their long, full skirts lifted and the hems tucked securely in tight waist bands; dogs leaping up and down, making pranks with their little masters, their legs and bodies caked in mud.

When the mortar is thoroughly mixed, the men heap it into a neat mound and cover it well with clean straw, to keep it damp. Meanwhile all the others are off to the village dam, laughing and shouting, to wash the mud off their legs, and to wash the mud-caked legs and underbellies of the oxen.

We are to keep the straw damp. Now we are ready to take a day's portion of mortar to form into blocks. We do this by using a wooden frame open at the top and bottom, measuring two large hands wide by four hands long, the fingers spread wide.

We have two frames, so I help David. It is a simple matter. You set the frame where you want the block left to dry. Now fill the frame with mortar, press it in tight, smooth it off and lift the frame. The block stays where you made it. Easy? Yes, for a man. But for me it takes two to three good hefty bounces with arms and shoulder, and sometimes elbow on thigh, to shake the mortar loose. We are careful to set the blocks far enough apart so that we can flip them over when half dry. It takes a lot of space, but we have it. David scolds me and says I should go and sit down, in my condition, but I won't listen. I want to help, and I want a house.

When the sun and wind have dried the blocks halfway I go out to turn them over. The little ones have fun playing house, but for me it is back-breaking work. My hands are torn and bleeding. My thighs are black and blue. Still I will not stop, I keep thinking of our overcrowded lodging.

Because I work so hard, I make David work even harder and longer. He teaches and oversees the fields and after supper he goes to work on the house. Some of the day laborers help him.

When David leaves for work in the morning, I take my children and go to my house building. While my little ones play nearby, I carry one clay block at a time and add it to where David has left off. I mix mortar when I need it.

Again, David rants and scolds. Nights he can't sleep. In the mornings he scolds again. And I decide I had better quit. Yes, I think, I will quit. My mind is made up.

But, something happens. My children, like the others, must sleep on the dirt floor. And this morning while I am outside shaking the dirt out of their bedding, I hear five-year-old Elizabeth crying.

"Mama. Mama," she comes running to me.

"What is it, Lizya?" I ask, brushing her brown hair away from her tear-filled eyes.

"Nikolai, he wet against my legs," she sobs.

"*Ach, Gott!*" I look at her bare legs and feet, all splattered with dust and mud. This cannot be. This is no way to bring up children.

I fold the bedding and take it back into the house. Lizya follows. "Don't cry," I say, "Mama will wash you clean."

When the task is finished I send her out to fetch Nathalia and Leah. They, too, are soiled from play. I wash them clean and comb their hair. I dampen each strand and braid it tight. My girls are all brown heads, but each one is different, so sweet. Nathalia, nearly four, with wide set eyes, always sparkling, now has a startled look with the small tight braids drawing back the skin. I laugh and kiss her forehead, knowing that she will not be tousle-headed all day. Leah, the youngest, has thick hair, very brown and very long. Her eyes are as deep brown as a wet leaf caught beneath the water of a clear running brook. A pretty child.

This done, I say, "Come, children, we will go build our house." I do not let them see the deep concern that is churning inside of me. My little ones hang onto my skirt as we walk. The wind is in our hair. The morning sun, no doubt, is glistening in the tears that are welling in my eyes.

It is a surprise to see that all the walls are up. David and the men have worked hard. The door and window frames are in and all that is left to do is the roof. There is a dirt floor as is the custom here in the Volgaland. When the house is entirely finished I will take water and a scrub rag and wash the floor smooth to harden it, then sprinkle on clean sand. And each day thereafter when I sweep the floor I will sprinkle on more damp sand. The sand has a tendency to keep the dust down and gives a clean look. Each house has a built-in sand bin for this purpose.

Now that the house is so far along I can start by plastering the inside walls. "While Mama works, you watch the girls," I admonish Lizya. "See that they do not get hurt."

"Yes, Mama," she says. She is so dependable.

I take a basket and mix a fine mixture of clay to plaster the inside walls. When they are finished I will white-wash them. I can hardly wait to see it. This process is backward, since the house hasn't a roof yet and David will scold, but I must work while I still can.

In a month the house is finished. It is a fine house. So roomy! The children laugh and clap their hands. They run from one room to the other and back again. David and I find more white clay in the countryside and with brooms made from native *Schilf* grass we white-wash the outside of the house also. The weather will take it off in time, but each spring, on Whit-Sunday, the birthday of the Christian church, all the village houses will get a new coat of white to commemorate the date. Among our Volga-Germans it is a day of baptism and confirmation, for the wearing of white and the singing of the hymn, "*Herr, wie du willst, so schick's*":

> *Seek ye who will some other way*
> *To find your soul's salvation*
> *My heart shall build on Christ alone.*
> *The only sure foundation.*
> *His saving Word and works endure,*
> *On them I rest and feel secure,*
> *With foes around me raging.*

Early Whit-Sunday morning is the time a young man steals into the courtyard of his sweetheart and plants a flowering twig near her door. When the sun comes up the sight of the village is a joy to behold, so white and clean and holy.

When finally we move into our house, the children are more interested in the bed on top of the wall oven than in anything else. "Never again will we be without a bed, huh Mama?" Lizya asks, old beyond her years, her face so serious.

"No, child, never again," I assure her.

"Will we fall off, Mama?" asks Nathalia, now four, her large brown eyes sparkling in the candlelight.

"*Ach*, no, sweet child, you will not fall off," I laugh. "Your *Baba* will make a railing around it, and build a small ladder. Your *Baba* is good."

"Yes, Mama, *Baba* is good," they pipe, together.

"I like *Baba* best when he buys me blue plums from the Cossack fruit vendor," says Nathalia who as a rule has little to say. "I like plums better than anything!"

Sure, I remember how large and sweet the last plums were and David and Nathalia ate them all — well, almost.

"I like best not to sleep on the floor," says Lizya, and adds, "I like even better the clear, cool water from Frau Seewalt's private well — not from the dam where cows and oxen splatter."

"*Ach!* What has that to do with your *Baba?*" I laugh and hug them to me. "Better you get in bed, before he comes and finds you still up. Scat!"

It only takes a minute; they sleep in their underclothes. But there must be time for prayer:

"*Abba, lieber Vater, im Himmel. Amen.*"

To celebrate our new home I bake *berok* for the family. I start with bread dough and while it is rising I steam diced pork, onions and cabbage, seasoned well. I set the rather dry mixture aside to cool. After the dough has risen a second time I roll it out and cut it in squares. Next I ladle two spoonsful of the meat mixture onto the square, and bring the corners of the dough up to touch and press the seams shut with my fingers to form an X. I lay the meat packet X-side down in a well greased baking pan, grease the top and let them rise again. Then bake, and eat, while they are still hot. I serve *Süssholz* tea made from licorice root, or *Steppe Tea* as we call it, with the *berok*.

There is joy in our hearts and a song on our lips:

*Allein Gott in der Höh' sei Ehr'*
*Und Dank für seine Gnade!*

Life is good. Herr Seewalt has allowed David a plot of land to sow wheat. If the crop is good, we will have enough flour for the winter, and enough straw for the ox team David has bought from my father.

Every morning at breakfast and every evening before going to bed David reads a Bible text and prayer from the *Gebets Buch*, a confirmation gift from his father. Sure, our life is set on a firm foundation.

After two months, my new baby arrives. It is a girl, light haired and blue eyed, like David. We call her Mia, a Gypsy name for Mizelli. David looks at her. "*Ei*, a houseful of girls," he says, shaking his head, but there is a twinkle in his eyes, too. "A *Bauer*, a farmer, I will never be at this rate." He laughs, but all the time it is sons he wants, I know.

Mia is two weeks old when my oldest brother, Wilhelm, Anna, his wife, and their two young girls leave for *Amerika*. *Ach*, I think I cannot bear to see all of them go. Now my father and stepmother have only two young people in their house, my stepsister Lydia and stepbrother Jakor. Otto is away in the service. Wilhelm comes to our village, Kindsvater Kutter, to say good-bye before he leaves. There are tears, and more tears.

"Good-bye, good-bye. *Auf Wiedersehen!*" I wave after him. "Remind Friederich to send us money for *Amerika.*"

"*Ja, ja,* I will," he calls back. I wonder if I will ever see him again. My heart nearly breaks in two.

In the middle of harvest there is an epidemic among the children in the village. So many of them die, and the mothers who must help in the field are especially worried. They are needed in both places. What can they do? The weather is so threatening that the threshing of grain cannot be delayed. There are no doctors in the village, nor in any of the nearby villages. The few midwives have their hands full; they cannot help everyone.

The disease is a dreadful choking in the throat. When, at last, a doctor from a faraway village is sent for, he calls it diphtheria. The disease is terrible. Children are dying every day.

I pray day and night that my children will not get it. I, too, the same as all of Herr Seewalt's help, am out in the field. The weather is so threatening.

"Hurry, hurry," Herr Seewalt says, looking to the skies.

David must say the same to the men he has under him, he, himself, working as hard as they. He even hurries me. "I am sorry," he says, "but we cannot stop now. Thank God that our children are still well."

Herr Seewalt has new-fangled machinery shipped in from *Amerika.* The speed and power of these machines is so great that human beings find it hard to keep up. Tired, I fall into my bed at night, and just as tired I crawl out again in the morning. I take my month-old Mia with me to the field. She sleeps in the wagon, but the other three must stay at home. My heart is filled with fear for them. But this is nothing new. Women here in this land have always left their children at home, and still do. Often an older child stays with them. But this is not always good. So many things can happen. Sometimes, it is better to leave them alone.

When I return from another hard day I find that Lizya has a headache and her throat hurts. *Ach, Gott,* this is it. Diphtheria! What will I do? I stay up with her all night. I lay cool cloths on her forehead. I make her gargle with warm salt water. Nothing helps. My poor, poor Lizya!

Morning comes, at last. The sun rises blood red in the eastern sky and peers through a cloudy mist. With a heavy heart, I pack our lunch to take to the field. David and I have deep concern for our child. But we have no choice. "Stay in bed, *lieb'Kind*," I whisper to Lizya, my lips against her hot forehead. "Mama will be back this evening."

She only nods, but I see the pain in her eyes. How can I leave her? My heart cries inside of me. I turn to Nathalia. "Be good, child," I say, "take care of little Leah; keep her in the house, and be very, very quiet; Lizya is so sick."

"Yes, Mama," she says, tears swimming in her large eyes.

It seems this day will never end. The sun, no longer red, but white with heat, hangs in the sky and will not move. My tiny baby in the wagon bed cries after I nurse her. Because I am so worried, my milk upsets her. Besides, the flies are all over her. I fashion a canopy over her to keep the flies away. But still she cries. Finally I am so far away I do not know whether she sleeps or cries.

When we get back home, things are even worse. Now Nathalia is sick also. My little Leah will be next; I see it in her quietness. Now I must have someone to stay with them. But whom? Finally I find Alexander Wiessner, a neighbor lad, age nine. His mother is my good friend, and he is a nice boy.

The days drag on. My children do not get better; all three of them are sick now, all but the baby, Mia. All night long David and I are with them. But it is the same all over the village.

This evening when I come home Lizya has a choking spell. Perhaps, she has lain here all day without a drink of water. And Nathalia is sobbing with a swollen throat.

"What is it, *Liebchen?*"

"Alexander hits me with a stick, because I am not quiet, like Lizya."

"*Ach, Gott,*" I say, "this is enough. I do not go out in the field again. My children will die without me."

I go to our bed where Lizya lies so quietly. "*Liebchen*, Mama stays with you from now on," I say to her. Her dim eyes hold the faintest smile and she says in a thick voice, "I'm not sick, Mama."

"Would you like a drink of cool water from Frau Seewalt's well?"

"No, Mama."

And this night, before the moon is up, she closes her tired eyes in final sleep. *Ach, Gott,* my heart is breaking. David stands beside me, holding me tight, tears streaming down his face. But Nathalia is so sick that we cannot stop to think of Lizya. The scabs in Nathalia's throat are so thick she can neither eat nor drink.

Now on the evening of the second day David holds her on his lap. "What does Nathalia want?" he asks.

"Plums," she answers, with difficulty. She remembers the blue plums she loves so well.

100

"*Baba* will get you some plums," he promises. A tear falls on her brown, silky hair and glistens there like a star fallen from heaven. Then, the star goes out.

"Oh, David, David," I cry, as we cling together.

Now David is making the second coffin. And the two lie side by side in the graveyard.

I'm afraid to come home from the burial for fear that Leah will be dead also. But she lives. Let God be praised! And my baby, Mia, does not even get sick.

Our house is so empty now. Our hearts are filled with sorrow. But other hearts throughout the village are as bereaved as ours. To Russia we give our children, in death.

Once again we hear rumors of riots, of robber bands, and plunder. Rumors say:

"Greater Russia is ripe for revolt!"

"War with Japan is imminent."

"This will be Russia's downfall."

As I lie awake by night, my mind wanders back to when I was a girl. I remember some of the tales that were told then about the coronation of Emperor Nicholas and his bride, Alexandra. It was a day of massive gathering, of peasant crowds packed on the sidewalks, shouting wild hurrahs and pressing forcibly against the lines set out by Cossack convoys and squadrons of hussars. It was a day of feasting, a day to receive presents. But, halt! What was all this? The crowd broke through, into the street, into the courtyard. Fifteen thousand people were trampled to death in a frenzied stampede. A bad omen for the new czar and his czarina, the saying went.

And, now it seems, the bad omen is upon us. One cannot be sure what will happen. All evil, I think.

# CHAPTER 8

# The Russo-Japanese Conflict

I t is the fall of the year and I am gathering in the last of my garden. David has made me a root cellar where things will be safe from winter frost. Potatoes and onions rest in a deep nest of straw. A large cask is full of sauerkraut with a white cloth and wooden plate and stone on top to keep the brine level up. Firm cucumbers and small, white watermelons, in separate containers are curing in salt brine; the seed of which, according to my father, dates back to the mighty Khans of Samarkand.

There are jars of red beet juice boiled down to the consistency of syrup, an important source of sweetening for our meals, and especially good in baking fancy breads. I have thick white lard in which are buried pieces of fried pork and fried sausages; these are in stoneware crocks, with only a cloth over the tops. The meat keeps perfectly as long as it is covered with lard. There are two large cheeses, sewn in cloth; these I have made from the milk of our goat, Ba-ba-ra, with the sweet disposition; she never butts. Truly, I am thankful for all I've got.

I have one more tedious job to do, that of boiling watermelon syrup. I do this out in the yard near my cooking kettle. First I must cut open the melons and scoop out the red meat and boil it in the large iron kettle. Later I strain out the pulp and seed and reboil the juice until it is a syrup we call *Melasse* or *Schlecksel*. It, too, is a sweetness for fancy baking.

I have finished one batch and am starting on another when Vanka Wassemiller, the *Bürgermeister*, calls a greeting to me from the street. "Where is David?" he asks, as he comes near my cutting table. He samples the red heart of a prime melon, the juice dripping off his fingers.

"He is down in the Dovorinka flour mill by the river," I say, calmly, but a sudden fear overtakes me when I see Vanka's sober face. But he smiles quickly to offset my fear.

"Ah, but this is fine melon to boil into *Melasse*." He takes another piece, throws back his head and tosses the tidbit into his mouth, careful not to stain his long moustache. He smiles again. Vanka is a good friend and full of teasing ways.

"What do you want with David?" I ask, searching his face, yet not seeing anything.

"Tell him the czar wants him," he says, with light words. "Do not forget, Evaliz."

"*Ach*, go away," I say. Vanka is always playing harsh jokes, first with a seriousness on his face and then, a smile. I really think he is joking, for he says no more about it, only that he will be back.

The making of watermelon *Melasse* or *Schlecksel* is a custom handed down to us by our foreparents. *Schlecksel Kuchen*, a fancy sweet bread, has graced the tables of wedding feasts and church holiday gatherings down through the generations. It is a rich reddish-brown jam that can also be poured hot over plump dumplings!

The work is time-consuming. It will take me two days to complete the process, and it will take much grass fuel. The fire, fanned by the wind, sears my bare legs and feet. I must have my skirts tied up high, away from the open flame. All day I stir the thickening brew with a wooden ladle, careful not to let it burn to the bottom of the caldron.

But I cannot keep my mind off David. What about Vanka? Why would he say the czar wanted David? *Ach, Gott.* I wish David would come home. Surely, he will laugh at my fears, I think, but still I cannot keep my hands from shaking. It has been a long time since he has told me anything about the army, but he still reads the pamphlets.

It is nothing new in our village to see young men of conscription age leaving for military training; I see it from time to time, and think nothing of it. Here a son is gone and there a son is gone. My brother Otto is stationed near Odessa. There can be no immediate danger of war or David would have told me — or would he?

104

I glance down the road a hundred times or more and finally he comes. "Hello, hello," he shouts, from afar. "The wanderer has returned home. Come, and embrace him." He is sitting atop a load of sacked flour, waving and smiling.

As soon as he is in the yard and jumps down I run to him and hold him tight. "David, you cannot leave me," I say.

"Leave you, why? Where?" he puzzles, holding me at arm's length.

But before I can answer Vanka confronts him. "Make ready, David," Vanka says, "waste not one single minute." It is no joke this time. It is like a *Kapitän's* command! And at his very word David turns into the soldier that he is. Has he forgotten, I think, that this is only Vanka Wassemiller, a friend, who sits at table with us; he who gives our little children rides on his bouncing knee and laughs with them full of glee?

Vanka has delivered his message. He leaves our yard, head bowed. Then he pauses, as if he remembered something else to say. "Tomorrow morning at sun-up they leave, David," he calls back.

"Yes, Vanka. I am ready," says David, his voice steady, as though he is under Vanka's command.

David isn't happy to go. We go into the house together. "This is it, Evaliz," he says, his hands on my shoulders, his eyes looking deep into mine. Then he draws me into his arms and holds me tight. I feel emotion struggling in his throat. "I have not told you before, so that you would not worry," he whispers into my hair that has fallen from its bounds and is hanging loose.

"Oh, God. Oh, God," I cry, hanging onto him. My little Leah cries because her mama is crying. And sweet little Mia is crying because Leah is crying.

"Sh-s, sh-s," I say, going to them, gathering them to me. "Sh-s, your mama is alright."

After David has taken care of the ox team and the flour, he explains to me what has happened, according to the pamphlets. "Since February Japan has blown up our naval base at Port Arthur. Great Japanese forces are pushing back our troops on the mainland. The Trans-Siberian railroad has been cut in half. Thousands of our men are losing their lives! This has been happening right along, but I only read it last week."

"*Ach*, sure, I see why you must go," I say, but inside my heart is like a stone. I cannot be reconciled.

This night I lie close to David and weep silently into my pillow. He has a troubled sleep. His body twitches. His breathing is heavy as though troubled with a terrible fever. After a time he rouses and lies awake, and I know he is filled with grave doubts, the same as I am. Then, he too, turns his face into the pillow.

105

It is a restless night and yet pre-dawn comes all too soon. All is hurry, hurry. There is no time for tears. We gather our two little girls, Leah and Mia, and head for the market place. Almost every house along the way has a light burning. The dim lights have an eerie glow in the morning fog.

When we reach the market place there is bedlam, whole families weeping.

"Read the Word of God, Evaliz, and have hope," David says, looking into my face. "I will return."

"Oh, God," I think. "How will I stand it?"

The autumn sun, blood-red, is just coming up over the horizon as the Cossack convoy comes riding through the streets to take our men away on spare, saddled horses and horse-drawn *dotsckas*. "Make haste!" the hetman shouts. "Make haste!" And those men who are slow to heed the command are helped along by the resounding blows of leather braided *plotkas*.

For all of us present, it is a day of doom. Women who do not know what this war is all about take it very hard. My good neighbor, Marie Wiessner, for instance, waves a clenched fist. "Plague you, devils!" she cries in a voice not at all like Marie's. Marie, a good woman, is the mother of eight children. I must turn away from her. Her anguished sobs are breaking my heart. She is not the only one shouting; there are many others. Children, too. All is eerie in this morning mist with only the top half of man and beast showing.

"Forward . . . Forward! You dogs. You swine."

The sight before me is like a boiling pot of humans and animals all thrown together. Weeping women grab the reins of startled horses, and hanging on, are trampled under foot.

David's last words to me are "Promise me, Evaliz, as soon as I am mounted, you will leave the street."

"Yes, yes," I say, "*Auf Wiedersehen.*"

Then, David is gone and I cannot go back to my house. I must follow him down the road. Like a surging river after the flood gates are opened, the women and children follow after their loved ones. Frantic women, who are with child, hang onto the backs of wagons that are taking their men away, and let themselves be dragged to death.

Then, this scene is over and the days spin on and on. Winter sets in with teeth of ice, and each day its endless fury reaches a new height. Winds howl and rage, and the snows swirl without end. I lie awake nights and wonder if David is still among the living. The months come and go. It is Christmas; then the new year begins.

At last, comes a surprise: a letter from my brother Friederich in America. *Ach!* I hold it in my hand, and the strangeness of it

106

reminds me of my childhood, when Frau Tittle had a letter from America. It was that letter that started my dreaming. I recall the words Otto said about that letter so long ago: "Poo — I have too much sense to believe that a flimsy paper could travel that far without mishap."

I look at my letter, and for a moment I am like Otto. I can hardly believe it. But it is true! It is mine and David's. It has Friederich's writing. Quickly, I reach for my *Halstuch*, my head scarf, and rush to have Vanka Wassemiller, the *Bürgermeister*, read it for me.

Vanka is glad to oblige. He reads:

WaKeeney, Kansas
*NORD AMERIKA*
*den letzten November, 1904*

*Lieber Schwager David und Schwester Evaliz, zusammen mit eueren lieben Kinder:*
Greetings, in Christ Jesus, to all of you from all of us here in *Amerika*. We are, *Gott sei dank*, all well and have established ourselves, not without a measure of strangeness, in this great land of promise. Level and far reaching are the fields and pasturelands — not unlike the wide steppes of *Russland*. The loam is rich and virgin and especially adapted to growing wheat and corn, and all manner of lesser grains, although much, much cattle is grazed here. And that brings us to the subject at hand, that of the money.

Here enclosed is the money for your passage. I secured it from Mr. Frank Walker, a rich cattleman, on a loan to be paid by David, when you arrive.

It is better that you take ship in Hamburg, *Deutschland*. It is our hope that you will be able to flee *Russland* now that there is so much war and turmoil. We have read in German print here in *Amerika* of the riots in the cities and of the reverses in Manchuria.

In closing, we are leaving all in God's hands for a safe journey. From your loving family, *Bruder und Schwägerin*,

*Friederich und Gredel*

Vanka hands me the letter and the money note and says, "Now, go home and hide it."

"Thank you," I say to him. "Pray for me and David, that he will come home."

Vanka nods, "That I will."

When I get home, I hide the valuable paper in the wall of our house. No one knows about it, not even my children.

Again there are rumors: rumors of atrocities coming ever nearer, of the possible overthrow of the czar. There are rumors of Russian soldiers deserting and bringing back their armament to plunder and kill, rumors of robber bands moving over the land. There are tales of railroad strikes; of hunger in the Far East; of peasants, crazed with lust, burning the rich estates of noblemen and growing drunk with their plunder. Riots. Searches. Arrests. Fighting in the streets of the great northern cities. College students inciting the people by loud speeches on tightly packed streets. Russia at war with Japan and, at the same time, torn from within! Where will it end?

This is a peaceable village. Our people seldom demur. Nor do they even now. All are thankful that we are far enough away from the rioting cities. Then it happens.

Deserters, gone mad with gain and plunder, are infesting our province. Here and there, in the night, one sees the glow of fire against the sky. And in the morning tales of plunder and crime spread throughout the village. Our old, learned men are saying that the government is losing control over Russia. If this is true, how then can we win the war? David is in the war.

I hurry home from the market place and shut the door and weep bitter tears. "Oh, God," I pray, in the dark of night, "give me strength and faith in Thy goodness." And again, each morning, I look out over the vast snowlands, so bleak and cold, and I have hope anew. David will come!

In loneliness I seek out my neighbor, Marie Wiessner, and we console each other in our miserable lot. Both of us have not heard from our men since they went away. We do not know if they are dead or alive. But we keep our families going: mending, cleaning, weaving, and doing the family wash through holes in the ice on the village dam, while frigid winds buffet us as if we were match sticks; digging snow tunnels to care for our livestock. Once a week we bake bread; we also knead out extra dough and shape buns and bread dumplings to set out in the lean-to to freeze hard as a rock, for Saturday baking. On Saturday morning we bring in the bread board with buns, all frosty and feather-laced with hoarfrost, to let them thaw out. They are good brushed over with a beaten egg glaze and baked in the oven to a golden brown, or boiled bubbly in meat and sauerkraut. Marie and I laugh at our shortcut; "lazy cakes" we call them. I also make my Leah and Mia some dresses out of used clothing from Frau Seewalt. I cut my own patterns and sew them all by hand. My little girls look so sweet in them with their long sleeves and high band collars and buttons down the back. David would be so pleased, if he could see them.

Suddenly, there is weeping and great anxiety in our village. We hear that Port Arthur, our naval base, has fallen. The war with Japan has ended in remorse and shame! What a blow this is to Russia. Even the weather adds to the dismal circumstance. Each consecutive storm piles more snow upon snow until it reaches the housetop.

Then, here and there, we hear that soldiers are returning to their Volgaland. Families are weeping for joy over their loved ones. And more than a few weeping without them. Which will it be for me? I walk through my house, hoping and waiting. . . . Then, suddenly, the gates of heaven open and God pours out a blessing. David comes home! Word also comes from my home village that Otto has returned safely. Also Marie's husband comes home, eventually.

Now that the war has ended so shamefully for Russia, there is a growing uneasiness among our villagers. There is talk of whole families leaving for America. People are getting ready everywhere. They are selling their livestock and household goods, even while the winter snows are piled high.

David and I, too, have caught the fever. "See, we can go. Here is the money!" I say, digging the paper out of the wall where I hid it. I watch David as he reads the account; he is as excited about it as I am. But David is also serious.

"I will not leave until I get my discharge papers from army headquarters in Tsaritsyn," he says. "I will not be caught at the border, and brought back. If I go, I will go clean." David is right. We must think how we will do it.

Next Sunday, in church, we learn that our pastor is very much against the people's going to America. His sermon is on sheep going astray. "Dearly beloved, do not walk blindly. It is not a land of milk and honey. It is a land of. . . . " From a barely audible tone his voice rises brusquely and bursts like thunder over the timid congregation. The people sit in stony silence, their eyes held to him by force, while he delivers his next assault.

"Brethren, be not like stupid, frightened sheep, running, you know not where." His voice has all the wild fury of a Siberian bora, a storm before which one must bend.

He is a tall, powerfully built man. His countenance is handsome, but stern. His black robe flows majestically in heavy folds from his impressive shoulders. There is something unflinching about his bearing and his commanding voice. One simply has to look and listen.

I do not like what he is saying about America. What about Russia? Has he forgotten about the people's revolt in the cities, the pogroms in Jewish ghettos, the plunder and murder?

I lean my face against the broad pillar next to my bench and feel the coolness on my feverish cheek. *Ach, Gott,* I think, what is this man saying about my America? Is it true? It cannot be true! David would have told me.

I look for David sitting on the men's side of the church, but it is too crowded; I do not see him. All around me women are weeping silently, for some of their families are gone already. I see their lips quivering in prayer. They believe what they hear. I want to stand up and shout that it is not true, that America is a good land, full of promise. But I do not.

At last, the powerful voice mellows. The sermon is over. "Now, peace and mercy . . . may the blessing of our Lord Jesus Christ be with you. Amen."

When I find David in the crowd I see that he is as undaunted by what he heard as I am. We hurry home to once more look at the paper that will make America possible for us.

"See it; touch it," I say, "it's real!" We all laugh. Even our little girls, Leah and Mia, laugh and dance around the room. *Ach,* such happiness! Such overwhelming joy! An American trusts us with his money — us, whom he doesn't even know.

# CHAPTER 9

# *Far Horizons*

My heart is light these days. We are really and truly going to America. America . . . my heart pumps the gladdening word through my being, until my happiness knows no bound. Like a child, I cannot eat or sleep. I cannot understand the tears my neighbors weep for me, the wasted pity. It would be better that I weep for them, I think.

The first chance he gets, David leaves for Tsaritsyn to get his discharge papers. He uses Herr Seewalt's horses and sleigh. The day is bright and clear. I am glad he has good weather since it is a three to four day trip.

But before noon, a strong west wind is blowing. This is it: the breath of spring! And David is barely gone. How can he get back before the thaw?

Night comes on and still the mild west wind blows. In the morning, the gusts increase and a rapid flow of water is running down the steps into my root cellar, causing the straw over the potatoes and onions to float higher and higher, yet out on the driven snow there is no visible change — and therein lies the danger. I am so worried about David. When the spring thaw begins no one dares wander too far for days on end. Soft, warming spots appear in the deep snow, and oftentimes sleighs and horses have sunk down in the slush and disappeared from sight, not to be found until the snow melted.

I must also worry about my potatoes and onions; I can't let them go to waste. I kneel on a high stool over the icy water and fish them out one by one, nearly freezing my wrists, then my elbows, as the water rises. I can hardly stand the pain in my arms and shoulders. But I save the vegetables and carry them into the house.

Then, before the night comes on, the weather makes a complete change. Soon the whole world is shut out by a blinding flurry of new snow. It is the bora, a north-eastern hurricane blowing in from Siberia, the land of ice. Snow clouds sweep the land and swirl into the air, gathering fury as they meet. Windows and doors clatter. The thatched roof shakes and sprinkles us with bits of dirt and straw. The wind howls and rages, whistles, and shrieks. It frightens Leah and Mia. Leah tries to peer through the frosted window pane and cries for her *Baba*. "Mama, he will freeze. He will freeze," she says over and over as I hold her to me, and I cry with her.

I can only hope that David is in a safe place. It will be several days yet before he gets home. I go about my work getting ready for the trip. I bake large loaves of black bread and cut them into slices to make zwieback. To do this I toast it in the oven until completely dry, so that it will keep a long time. It will be good on the long way to America.

I also make butter to take with us. When the butter is churned I break the ice in the drinking pail to get water to wash it clean. Then I wring out a tea towel in strong salt water and wrap the butter in it. And all the while a wee small voice inside of me is saying, "Are you doing this for naught?" Yet I refuse to listen.

Then, after a long week of waiting, David returns, safe and smiling. He has his discharge papers. "Now I am a free man," he says.

The storm has blown over, but the cold weather holds. This is good so that Alexander Meissner who has promised to take us to the railroad town will also get back safely. The station is forty versts away.

And yet, we have many things to put in order before we leave. David makes a box to hold our bedding, the featherbeds, large, square goose-down pillows, and the heavy quilt from my father's house. The children's quilt I will keep for them to cover with on the way. We must sell everything we can't take: food, houseware, chickens, hogs, and oxen. There is no time to waste.

Otto brings my father and stepmother, my stepsister Lydia and stepbrother Jakor to see us once more and wish us Godspeed.

Friends and neighbors swarm into our house and swarm out again, taking our precious belongings with them. And so the days hasten away while the spring thaw is coming dangerously close.

Then, Alexander is waiting in the dooryard. With him is another man and sleigh to hold the box and extra bundles. Quickly we load things in. Friends and neighbors are standing by to bid us farewell. Herr Seewalt's fast troika team is eager to be on its way. The troika bell jangles nervously. Then it is: "Good-bye, good-bye . . . *Leb't wohl . . . Auf Wiedersehen!*"

There is no time to say the good-byes the way I had planned it, to look long and lingeringly into each face, so that I will remember until the end of time, each look of sorrow, each eye gleaming with fierce hope, each warm hand clasp so toil-worn and heavy-knuckled. All this I would see, and feel, to engrave crystal clear on my heart forever.

All this, and more: a well kept door-yard, flaxen haired children tumbling over new-born grasses, old faces, wrinkled and sunbaked; a peasant babe suckled on its mother's breast. All this, and still more, I would look at with pondering, aching love. A lump sits in my throat and hurts and hurts.

Never shall I forget this last backward look at my village Kindsvater Kutter on the Don Artchada, the morning sun flooding it with sunlight. A sorry little village, half-stooped and buried in deep snow. *Ach*, I am not so happy to leave it as I think. Never shall I see the endless green and gold of the open steppes again, nor the black furrowed fields with humble barefooted peasants following the plow.

Never shall I see my *Kosakenland* in wild bloom again, and hear the thrill of the bird-throng in the spring. Never, shall I see the roving Gypsy bands flooding over the land, spilling into every village — dressed in bright scarlets, greens and golds; brown skin, black tresses, glinting eyes, songs on their lips, music both soft and fierce at their finger tips — filching, bartering, begging:

"A mere cup of flour, a handful of salt, please my honorable *matuska.** Your fortune for a spool of thread . . . a loaf of bread . . . three small eggs . . . O, you of lily-petal skin, a leaf of *Tabak* for a thin *duretzga*, ere I die. Enough *mahorka* for a *papier-cigarre*. A needle. A measure of gruel, kind lady, for the little ones. . . . "

This is how it went, until they had accumulated far more goods than any one family had in the entire village. And while the not-always-too-kindly *Hausfrau* doled out a pinch of this and a pinch

*Matuska* — (Russian) mother.

of that, plump hens and ducks were cunningly tucked inside the tattered blouses of Gypsy *chai's* and *chal's*, girls and boys.

But, all this, I shall know no more. For me, Evaliz Becker, there shall never be the likes again. I am winging to the tune of the troika bell to a life that will be different. I wipe a scalding tear from my cheek and I see my village no more. It is wiped out forever. Only the wide, blue sky reaches over all the snow land. And our slim tracks run swiftly backward to lose themselves into nothingness.

And then it is also time to say good-bye to Alexander and the other driver. "Adieu. Adieu!"

"Farewell! *Leb'wohl! Sei Gott befohlen!*" Poor Alexander, he's such a dreamer, a youth in his twenties. I know the deep yearning he has for America, the endless, sometimes futile hope. In pity, I wish we could take him. But he must hurry back with Herr Seewalt's horses.

There is hoarfrost on the winter pelts of the fine horses. Their sensitive nostrils stand wide, lined in delicate pink. They are a special breed of horses. And Alexander handles them like a master.

I see humble resignation on his young face as he circles on the snowy street, runners screeching, and hurries away, leaving us standing beside our bundles resting on the snow at the railway station. I look after him with a sad heart and think of the words of an old German folk song:

> *Ach, Vater, Mutter, eure Tränen!*
> *O trocknet sie und seid beherzt.*
> *Ihr lieben Freunde, laszt das Grämen.*
>
> *Es ist bestimmt, in Gottes Rat,*
> *Der alles in den Händen hat.*
>
> *Drum lebet wohl, auf Wiedersehen.*
> *Ade, lebt wohl, wir müssen gehen.*

We wait a long time for the train to arrive. When it does, it is in no hurry to leave. The station is full of fleeing people, mostly Russian peasants, poor, and tattered and forlorn, looking as though they have no hope or destination.

Then, finally, the steps leading into the train are the beginning of a new life for us. We press forward into the car and the way is strange to my stumbling feet. Will we be received with open hearts in America? For the first time doubt fills me.

There are no seats in the Russian train, only a shelf or two along the side. There are some wire net bins in which one can settle down, if he is lucky enough in this press of people to get one. But mostly one sits on his own belongings.

I look on the shabby Russian peasants, so different from our people, so listless, huddled on their small belongings, a mud-crusted straw bed, a sodden bundle of clothing, a samovar at their feet being heated with charcoal. The Russian likes his hot tea. He drinks it all day long.

Our train car is crowded and yet more people are coming in. Each time the door opens cold rushes in and with it comes the strong smell of coal smoke, and from somewhere far across the village of Leschin comes the faint clamor of church bells, like an echo out of heaven. Instantly, the train whistle answers the sweetness with shrill, querulous anger. Darts of black smoke clouds puff upward to mar the silver-blue sky.

At last, the train gives a mighty jerk, shudders momentarily, and then the ground begins to move slowly out from underneath us, as the train begins to labor into action. Frightened, our little girls rush to David and bury their faces in his long-haired pelt coat. He holds them tight, smiling at me.

I look out of the window and see the coughing, smoke-filled breath of the locomotive envelop the small station in black clouds. Then the mass slides backward and becomes invisible, as the train goes faster and faster, rattling a thousand claws of steel.

I press my forehead against the frosted pane of glass and close my eyes, but a tear comes stealing through. Never before have I taken wing. Now, I am winged with time, meeting tomorrow before it comes.

The days and nights that follow go sailing off in a mad whirl. It is nothing but hurry, hurry, trains and more trains, whirling through small villages and larger cities, shrieking madly, going faster ever faster. Strange sights meet the eye, all splendid and beautiful and sad.

Here are tall buildings with windowed shops — though some of them are boarded up — people hurrying in and out of depots . . . Russians, Armenians, Kalmucks, Kirghiz, Greeks, Tcherkess, Cossacks, many carts, great and small, even the *balagoola*, the Jewish covered cart. Owners drive animals of all kinds: dogs, camels, sheep, hogs, oxen and winter-shaggy Cossack horses prancing on the frozen by-lanes and winding streets. And still more crowded depots. It seems to me that everyone is fleeing Russia.

Everywhere in stations wandering peasants dressed in rags are eating black bread and garlic, and salt herring, while waiting for their trains. Others, bearded and dirty men in loose coats and shaggy fur caps, and women and children in tattered shawls, sprawl on benches, or on bare, cold floors in the midst of more tea-kettles, lunch baskets and bulky bundles. Still others are standing in line to fill their samovars from the *kipatok*, the station's hot water reservoir. Still others who have no food eat sunflower and melon seeds, spitting the wet husks down the front of them and all over the floor.

Weaving in and out of the crowds, or standing on train platforms, are tacky peasant women selling washing privileges for a few kopeks, providing passengers with basins, soap and towels. Some sell jams and fruit, and hot borsch, the Russian's favorite cabbage soup. One woman tries to sell us a huge round loaf of black bread over which body lice are running. *Pfui!* Such filth. Others are selling boiled eggs that are rotten to the core. Oh, the smell! I must hold my nose shut; my children also can't stand the stench. David says that only the lower class city dwellers eat them, for they have never seen a fresh egg and therefore know no better. It is a simple matter, David says: "Since it would be more profitable, the farmer first tries to hatch the egg."

Sunlight and darkness flash by and we have left still more people behind. Village after village. City after city. The climate is somewhat changing and fir trees dot the landscape. Gone is Orel and Smolensk. Gone are those parts of Russia where the fugitive Jews are herded together in miserable ghettos, but I remember the sight and recall St. Andrew's hymn which I have heard so often:

> *Well I know thy troubles,*
> *O my servant true;*
> *Thou art very weary.*
> *I was weary, too:*

It seems I have eyes only for the outside world. I have hardly noticed the families in the train with whom we are packed in. But David has a way of getting around. He makes friends with everyone. He points out two families who are going to America. They are seated on their luggage at the rear of the car. I smile at them and see that they are also Volga-Germans.

David explains to me, "The couple with the baby on the right are Ludwig Reinert and his wife Ammarie." I look at her and she smiles at me. Frau Reinert is pretty and young, with dark hair and soft brown eyes. She is holding her child who has fussed and cried from the day they boarded the train.

"The other family," David says, "is from *dem kleinen Russendorf*, the small Russian village, Dubovka, on the Volga. They are Christian and Marieliz Ehrlich and their daughter,

Margrete, age eight." Frau Ehrlich is a neat, plain woman of about thirty-five with a tight hair bun. She is weeping half of the time because she is afraid to go to America. David and Christian both speak Russian, and that comes in handy whenever there is official business to be taken care of at the change-over stations.

Whenever the train stops long enough, David goes out to the small food markets next to the station and buys dry smoked fish to go with the bread and butter I have brought. Sometimes, when it is available, he brings a small pail of milk for the children. But the milk must all be used before the train leaves, so we can give back the pail. One time he buys a freshly baked chicken from a clean, plump and rosy-cheeked Jewish woman. "That is in remembrance of this journey," David says, smiling broadly. "Just once will I splurge. Let the fish and hard bread rest."

The whole trip has been dreadfully cold. The windows are covered thick with hoarfrost. There is no heat in the car. Leah and Mia cry because they are so cold. I wrap their shawls tight around them and cover them with the extra quilt, but still they are cold. David spends a precious ruble for a flask of vodka. He brings a beaker of hot water from the station *kipatok* and mixes them a drink, and it is a relief to see them sleep with glowing cheeks.

Ammarie Reinert, too, has had a bad time with her baby; it has been very sick and she has had no sleep for two days and two nights, except for short naps. There is a weariness and hopelessness on her face. Her baby is getting weaker every day.

Frau Ehrlich, bundled in heavy shawls and high felt boots, the same as I, still weeps at times and speaks very little. But now that the surroundings are getting stranger, the people different, she devotes more time to her girl, Margrete. She clings to the child as if she has a premonition that she will lose her on this endless journey.

The days have dragged themselves into a week. Then, one afternoon, we see water. "The Baltic Sea," David says. There is excitement in his voice and eyes. "We have completed one long stride in our journey," he says.

*Ach*, I am so excited. I scrape away more frost from the window for my children to see. Then the houses of Libau, Latvia go sailing past our window, first the hovels, wharfs; then straight, tall houses, shops, people, animals, and still more buildings and people.

"This is the old Kurland naval station. It has a great history. I have read about it many times," David says by way of explanation. "The name Libau is German, but also Sweden and Poland have had it, but in the third partition of Poland, in 1795, it passed to Russia."

The people here in Libau differ greatly from those in inner-Russia. These are not muzhiks, kulaks, nor Tcherkess,

Cossacks or Buryat, but clean, energetic Letts, Poles, Jews and Germans. The train, seemingly exhausted, eases to a stop at the station. We have come two thousand miles.

David takes charge of our official business while we are housed at a Jewish hostel. Here I earn our keep by cleaning rooms, changing beds, lighting fires and lamps and extinguishing them at night, for it is getting close to the time of the Jewish Passover when custom forbids them to blow out the light themselves. A week goes by, then we are to leave by ship for Hamburg, Germany.

"Now you will ride a ship across the Baltic Sea, and through the Kiel Canal to the Elbe River," David tells the children, and they are overjoyed at the new adventure.

But all is not happiness at the seaport station. Ammarie Reinert's baby that has been sick these many days dies in her arms, an hour before we are to embark. Ammarie is frantic. She holds the tightly wrapped bundle to her and won't let anyone take it away from her.

But all around us there is hurry, hurry. How can one stop to take pity on a mother who has just lost her baby?

"Quick, we must have our baggage. It is all our worldly goods," is the cry, everywhere. It is hard for the poor emigrant to believe that his belongings are not deliberately misplaced. Porters and officials, hindered by the bewildered peasants, are sorting and resorting bundles, boxes, bags and baskets. Most are opened and examined in great haste. All of us are inspected as to health and destination and all the while the hour is going by.

Ludwig Reinert and his wife, Ammarie, are standing outside the inspection station, on a dimly lighted platform, arguing bitterly with an official. Ammarie is hysterical. She is shouting loudly and weeping bitter tears. She refuses to give up her dead child. What the official shouts is no secret:

"You cannot, you shall not, take the body with you."

"We will bury it at sea," Ludwig shouts back, just as determined.

But it is of no avail. Poor Ammarie must lay her precious bundle onto a baggage cart, there on the windswept platform, and leave it, even before its little body is completely cold.

The Baltic Sea is a large body of water at the end of which are islands where we stop. Then comes the Kiel Canal and the Elbe River, then Hamburg. We arrive on a wintry evening at sunset and see the waterway into the German city. All of us marvel at the sunset glow on the towers of her mighty churches, the tree lined promenades, and the *gross Brücke*. The western sky is aflame with vermillion shreds of gild-lined clouds that are almost too beautiful to behold.

118

So this is Germany! The Fatherland of our ancestors! The Fatherland that turned a deaf ear to their mournful cry of homesickness, and disappointment when they found no houses or anything on the Russian steppes, which the Empress Catherine had promised.

I look out on the land, at its strangeness and its beauty, and am surprised that I feel no kindred tie to it. Only its outward beauty touches me. If this land has beauty, what then, will my beloved America hold? I can hardly wait.

The flaming sunset over Hamburg is all the beauty allotted to us. Presently we are herded into a smaller boat and brought by water to the station proper. Once again the emigrant is worried about his baggage. But the welfare of our baggage it seems to us is of no concern to our new and efficient officials. The important thing is to get us in quarantine as soon as possible.

Frau Ehrlich, who, at last, has wept herself dry, now finds her tongue. She bewails the fact that we must be put in quarantine. "So, we are not clean enough — we, whose ancestors belonged here. Now, look at us, we must be cleansed before we enter," she storms, at no one in particular.

I hide my eyes in shame, knowing that we have picked up bedbugs and lice in the crowded trains and stations all across Russia.

We are loaded onto a double-decked horse-drawn wagon and taken to a large building set in a lonely field. The place is enclosed with a high fence. Quarantine!

White-clad men and women take charge of us. We women and children are marshalled off into our special quarters, the men and older boys to another. If other stop-overs caused confusion then this by far is the greatest, for the men, who heretofore kept their families intact and informed are entirely separated. Women have fear of losing their husbands, for without them, what would they do? Besides, sickness is breaking out in all quarters. In some cases it is a child, a mother, a husband, or a young lass or lad. We hear a rumor that one boy of fifteen has fallen in the bath house and has broken his leg. On every hand apprehensive mothers are losing their children only to find them down some long corridor or off playing with other venturesome children; or again, little ones are crying in fright and terror because they have lost Mama.

So the days go on. One week slowly drags into another and Marieliz Ehrlich behaves badly. One would think that she will never see her husband again. Meanwhile Ammarie Reinert sits dry-eyed and empty-handed, hardly aware, it seems, of what is going on around her.

119

I keep special watch over my children, Mia and Leah, who, like me, have been washed clean and deloused. I have to laugh now, when I recall that first day in quarantine. We were herded into a steam room, our clothes quickly taken off us and our bodies smeared with a slippery, evil smelling paste. Then, without a warning, a shower of warm water was let down on us until all the slimy soap was washed away. We were given a dry blanket to wrap in and sent to another room. While we were drying off, large, coarse woven bags were brought in, the heat still pouring out of them, and dumped out on large tables. These held our combined belongings, also fumigated! We were told to pick out our clothes and put them on. I look for my extra small bundle, the one that holds our song book, Bible, dry bread, butter and my children's second best dresses, and I find them all soaked in melted butter. *Ach, Gott!* So this is *Deutschland*, where everything must be clean.

Here in quarantine we sleep in numbered compartments built in a row. Three times a day we receive short rations of food. At each meal I see mothers hiding their share of bread inside their bosoms, to put into their bundles later on. This they do for their childrens' sake, should they need it later on.

Every morning and night we have roll call. Then, one morning, there is terrible confusion. Frau Ehrlich and her girl are missing. The white-clad women are very excited. Instead of whispering, as always, they are now shouting. And even though they find Frau Ehrlich and the girl they are not brought back to the women's quarters. The furtive whispers take on meaning now. There is smallpox in the men's quarters and Frau Ehrlich had gone to her husband in the night. Now she and the girl, Margrete, are in the isolation ward.

Margrete is vaccinated in all haste, but her arm swells and throbs and she writhes in pain. Before many days the doctors are talking of taking her arm off. But Herr Ehrlich and his wife will not hear of it. We get the story from the white-clad women who go in and out of our building.

"Sooner she dies than loses her arm," Herr Ehrlich shouts at the doctors. He will not give his consent. And Frau Ehrlich stands solid as an ox behind him.

Upon our release from quarantine we are ready to sail. The Ehrlichs refuse to stay behind, even though Margrete is still very sick. "We will go and take the girl with us," they say flatly. They pick her up and carry her to the station where the big gates open onto the loading planks.

It doesn't take David long with our visas and final papers and we find ourselves out on the cold, wind-swept docks. I see men loading wares into the ship that will carry us across the ocean. Sharp orders are yelled by stevedores and answered by the shrill cries of soaring, diving gulls. Never have I seen so many fish, even on the Volga. They are loading them into the ship all wet and shining in the morning sun that is breaking through the chill fog.

On the dock are cages of brightly colored birds and wild animals behind bars, all being hurriedly moved away. Great bales of cork and huge casks of Algerian wines are easily and swiftly moved about. And here, for the first time, I see large bunches of slim green fruit that David calls the banana. "It is a warm climate fruit," he says, "from far away islands." How huge God's earth must be! How different from the things I know. Surely, this is a sight to remember!

Heavy fog is a world all its own and danger lurks beyond every treacherous wave. It is a blind, narrow world, where huge waves rise to great height only to crash asunder, into seething foam. And all about us the throaty wail of our ship's fog horn is drawing answering calls from invisible ships and barges plying the waters between Hamburg, Rotterdam and Dover.

Our steamer stops in the port of Rotterdam to take on more cargo and passengers. Then again, on the grey wharfs of England more passengers and wares are loaded in. This takes a great deal of time, while sea birds dip and soar and swoop out of wisps of fog, cleaving the sky with sinister cries.

Then, at last, having left the choppy waters of the channel, we are out on the wide ocean, steaming toward America!

But third-class passage is no pleasure. Here, deep within the ship, we are packed together with hardly any room to spare. We are pilgrims of many nations, all fleeing Old World strife, looking for a new life of liberty and freedom.

There are small booths built all along the wall with narrow, hard beds. And though the room is very large and there are many beds, the beds are overcrowded with small children and the aged. The rest of us must be content with hard benches or the floor. The family who has a straw mattress or featherbed with them is lucky indeed.

Or are they really lucky? There is much seasickness among the people and the ship has not provided enough urns for all of them, and accidents do happen. Sometimes it is just plain carelessness, and the mattresses become terribly soiled by strangers. *Ach*, such stench! One can hardly stand it.

David looks so pale that I beg him to go topside to get some fresh air.

"We cannot all go, so I will stay," he says, flatly.

"You can do nothing here," I scold, and make him go. It is enough that I must stay in this hole. I do all I can to help the sick, but soon I must close my eyes to it. I struggle hard not to let the sickness get me, but in the end it has me in its grip. I am so sick I cannot hold my head up. Even my children are better off than I am.

Every now and then, Vasilla, a burly Russian, comes to wash up the stench. He has a large wooden scrub bucket. He is not the best person to have around, because every word he utters is a swear word. His words are as vile as the mess he has to come to clean up; I know, because I understand them. And because his work is what it is, he drinks a lot. He is never sober. The moment he enters it is as if a storm has descended upon us.

I must keep close watch on my Mia, for she is forever spilling water. Up to now she has spilled his pail twice, the lurching of the ship sending water in all directions, adding to the mess.

*"Durak! Swovitch!"* he roared, both times, snatching up the bucket, threatening to kill her. But I hide her behind my skirts, away from his bleary eyes. Twice she has been safe, but what will it be the next time Vasilla comes? I must keep a constant watch on her. The seasickness persists.

The days go by one after another. The ship lurches and rolls and sinks, only to rise again. The hours while themselves away and night comes on without end. The sleepless moan in their discomfort. A grey haired, stooped *Grossmutter* sighs, huddled in a miserable heap on a hard bench, and her burdens weigh heavy on my heart. My family is asleep about me as I sit in silence. Underneath me is the constant throbbing of the engine that is moving us forward.

Another night, and an old man dies. He is carried up the stairs to a watery grave. After that there is a strange stillness among the sick people. A young Polish mother, dark of skin and beautiful to look upon, is sitting close to me. So far we have only smiled at each other. But now she is sad-faced, hugging her tightly wrapped baby to her, rocking her body back and forth, back and forth. From the small bundle come low whimpering sounds. And though she often tries to feed the baby, it refuses the breast. Nothing seems to help, so she sits and rocks.

When her mind, seemingly, wanders to a watery grave, she instinctively draws the bundle even closer. And I see the fear in her eyes multiply. It is on such a moment as this that there is complete silence inside the blanket. I am aware of it as she is. Then suddenly, and frantically, she searches within the folds. After a moment of intense anxiety her hands grow still, even calm. And I cannot tell what has really transpired inside the bundle.

Morning comes, and I have fallen asleep, hunched forward, my head resting on the bundle I am holding in my lap. Then I become aware of terrible screaming.

The words being shouted are in many languages, and I think we must be sinking. I open my eyes and see soapy water swishing by my feet. "Where is Mia?" I cry, leaping forward. "Where is my little girl?"

"Vasilla has her by the nape of the neck. He is drowning her in the sea," screams Leah. "Mama, do something! He swears he will feed her to the fish."

There is great excitement in the room and people are milling toward the stairway. *"Ach, Gott,"* I cry, "let me through." I elbow my way to the stairway, thinking all sorts of things. But there is no need to worry further. Already Ludwig Reinert is coming down the stairs, carrying Mia in his arms.

"He didn't hurt me, Mama," she says, not even crying.

*"Ach!"* What can one do with a child such as this?

On the sixth day at sea, David comes down from the upper deck with bad news for all of us.

"We must be vaccinated for smallpox. We cannot enter New York unless we are," he informs me. He asks me to get myself and the children ready, to scrub our arms clean. He brings us water to do so, and has me scrub his arm also.

When the doctor arrives he asks David to help him single out the people to be vaccinated. And so it is that David gives Leah and Mia the vaccine, each in turn. I hold their quavering heads against my breast while David scratches their left arms with a needle. After that David also gives me the vaccine.

After a few days our arms become quite painful, but one good thing is that Mia is very subdued. She sits quietly at my feet and leans her head against my lap. There is no more need now to worry about Vasilla and his scrub bucket.

Frau Ehrlich, who has moved from the other side of the crowded room, is more of a companion now that her girl Margrete, who had the vaccine in Germany is steadily improving. The three of us, Frau Ehrlich, Ammarie Reinert, and I sit together with our knitting. I do not let my sore arm bother me, the woolen thread skipping across Mia's golden tresses where her head rests on my lap.

Nine days and nine nights have rolled by with the billowing waves washing past the portholes. And still the young Polish woman is cradling her baby in her arms. There is a definite change though; most of the time now she sits and stares blindly before her. In all this noise I cannot be sure if the baby has whimpered lately.

It cannot be dead, I tell myself. There would be a stench. Then, I say, stench? What could add more stench to what we already have? I keep the secret to myself. I would not dare to betray her, if it really is what I think.

Then I begin to notice, whenever officials are near, that she pretends to talk or coo to her baby. Whenever our eyes meet I smile kindly and I do not burden her with any questions.

We spend ten miserable days and nights cooped up in the bottom of this ship, with no appetite, hardly any sleep, and now sore arms from the vaccine. We go through good weather and bad, through snow and sleet, ice and wind, but I am hardly aware of it except for David's telling me. Constantly huge green waves wash past the portholes. Yet, sometimes, when I sit and gaze at the green-white foam welling outside, it falls away, and I find myself looking at the blue sky. Heaven is indeed close by! But where is America?

Once David comes down the stairs all excited.

"What is it, *Baba?*" Mia asks.

"I saw a large steamer out on the ocean. That means we are getting close. We are not alone," he tells her.

David chucks both girls under the chin to make them laugh. "Guess what," he says. "I saw a monstrous whale, spewing a huge stream of water." We all laugh at the way he throws his arms high, indicating the height of the stream.

Leah asks a more serious question: "When will we reach America, *Baba?*"

"I can answer that, too," David says, smiling. "One more day and night, is all. Now, what do you think of that?"

"We like it," both of them chime together.

Then that time passes too and we prepare to disembark. Everything is happiness. All about us people are taking on a new zest for living. Their eyes take on the glint of renewed hope.

All are happy save the young Polish woman. She alone sits mute, staring. It is true. Her baby is dead. For the past day and night she has sat dry-eyed, filled with an agonizing sorrow, rocking and humming softly over her tightly wrapped bundle, determined, I know, to save the body of her child from a grave at sea.

But now, as officials are taking the baby from her, the pent-up torment bursts forth, shattering and terrible. I rush to her and put my arms around her as she sits; she presses her face into the folds of my skirts, sobbing bitterly.

"There, there, *Freundin*," I soothe in German, tears streaming down my own face, falling on her head. *"Still, nur still,"* I coax, my arms around her sobbing form.

After a long time her hunched shoulders relax. She is exhausted by the violence of her grief. Yet her deep mother love has saved her baby from a watery grave, preferring an alien grave, in alien soil — you America! A Polish mother enshrines her heart and soul within your shores, ere her feet enter.

# PART TWO

# *AMERICA . . . . .*
# *MY AMERICA!*

*I am the vine, ye are the branches: He that abideth in me, and I in him, the same bringeth forth much fruit: for without me ye can do nothing.*

*John 15:5*

# CHAPTER 10

# *The Trip*

*A* merica. . .the name is happiness! And to my eyes the Statue of Liberty is a sweetness almost painful to behold. See, how majestically she holds the book and offers the light! All at once the old yearning returns and I renew the pledge I made in *Russland*: unknowing like me my children shall not be. Here we will try to make something of ourselves.

Tears of happiness fall down my cheeks and I let them fall. All about me is excitement and a murmuring of many languages.

> *Give me your tired,*
>     *your poor,*
> *Your huddled masses*
>     *yearning to breathe free,*
> *The wretched refuse of*
>     *your teeming shore.*
>
> *Send these the home-less,*
>     *tempest-tost to me,*
> *I lift my lamp beside*
>     *the golden door!*

I think I must be dreaming the words; I have heard them before. I am not dreaming; David standing beside me is speaking them softly in our own language. He is looking off into the distance, beyond the goddess of light, to the land where a great city lies red in the setting sun. His voice is low and reverent. I look on his face and see the brimming tears, the moving lips, and I know it is his very soul that speaks.

Suddenly he turns to us, reaching out his strong arm and pressing us forward. "Look, my *Familie!*" he exclaims. "Look! So that you will see her, and always remember."

He lifts up Leah, the better to see. She is excited. "Oh, *Baba*," she cries, pointing into the swirling mist blowing up from the sea, "the goddess has waded out into the water to meet us, to bring us the light!"

"*Ja, ja,*" David says, in a choked voice, holding her close to his tear-stained cheek. "*Ja, Liebchen,* she comes to bid us welcome and offers us freedom." He swallows abruptly and his voice leaves him.

Holding onto him I feel the excitement pulsing through his veins as we view the statue that symbolizes a new life, and my own heart will not lie still. Surely, this is the beauty of freedom, the beauty of things to come!

As we stand silent, with David's strong arms about us, the setting sun washes the sails of many small ships with scarlet. And, over all, the sea gulls fly, their lifted wings like narrow banners glinting in the sun, dipping, soaring, dipping again, and screaming like shrill gusts of wind in the night.

Our ship doesn't draw up to the docks of New York as I think it should. It anchors in the deep water a mile or so out, and we must stay on board another night and day.

Here, at standstill, inspection is more rigid. It soon becomes apparent that not all immigrants will enter the dreamed-of land. Many kinds of illnesses have broken out, especially a dread eye disease which has the officials worried. All about us are families who have one or more members whose eyes are mattered shut. These, the sick ones, cannot enter the country. That is certain. It is pitiful to see the anguish among our fellow passengers. There are Jews, Hungarians, Serbians, Ukrainians, Poles, Germans, Austrians, and Russian-Germans, our nationality. Some of each race are afflicted.

Shortly before nightfall a small ship comes alongside to take us to quarantine. In the process the blustery March wind blows a dampness off the ocean and chills us to the bone. Still it is good to have our feet on solid ground again. Even so, here at the immigrant station the actual weeding-out of the sick will take place. It will touch many a family.

We walk in great throngs down narrow passages enclosed by wire netting. There are many passageways running side by side all swallowing up more and more people and pouring them into the building proper. It is a stream of strange and varied people of many languages. A good many, like me, wear the head shawl and full skirts and heavy felt boots. Some are dressed in nothing more than pitiful rags, not enough to keep the body warm. They are so cold and miserable looking, I think they will die before they reach their destination. I notice especially a mother who has two girls about the size of mine.

In pity, I decide quickly to give her my children's two extra dresses. But in all this press, I have difficulty getting them out of my tightly bound bundle. And while I am pushed and half-stumbling down the ramp I lose sight of them, without the mother's knowing my good intent. I am so worried about these shriveled and cold children that I also lose sight of David. The last I saw of him, he had our two children by the hand, going with the crowd.

*Ach, Gott,* I am lost! What must I do? I hold tightly onto my bundle and hurry forward. The faces around me are strange, and I'm certain they do not speak my tongue. They are harassed themselves and do not care that I am lost.

I hurry forward into a large enclosure, dimly lit, and come to a small cage-like room where a woman sits with two small children, a boy and a girl. She is German and she beckons me to sit with her. I enter and see that both children have sore eyes. The thought never enters my head that if I stay I might never be let out of here.

Her name is Gettes. She does not know what will become of her and her children. She has not seen her husband since he went away arguing with an official. "*Ach, Gott!* Maybe they will send us back," she says, seeing the terror of it for the first time. "Where is my husband? Where is my husband?" she wails, and her eyes take on the look of an animal held at bay.

I try to soothe her in my small way. "He will come," I say, patting her shoulder. "He will not let you be sent back."

But she wails all the louder. "No, no, I will never see him again." She frightens her children with her loudness and they whimper in anguish. Then with mother love she gathers her little ones to her and sobs with them.

When, at long last, David finds me here he isn't glad as I think he should be. Instead, he is almost rough in hurrying me away. When he gets me far enough away from their hearing, he tells me that the woman and her children will be sent back because of the children's sore eyes. "They will need their mother," David explains. "The husband is free to stay, if he chooses. In any case he must stay, if he hasn't the return fare."

David tells me it is a good thing that he found me first. He hurries me into a large station room where many immigrants are

131

waiting on benches, and where he has left our children with the Ehrlichs and Reinerts, who were on the ship with us. My little ones start crying when they see me. "*Sei ruhig,* be still," I say. "See how everyone is looking."

Robed priests and ministers mingle with the people, asking about their welfare and destination. The Lutheran minister who befriends us says that it will take us five or six days, with a stop-over in Chicago, to get to Kansas.

"That far?" I say, hardly believing. "As far into the United States as out of Russia?"

"*Ja,*" he says, smiling. "*Amerika* is a large country. Kansas has great wheat fields, the same as Russia." The German-speaking minister's eyes sparkle. *Ach,* sure! Even a minister six days away from Kansas knows that it is a good place. I will be happy there!

Here at Ellis Island, the immigrant station, sad things are happening to some of the people, while we are being examined and dispatched by officials. We are aware of two men and one woman who are denied entrance to America because they have the eye disease. They are strangers to each other. The Russian woman is told she must return to her hometown, Tambov. Her four children, ranging in age from one month to six years, must return with her, even though they are perfectly well. The husband has no way of keeping or caring for them.

"Children must have a parent. It is better that they go with the mother." The officials are emphatic. Their word stands. Return fare is granted for them, because of the peculiar illness. But this does not appease the mother. She wails aloud, causing her children to scream in fright. The husband begs to return with them, but he lacks the money for the return trip.

The situation with the other two men is no better. They must return while their wives and children stay. We, ourselves, are fortunate that we are all well. Our papers are all stamped and approved by German-speaking officials, and as soon as David can gather up our belongings we are free to go — to Kansas, where my brother, Friederich, and his family are waiting.

David has bought enough food for the trip, bread and cheese and a thick round sausage they call bologna, and he has seventy cents left in American money. "Enough," he says, jingling the coins in his hand and laughingly slipping them into his pocket, "enough, to start a good living."

We say good-bye to the Reinerts, who will stay in New York, and to the Ehrlichs, who are not quite ready to leave for Ohio, where Frau Ehrlich has a brother. "Good-bye. *Viel Glück. Auf Wiedersehn!*" All of us shed tears. Perhaps we are never to see each other again.

Then, once again, we are on a small ship, and I am frightened. "This is not the way," I cry. "We are to travel by land."

"It is all right, Evaliz," David says, "the boat is taking us to the train station." Both of us laugh at my stupidity. I forget that this is America where everything is good.

I am surprised. The boat does not take us to a bright, shining station, but to the bleak and cold railroad yards. As far as the eye can see there are train tracks, one next to the other, with locomotives everywhere, steaming, puffing smoke, clanking and moving backward and forward pushing box-cars with them. Long sheds with high platforms are built along the side, where we are asked to wait. There are many people gathered here; many are going to different parts of the country. But while we wait for our train we huddle together in this cold, poorly-built station.

All at once the right train comes and we rush out to see it steam into the deep lane between the platforms. A train man looks at our tickets and points out a certain car, but somehow we pick the wrong one and he shouts, "No, No! You crazy foreigners." I guess what he is saying and I wince with shame. David no longer knows the language. Now he is a stranger in this new land.

The porter to our car is trying to lay a plank for us to walk on, and David tries to help him, but the porter, a stout, ruddy-faced man, doesn't want his help. He resents David's good-natured help. He violently jerks the board from David's grasp, the board falls, and in the process the porter suffers a blood blister. He is so infuriated he calls David a bad name:

"You son . . . . . . . ."

*Ach!* Twice within minutes David has been called names. Don't they know this is a day of remembrance, a day of gratitude and love? Is this then, our welcome to America? No, I will not believe it!

I am surprised that the American trains are much, much better than the Russian trains.

"Look, Mama, they have seats," Leah and Mia shout when they get inside. "Look, *Baba*, seats for everyone and more."

"*Ja, Mädelen\*; Baba* sees," he smiles, settling down.

Soon we are flying through the city that is more than one city; before one ends entirely another one begins. The train shrieks madly, going faster, ever faster. I thought the trains of Russia were fast, but they are nothing compared to this. One hears other long drawn-out wails of speeding trains, coming toward us. One especially, from the sound of it, is piercingly near, then, a veil of darkness, a flash of light, and we have passed each other, our own shrill whistle mangled by the clatter of a million steel claws. Sure,

---

\**Mädelen* — (German) plural of *Madel*, girl.

the buildings go whirling past faster than did any of those in Europe.

There are houses and factories and stations and rivers and tremendous refuse dumps, and still more of everything over and over again. My children look through the window and marvel at the spirals of smoke and the glittering rubble shining in the sun. I cannot tell what it is, but David calls it tin cans. "They are discarded food containers," he says.

What else shall I see in America? I wonder.

After a day and night the land is changing, still snowy, but more open. This is the way I like it. It's to the wide open fields of Kansas that we are going. But that is still days away; we haven't even reached Chicago, the stop-over.

I thrill at the sight of large trees and rich farm houses, the lakes, the square fields and the pasturelands that swim past our windows.

"The fields of Kansas are like those of Russia," David says. "That is what the minister at the island station told us." Sure, I think, it will be a fine land. Even better than Russia.

Leah and Mia are no trouble. They are playing a game. "I will take that tree and pond with the ducks on the ice for my home," says Leah.

"No, the house with the pony tied up is better," pipes Mia.

Then comes Chicago, the lay-over town. For us it is a place of misery for we have to sleep on the hard benches. Our food is beginning to spoil. The bologna David bought is getting sticky and greenish in color, but we must eat it; we have only a few coins left. Careful so that the people across the aisle do not see, I peel off the outside covering of the meat and break a loaf of bread. We eat our meal. At least we have some bread and cheese left for the rest of the trip.

Moving forward, we leave more and more country behind. Now and then the snow on the land is not so deep. Maybe when we get to Kansas there will be no snow, I think.

Our train stops in a small town. A young, freckle-faced lad comes in selling food. A hunger-provoking odor heralds his coming. "Pies. Apple pies?" he calls out, coming down the aisle. I look close as he comes near, selling to the people in front of us. What are they? I have never seen them before. What is pie? I do not know.

My children also watch with great longing in their eyes. Oh, for a coin to get one for them. I cannot bear the look in their eyes. I turn to look at David, and I see that he, too, has turned away.

But I'm compelled to look; I am the closest. The boy is standing near, holding the goody toward Leah.

"Pie?" he questions.

In all innocence, Leah thinks he is giving it to her. She reaches out and takes it. Then suddenly, she realizes her mistake and a flush of shame spreads over her face. Bewildered and embarrassed, her eyes dart from me to David, and back again. The boy is waiting for his pay. Silent tears flood her brown eyes and roll down her cheeks. *Ach*, for a brief moment a six-year-old foreign girl has forgotten that it takes money to buy these things.

"*Nein, danke,*" I say, taking the tidbit from her and handing it back to the uneasy lad.

My poor little girl. Her longing has driven her to shame. I draw her close to me and hold her tight, patting her. My eyes veil over. Dimly I see that the elderly American across the way is buying a pie.

When the boy is gone and the train has started I feel a gentle tug on my arm. It is the American gentleman. He is asking Leah to look at him. Then, in all kindness, he hands her the baked delicacy. Our eyes meet. We smile the universal smiles of friendliness and gratitude. There are good people in America, I tell myself.

When at long last, our conductor calls "Kansas City," a sheer joy wings through me. Here is a word I understand. The word "Kansas" means home to me!

I look out over the land, eagerly trying to picture my new home. But a string of crazily tilted buildings comes sailing along and then another city is flying past our windows. It is only a city. This is not my home! Instead, we have a lay-over in the station. More hard, cold benches.

Again, the train rushes on and on, through the rest of the night and into the light of another day. Then come the prairies, desolate and brown. Shaggy grasses once tall, now broken in disarray, are weighed down with scattered streaks of dirt-crusted snow. Cold, March winds blow out of the open country and buffet our train on its moving wheels.

Where the land is dry, strong prairie winds swoop up puffs of dust. Huge, round tumbleweeds roll out of fields and skim crazily over the broken-down grasses and patches of snow, like something possessed. More and more follow after them as the wind tears them from their winter mooring. We are accustomed to the thistles, because we had them in Russia.

Some of the tumbleweeds come straight for us and dash as though in panic against the side of the train and are ground to bits under the fast turning wheels. *Ach*, to me it looks as if the whole world is fleeing in terror.

My heart feels as desolate as this brown land, as desolate as the small farm places that are scattered so far apart on this wide open land, the solitude of the windy sky broken only by their spindly windmills.

There are only two other persons left in our train car. They sit up front, looking solemnly out of the window. All the others got off where the land looked rich and the farm places plentiful.

The eagerness has also gone out of David's eyes. I turn away from the moving prairie and pretend that I do not notice the bleakness. But the ache is there. It grows and grows. Still I let my face show nothing; David must not lose faith, too. My head throbs. Is this what we have come to? Has this been my dream? *Ach*, no! I cannot hold back the tears. Hot and scalding they fall down my cheeks.

David sees me crying. "*Ach*, Evaliz," he consoles. "Wipe the tears. This has been winter. Wait until spring comes. You'll see, things will be better." He puts his finger under my chin and forces me to look at him. "Come, be done with this foolishness."

"*Ja*, sure," I say, and we smile at each other. Things cannot be this bad all the time.

The porter enters our car from the front. He sways on his feet and takes hold of the back of the seats to help him walk. He looks at us and says, "WaKeeney, WaKeeney."

"*Ach, Gott!* This is it," I say. "Our home." I hustle things together and smooth down my children's hair. David takes care of the bundle. The train is beginning to slow down. I can hardly breathe for excitement. Now town houses are beginning to move by, not too many, because this is a small town as Friederich said in one of his letters.

Then we see the depot and people standing around. The train stops and we stumble down the aisle to the steps. I try to see all the happy faces at once but it doesn't work.

"Welcome to America!" my brother Friederich shouts, and throws his arms around me, hugging me tight. Everyone says hello and there are happy tears all around. With Friederich is his wife Gredel and their four sons, one more than they had in *Russland*. It is wonderful to see them.

Friederich lives on a farm eight miles out of town. He takes us out home to visit with them for a week. Later we will live in a rooming house in WaKeeney which Friederich has rented for us. We must live in town so that David can repay the loan to Mr. Walker by helping him build a new house. After that, we hope to farm.

We have a room on the second floor of what is called "The Bee Hive," because all manner of people have lived here. It is a large grey house with twelve rooms, six on top and six on the bottom. Each room is a unit within itself suitable for cooking, eating and

136

sleeping. It is very crowded for four people. At present it houses several railroad workers and their families, the livery stable manager, and a newly arrived minister and his family. There are others.

The Bee Hive sits on a city lot all by itself, just a block off Main Street. The back entries to stores are only a stone-throw away. The vacant ground around the rooming house is a jumble of blackened, broken-down sunflower stalks and weeds. No one has bothered to clean it up.

Then, lo, the miracle: spring comes to the prairie! It does not come softly nor shyly, but in great magic strides. Spring! Lush, and green, and beautiful!

From my second floor window I see it coming like a green rolling tide. It is everywhere! It is in the eaves of the house where birds are busily building their nests. It is in the lilting winds, soft and soothing. It is in the tender buds on trees in the Courthouse Square, and in the green, lacy foliage along the edge of the town streets.

From my high window I see it all, the whole small town complete, with the wide green prairie running far away to meet the blue expanse of the Kansas sky.

It is a strange little town. The two main streets cut a dusty cross right through the center. Its houses are scattered loosely on outlying streets, all built on smooth ground. There are trees and bushes. But the oasis is the Courthouse Square, with its flourishing trees. Along the two sides facing the stores are neat rows of hitching posts, with wagon-hitched and saddled horses sleeping drowsily, occasionally swishing their tails and stumping their hoofs in the soft ground.

The weather-worn store fronts have wooden sidewalks, dry and splintered. There are trees next to them. On the north end of the street leading up from the railroad stands a large livery stable, corralled at the rear.

Scattered about loosely on the two main streets are a blacksmith, a print shop, the post office, the bank, a harness shop, the cream station, the mercantile store, a butcher shop and the implement store. The south side of the harness shop and numerous other sheds display posters of by-gone carnivals: skimpily-dressed women stand on the broad backs of prancing horses; regal drivers dressed in king's livery drive gild-edged wagons with caged animals, drawn by pure white horses with red plumes in their manes. Freaks and clowns with chalk-white faces follow.

Another building of importance, called the Penny Hotel because of the Penny sisters who own it, sits on a street by itself, near the railroad, and a block away from the business section. South, next to the train tracks are the grain elevators, the lumber yard, and further west, beyond the depot, the stockyards, where long-horned cattled are bellowing and milling about in a cloud of dust, while men on horseback are shouting, "Hike! Hike!" and snapping whips over their heads, forcing the bewildered cattle up the ramps into cattle cars on the siding. Here, from my high window, I can see it all.

In the corral behind the livery stable a strange team of work horses eats hay. Their sweat-soaked hides glisten in the sun. A man has brought them, watered them, given them hay and closed the gate. It is the noon hour. I marvel at their strangeness. I have never seen their kind. In Russia we had horses, oxen, and camels, but these I know nothing about. They have very long ears and slim, smooth tails, with only a tuft of hair at the end. When David comes home I ask him, "What kind of horses are they?"

"They are mules, a hybrid, produced by cross-breeding of donkey and horse," he explains, and adds, "They are much stronger than horses. They are often used for heavy pulling or road work, like building railroads."

Sure. It is good that I have David to explain things to me in this strange land. Sometimes I wonder if I will ever get used to it.

I do not like living in town, where there is nothing for me to do, and where I have nothing to do with. I am used to hard work among my kind of people. I must work to be happy!

The people look at me and my children with great curiosity. They smile at the way we talk, and stare at our stupidity when we ask for things over the store counter. I feel shame. And each time I go, I must believe that I am a know-nothing.

I do not fit in with these people. To them I must look like a clumsy ox. Here I am, dressed in heavy felt boots, long woolen skirt, a button down front, tight fitted bodice with long sleeves and high neck band, and on my head a *Halstuch*, a head shawl. They are all the clothes I have. They are dressed in ruffles and lace, and in dainty, feather-light shoes. Instead of head scarves they wear large, flower and net trimmed hats and carry silken umbrellas.

I think I should stay in my room. Yet I must go from time to time, especially when my two children leave their play and follow the path to the town streets. But before I go to find them, I must make a decision; I can wear my boots, or go barefoot. Which? One is no better than the other.

The children are drawn to town because several times when Mr. Walker saw them there, he gave them candy. Now I cannot keep them home. When I find them, Leah, the elder, explains that she came only to bring Mia back. But Mia makes no excuses. Neither is she ready to go home. She lies down on the wooden sidewalk in front of all the people and kicks and screams and will not walk home until I lay a hand to her. I could die with shame.

I am a big show, better, by far, than the carnival, advertised on the tattered posters on the sides of the town buildings. Some of the town ladies swish past me with a rustle of silk, trying hard not to notice me; yet, I know they turn and take a look once they are past. And sun-baked, weathered farm women, who are not dressed much better than I am and who still have barn manure on their awkward shoes, stand still and look me up and down, without so much as a flicker of shame in their eyes. They do not know it, but my shame for them outweighs that of my own. Their boldness is so unbecoming.

The young town girls dressed so daintily, with high, fluffy hairdos stand off a ways, whispering slyly, thinking I am too dumb to notice. Then, if I happen to look their way, they quickly try to cover their tittering with daintily-gloved hands or slowly twirling umbrellas while their mischievous eyes rove from my head to foot. A bumpkin, for sure! My face burns like fire. This is not the way I would have it in America.

When David comes home from work I complain to him. "Do they think I want to wear boots in hot weather?" I ask, scornfully. "There is no money to buy shoes." Oh, I cry so hard, I think I will never quit.

"Ach, Liebchen, wipe the tears," David says with light words. "Can't you see they look at you, because you are so beautiful?" He lifts my chin and looks upon my face. "Sure, there isn't another woman as beautiful or as good as you in all this town, or country." He smiles and kisses me on the nose. He acts as if this is nothing, but inside, I know, he hurts very deeply. How deeply, I find out soon enough because he comes home and announces that he has taken a part-time job unpacking crates at the store, in addition to building the house. "Soon, you will have shoes," he assures me.

I go barefoot in our room, but the floors are dry and splintered and it is hard to be careful. I am forever digging slivers from my feet, and from the feet of my children. It is far better for the poor to have dirt floors rather than splinters, I think.

But, even so, I go barefoot from now on, even on the town streets. I try not to feel hurt when I hear someone whisper, "Look at that Roosian. Barefoot! Has she no shame?"

This is not the way I had dreamed of it. I wanted to make something of myself, something good and helpful. But in spite of all, my strangeness brings only ridicule. I cry myself to sleep at night.

The day is always brighter when my brother Friederich comes to town and brings us fresh pork, cream, eggs, and milk. The children are so happy they jump with glee. Friederich and Gredel are generous, and I appreciate their gifts.

I take pride in myself when I go out in the vacant lot next to our rooming house to gather dry sunflower stalks for fire wood. But the young married women on the ground floor think me queer, and when I walk out into the country and bring back dry cow chips, they laugh, and think me unclean, and refuse to take anything from my hands. What do they think we should do? Starve? We cannot eat our food raw. I spend my night in prayer. I ask God to forgive them, as I have already forgiven them. How can they know what it is like?

Softly, before the sun is up, I steal out of bed and slip across the dew-covered grasses until I come to the intersection of the two main streets. This is how I like it best, when no one can see. I stand in the middle of the street looking to the east, waiting for the morning. In the courthouse trees, the birds are chirruping their early morning chatter. I listen and realize that they are not different from other birds. Their twittering is the Song Universal. All things are the same. If I want to be accepted then the change must start with me. I see it all for the first time.

Then, over the far rim of the prairie rises the sun. The vivid ray of light spreads and grows over everything, lifting higher, and higher, cutting a golden pathway down the street, creeping forward, glowing and warm, until it shines on my bare feet. *Ach*, the wonder of it, the beauty of it! Even in America the sunlight has found me, at last. I shall never feel abused again. Where has been my dignity? My pride? My thanksgiving?

The words that David spoke so long ago are true: "It is one flight to the housetop; it is the leap of the soul to the sunrise."

# CHAPTER 11

# *America*

N ow when I walk on the town streets I hold my head high and people show only kindness toward me. Most of my self-confidence comes because of David. He is becoming well known and liked by all. He has an offer to help build two more houses as soon as Mr. Walker's is finished.

It helps, too, that I have a pair of shoes now and a new calico dress that I made for myself. All this was made possible by David's extra earnings from the mercantile store. He is a good man and already he is learning some of the language.

As for me, I would rather be out on the farm. But first David must pay off our debt. Then we must save money to buy farm tools and livestock. This will take a long time. So I plan and think what I can do to help. But what? I do not even know the language.

I stand at my window and watch the bustling town below. Sturdy farmers are loading seed corn, barley, and oats, or laboriously carrying heavy sacks of seed potatoes. Over in the blacksmith shop I see a bare-armed giant standing over an anvil hammering sharp edges to red hot plow shares, sparks spurting at every blow. Tap. Tap. Tap. The sound goes on throughout the day.

At the hotel, two blocks away, dazzling white linens flutter in the strumming winds. Long clothes lines are stretched in the large back yard and every other day, without fail, they hang full of bed sheets.

I marvel at the convenience the American people have to do their washing. We did not have water at our doorsteps in Russia, nor even in the yard. And we certainly didn't have clothes lines. We did our washing at the village dam in winter and summer, first boiling our clothes in ashes then taking them to the dam to pound clean. In the summer we dried them spread out on the grasses and in winter we hung them on pegs or whatever. Sure. The women in this country have it easy. If they only knew it.

Today, as I look out my window I see no clothes on the lines at the hotel. Neither are there any on the following day or the next. A thought comes to me. Whoever does the wash must be sick. Perhaps, here is my answer. I decide I will go right away. I call my children and wash them clean, and slip on fresh dresses. I comb their hair and make braids, tying the ends with torn strips of white cloth. I tie a clean white apron over my calico dress and put on a white head scarf. And we walk straight to the hotel, boldly, without any nonsense.

I do not even think what I will say when I get there. But now that I stand at the door, I am afraid to knock. My whole body trembles. And the thought of the door opening suddenly fills me with cold fright. I want to run.

"What is the matter, Mama?" Leah asks, in her quiet manner. But Mia, who is curious about everything, trips over the foot scraper and falls against the door with a loud bang.

Before I can say anything, the door opens. The tall, spindly woman with cold eyes gives me a questioning look. The look says, "Have you come to beg food? How dare you!"

*Ach, Gott*, I think. What is done is done. It's too late to run. Her eyes are demanding an answer.

"*Bitte, verzeih'*. Please forgive," I beg, my face burning with shame.

The look on the woman's face changes. "So, you speak German?" she says in careful, understandable German. I can hardly believe my ears.

"Yes," I say, "I came to see if you need a wash lady."

She gives me no answer, but looks sharply at my clean apron and the whiteness of my head shawl, then at my children's dresses. Finally, she says, "I'm particular. Come tomorrow."

I learn later that she is only the cook. Two unmarried sisters own the hotel. They are very nice, but one has been sick in bed, and since they do most of the work themselves, the wash has piled up.

In the morning I am up at daylight. After breakfast when David has gone to work, I take my children and go to the hotel. The children will play in the yard while I do my work. Everything is very convenient. There is a wash-porch built alongside the kitchen. There is a hand-operated wash machine, and a water pump with a wide spout. Kindling is stored right here inside; the clothes can be boiled on the large kitchen stoves; the wash and rinse water can be dipped into a wooden trough which has a spout. A v-shaped wooden drain, in sections, is fastened to the spout to carry water far out into the yard, away from the vegetable garden. Surely, this is child's play compared with the way I am used to washing. There are washboards of corrugated metal with a place to hold the bar of soap, bluing for the last rinse water, wooden clothes pins to hold the wash on the line. It's unbelievable.

When I am through washing for the day, I count twenty-four sheets, thirty pillow cases, fifty-three towels, eleven family size table cloths and twenty-eight napkins, among other small stuff. I can see by the cook's supervising eye that she is pleased. And I wonder to myself if she knows how painful my back is. I can hardly stand up straight, especially in my condition; I'm expecting again.

The woman seemingly is interested only in the work at hand. She says, "Come back in the morning to iron." I am happy. I have done my first day's work for pay, in America. Two whole dollars!

Every morning thereafter I go back to the hotel to make beds, clean out the wash basins and night jars, and I receive seventy-five cents each day.

On my way home, my children and I stop at the butcher shop to buy fifteen cents' worth of boiling beef and the friendly butcher gives us a beef heart and some liver, free. I cannot thank him enough. He only smiles. He gives things to other people too. Americans are good people. I also stop at the mercantile store to buy a pound of rice, some potatoes, four onions and a skein of yarn to knit new heels and toes on David's worn-out socks.

These are busy days, and I am very tired when I get to bed at night. I must knit and sew for the baby that is coming. The two old-maid ladies at the hotel have given me used clothing and worn-out sheets. I cut up one of the full skirts to make little clothes. There are enough assorted pieces of clothing to make Leah and Mia some dresses, and even one for me. From the worn-out sheets they have given me I tear diapers. They are a luxury. We had no diapers in Russia. I have had five children; none used diapers; I trained each one right from the beginning.

After several months Mr. Walker's home is completed, and David takes me to see it. I have never seen such beauty, such spaciousness, such rich appointment. The walls are papered with silver and gold and vermillion design. The portieres are of copen-blue velvet. A crystal clear mirror of tremendous size hangs from rope and tassels of gold. A soft rug covers the floor completely. Before we leave, Mrs. Walker serves us tea and cakes. She gives the children glasses of milk to drink. I can only nod my thanks, feeling very clumsy. But she makes everything right with her genuine friendliness.

Soon after this, a new shipment of lumber arrives and David starts on the first of two houses he is to build. Our debt to Mr. Walker is paid, and I need no longer do the washing at the hotel.

At last, we are out on the farm. There are now five of us. The baby is born, a girl. I call her Hester, meaning a star of good fortune. America's child!

Once more, spring has come to the prairie with the smell of freshly plowed loam, and tender, new grasses; of violets and phlox; of butter-cups and wild garlic. Prairie larks fly out of the pasture land to perch on fence posts, thrilling their songs, 'till my heart swells fit to burst. And over all, white, fluffy clouds sail in a sky of blue, going where no one knows.

Sitting in the midst of all this is our one-room stone house, six miles out of town. It is not a fine house, for it has stood empty and desolate and was once a chicken house. But I take lye water and scrub it clean. David lays in a floor out of old wood, and fashions bed frames along the wall into which we lay our straw mattress and featherbeds.

There are two other buildings, a granary, and a broken-down barn. But David will make it strong and sound before winter comes so we can shelter the team of horses and one cow which we have bought. The farm is rented. We are a long way from buying land.

Even though the dwellings are not good, the forty acres of land have lain fallow and David is anxious to set the plow into it. "This is our beginning, Evaliz," he says. "Our beginning, in America!" There is excitement in his voice as never before.

At last, on an early morning with the meadowlarks calling their melodious tone, David is ready to set the plow to the soil. I gather little Hester in my arms and with Leah and Mia running out ahead, we hurry to the field.

We have a good team of horses, and David is very proud of them. He needs only to cluck his tongue and they start, pulling with one accord, their heads and flowing manes bobbing up and down. David has the knotted lines around his neck and under his right arm while he holds the handles of the walking plow with both hands; the rich, black loam flows forth, smooth and moist and springy.

Rover, the little puppy that Friederich gave us, is running playfully about, tripping the children and chasing butterflies, falling on his face in the soft black loam. The children laugh with glee at his antics and fall down with him. Our chickens, too, come running, flapping their wings in all haste. Soon they are scampering over the newly-turned earth, scratching and picking worms, and frantically scratching again.

Barefoot, as in the old country, with my child in my arms, I follow the damp, cold furrow and it is like a healing balm to my soul. It is true. The earth is the Lord's.

It is a summer of hard work and high hopes. It seems David hardly gets to bed before he is up again, before the sun rises. As soon as the weeds start to grow in the corn rows he cultivates. When the corn becomes taller he is out there again, this time smoothing out the lister furrow, covering the young roots to a firmer depth.

Rains visit the prairie. Clouds gather and thicken and crowd out the blue of the sky, and rains fall in full benediction upon the land. The land shows evidence that the winds have ceased their burning. To all sides the wide rolling land holds young wheat and corn and young pasture grasses on its breast. Cattle and horses graze to their heart's content.

In the first part of June the waving fields of wheat lose their soft greenness, turning bluish and taking on a coarser look as the stems thicken and the wheat heads fill with milk. From now on they swell and grow with fertile will. Then the hot winds come at the right time, to ruffle the field in gold, almost overnight. The grain is ripe, waiting for the reaper.

With grateful hearts we cut and stack our golden harvest. It should thresh out better than six hundred bushels. When sold, it will help pay for the few farm implements David bought on credit. We must also make a small payment on the team of horses and the cow he bought from our neighbor.

Now that the wheat harvest is in and the corn is still green in the field, David borrows a mower from our neighbor to cut the hay that grows along the roadway and in draws, for winter feed. He will repay the neighbor with help when he needs it.

With this out of the way, the winter wheat already planted, and the corn still not ripe, David sets to work on the barn. He tears it down in part and makes a smaller and better building out of it. He has also built a chicken house and a pig pen and shelter for our sow and her litter of five.

In the late fall when the corn is ripe I go with David, and while our children play in and out of the rows, we cut each stalk with

broad corn knives and tie them into bundles, setting them in
shocks. When we are all through David hauls them home and
makes another stack, next to the one of hay. We need all the fodder
we can get for the winter.

Other farmers hereabouts have binders that cut and tie the
stalks into bundles all in one operation. Since it takes a great deal of
money to buy the machine, several farmers have gone into
partnership, and though they would lend them, the season is too
short to wait.

Early November is still warm. The sky is a sea of blue where
white fluffs of cloud go sailing by. Leisurely, the last of the wild
geese fly south, lingering in the pasture sloughs. Rising
majestically, circling and soaring and making a loud clamor, they
glide into a line as they wedge through the sky and fade into
nothingness.

Then, with the mild weather still holding, David goes to help
build our small country church. There are enough Volga-German
Lutherans living here in the neighborhood to undertake the building
of an edifice. And since David and another member have been
appointed to supervise the work, he must go every day.

While he is gone I go out to the large stack and husk the ears of
corn. I carry them by the bushel to the granary. I pile the stalks
neatly to one side for winter fodder. When the corn husks pile up in
front of me I go through them very carefully, picking out the soft-
centered husks to make a corn-husk bed for our children. These are
softer and more springy than straw-beds. I fill the ticking and sew
it shut, just the way we made the featherbeds in Russia. It will not
be as soft as feathers, but with a thick quilt tucked over the top, it
will make a good bed. At bedtime our children romp in the plump
thickness and laugh at the loud rustling of the husks. They do not
feel slighted that they must sleep on husks instead of feathers.

My house is plain. The floors were slivered until I rubbed them
smooth with sand. My table is homemade. The cook stove is old,
but very clean. We had no chairs, so David made two benches. Our
clothes are folded in boxes and some are hanging on wall pegs. Wall
shelves keep my dishes in place, and curtains are a thing to dream
about. But I am happy. And busy.

With good homemade soap I bleach flour sacks and make dresses
for my children, saving every scrap to make small underclothes.
Neither do I let one feather go astray, for we always need more
pillows.

Evenings, when David is home, he mends harness or soles the
children's shoes, and while he does that he teaches Leah and Mia
the Ten Commandments and Luther's Small Catechism. We sing

many hymns such as *"Jesu geh' voran,"* Jesus lead the way. Always, before the children go to bed, David reads a portion of the Scriptures and we have a prayer. He does likewise every morning before breakfast. God is always near.

Our first winter out in the country is bleak and cold. I stand in my yard and watch the first scud of grey clouds come over the sky. They gather and thicken. Then, as night sets in, a sleety rain blows in gusts, freezing on. It glazes every blade of grass, every stem of weed left standing, until they rattle in the wind. The ground is a sheet of ice. Every footstep causes a crackling like breaking glass. David and I are careful to bed down our livestock. The driving, freezing rain coats the east and north sides of our farm buildings with a shiny sheet of ice. All that stands before it, the wagon, the farm implements, the fence posts, are transformed from the real to sculptured ice. The icy blast pelts the roof and windows in a thunderous clatter.

During the night the sleeting rain turns into snow. The gusty, howling wind blows its icy breath into every nook and cranny; it blows down the chimney and puffs at the stove lids; it blows in around the door and the windows.

The temperature falls at an amazing pace, finely powdering the snow. The window panes freeze over right before our eyes, and blowing our breath against them is of no avail. The drinking water and evening milk only a few paces from the stove turn mushy on top and form ice needles. The wind blows deep snow drifts into our yard, blowing it off the glazed fields and gathering it where none is needed, leaving the open fields barren.

This is winter in earnest. Days on end the winds howl and rage and moan their mournful song of the prairie. Each morning our drinking water is a solid piece of ice. On nights like this, it is impossible to keep the bread sponge for the morrow's baking alive without wrapping it and taking it to bed with me.

On mornings like this, David, wrapped in his warmest, takes the axes to break the thick ice in the stock tank so our animals can drink, and before night he must crack it again. The water line is getting lower and lower, and the chopped ice roughens and freezes even harder than before.

Luckily storms do not last forever. There are many mild and sunny days in winter. In the late spring David brings in our new-born calf and lays it close to the stove. Our children are thrilled at the sight of it.

"O, Mama, see what Papa has brought us, a *Hammel-ja-da!*" cries Leah as she opens the door to David's kicking. Big-eyed, and a little bit afraid, Mia hides behind my skirts peeking out at the long-legged squirming calf until David lets go of it. Little Hester who is standing at the bench, holding on, screams with fright.

"Sh-s, sh-s," I soothe, picking her up and holding her tight. I bring her close. "See," I say, "it is only a baby calf." The calf reaches out its tongue and licks her arm, and she squeals anew. The others laugh and start petting it.

"This will make a nice pet for us," Leah tells Mia. Mia nods, already taken to the calf.

I look at my children enjoying themselves and I am reminded of the times my father brought lambs into our house, and a wave of homesickness comes over me for my family. I have not heard from them even though David has written them twice, telling them of the fruitfulness of this land. I wish they would come, but my father is an old man and the trip would be too hard for him. I have hope that some of my sisters will come, and Otto; he surely will come to America some day. My brother Wilhelm with his family is here already, but he lives a hundred or so miles away.

Because there is snow again and the roads are blocked, David removes the wagon wheels and replaces them with sled runners to drive to town. Although we are out of lamp oil, sugar, and tea, we have nevertheless fared well, for we have lard, milk, and eggs. I have kept my children fed by cooking milk soup with egg noodles, a favorite dish among our people.

A month after this, when the wheels are back on the wagon, David comes home from town filled with excitement. "Evaliz," he shouts from the wagon seat, "I have rented a larger farm."

"Where?" I ask, a bit worried.

He leaps down from the wagon box and starts unhitching the team before he says more. "Eight miles further south and two miles east."

"But, David," I say, dismayed. "We are already six miles out of town. What about the children? How can they become Americans living at the end of the world?"

"*Liebchen*," he says, stopping what he is doing. "It is not the end of the world. There is a school. And there is much land, with more sod to break." His eyes are aglow with hope for the future.

"How will you farm so much land with the little machinery you have?" I ask, hoping he has no answer, but he has.

"Wait; you do not give me time to explain. The farm implements go with the place. I can pay for them by sharing a little more of the crop." As far as David is concerned the thing is settled. "I tell you, Evaliz, it is a good thing I saw Mr. Willman first. Farms are hard to get with so many people coming in."

What can I say? I know David is right. "Where there is a will, there is a way," is his motto.

148

But when I think about it I get terribly worried. In the first place I do not like it so far away from town. And second, we haven't even seen the place. So much land: three hundred and twenty acres! What if crops fail and we can't pay for the machinery we now have? Maybe, I should stand up to David and say no before it is too late. But I don't. There is one good thing: we will be less than five miles from my brother Friederich who has a new name in America, "Fritz."

The calendar says it is spring, but the weather does not. It is a wet spring, raw and blustery, not warm, as we need it for moving. With Friederich and our neighbor's help, we move all our possessions in one trip. The three lumber wagons carry all except the seed grain and the feed that is left from the hard winter. The pigs are in one wagon, the chickens crated on top; the cow and calf are tied on behind. David will go back later to bring the grain and feed.

We make quite a Gypsy caravan trailing along the road to our new home. All things are bundled together and piled high on top of each other, but the brightness of a Gypsy van is lacking. How well I remember the gaiety, the laughter, and the lilting music that went with real Gypsy moving. Ours is a caravan of plainness, plodding steadily onward. Leah and Mia take it as a holiday, riding on the seat beside their uncle Fritz who follows behind us, wrapped up to their eyes in a warm quilt.

David and I sit on the high seat, our little Hester bundled snug between us, and I look out over the endless prairie that is greening a little here and there through the frosted ground and marvel at the bigness. As our wagon slowly climbs the swells of the land there unfold still more empty plains and unending sky. Farm homes are sprinkled meagerly over the rolling land and wild grass abounds freely, fenced in only by far horizons. Here and there the solitude is dotted by shaggy-haired cattle grazing in the raw wind.

Another high rise in the road and our new little church lies before us, clean and white, with Gothic windows and a gleaming gold cross finishing out the steeple. "All that remains to be done is the altar," David says, knowing that my mind is on the church. "I will make it as soon as we are settled."

I know how ornate it will be because I saw the one he built in the Volgaland, all white with gild trim. David is a true artist. Soon our people can leave off having church services in homes or school buildings. Here sits the church as an anchor of faith, and it gives me comfort. But the road runs past its door and on and on to where a smoky haze blurs the line of land and sky.

Hester has fallen asleep, her head on my lap. I hold my arm around her tightly, and I think many lonely thoughts as we plod over the rough wagon trail that leads to our new home.

We pass a small house with good outbuildings and David says they will be our neighbors, almost two miles away. The woman and her four children are standing out in the yard watching us go by. The woman is clad in a clean, faded-out Mother Hubbard and is wearing a white head shawl; the wind is fluttering her wide skirt. Even before David tells me, I know she is German just by her white head scarf. She will be a good neighbor, I tell myself.

David waves and calls to her, "Hello, Frau Weber. We have come to be your neighbors."

She answers, "*Ja*, so," and smiles at me.

Our milch cow tied to the wagon hears the friendly voices and bellows, lagging behind, wanting to stay, until the rope stretches her neck tight, and she must follow.

The road leads to the top of another knoll, then dips down again, and there, for the first time, I see my new home. My breath catches in my throat. There are four cottonwoods by the windmill and stock tank, where the ground slopes away from the house. "You didn't tell me there were trees," I laughingly scold David. "They will be good for our children to play under."

"I didn't know it myself," David says.

"*Ach*, sure, how could you?" and we both laugh.

Then, before I look at the house, I see that the road leading past the place turns to a mere wagon trail. There can be only one more lonely house in all that expanse of wilderness. We are indeed at the very end of the world. My children will not become Americans very fast way out here, I think. David knows what I am thinking, for he says, "See, Evaliz, to the west, another neighbor."

I look and see a faded house across a plowed field a mile away; it hardly shows up it is so near the color of the land. The outbuildings must be set in a draw, because I can see only the roofs of them. "Yes, I see. Does anyone live there?" I ask. David will not look at me.

"No," he says. Then he catches my eye with all sincerity and adds quickly, "Someone is moving in very soon. I heard it in town." We both laugh then and turn our attention to our new farm place.

I see at a glance that the house is much better and larger than the stone house we had. As soon as the wagon stops I get down and hurry inside, but Leah and Mia far outrun me. Big-eyed, they meet me at the door.

"Mama, it has a table and eight chairs. Eight chairs! Can you believe it, Mama?" Mia cries, so excited.

150

I try to push them out of the way so that I can get in too. Both are talking at the same time. "Two rooms and an upstairs attic, Mama. Come see," shouts Leah, clattering up the hollow wooden stairs. "Oh, Mama, how fine, how fine!" She can hardly contain herself. "See, a window on each end. And an iron bedstead!"

I see it all and I am as excited as Leah. This attic is big enough for all the children we have, and those yet to come. One more is on the way, even now. My mind wanders for a moment, but Mia's voice brings me back. "*Ja*, fine," says Mia. "But see the light through the shingles. And see the splinters in the floor."

"It is still good," I say. "We have had splinters before, and Papa can mend a roof. But a bedstead is something else again. How lucky can we be?"

There is more. When I get downstairs again I find that there is another bedstead in the second room, and a cook stove and cupboard in the kitchen. It's too good to be true. Whoever lived here did not want to be bothered with anything.

At last, I get a look at the farm buildings. They too, are better and roomier. I see now how foolish I was to hold back. Perhaps here lies the answer to everything. I want all of us to be good Americans!

We are no more than settled when David drives over to the new church building and brings the lumber for the altar. The house smells good with the odor of new-cut wood and shavings as David fashions the intricate curves and Gothic designs here in our large kitchen. When the altar is finished it can easily be hauled to the church and assembled. David must hurry. The dedication is to be the first Sunday in May.

When the frost is out of the ground, David breaks semi-sod for a potato patch. He sets the plow share deep to cover the tufts of grass. Leah, Mia, and I have cut the seed potatoes, being careful to leave two "eyes" to each portion. We have filled a wash tub to over-flowing, and David has hauled it to the field. Now with garden hoes and hatchet in hand, my children and I cross the narrow strip of pasture to plant the potatoes. A new furrow will usually leave a break, or pocket, into which we drop a piece of potato, but if there is none, we chop a slit with the hoe or with the hatchet, and as soon as the seed is inserted we step on the place to close it tight. In this fashion, we go on and on, each seed a foot stride apart.

When we are finished, David covers the field over lightly with old straw. This has a three-fold purpose: it holds the moisture in, keeps the weeds down, and prevents the sod from regrowing. Too, it will protect from frost.

151

It is during the spring planting season that my Maria is born. Another girl. Now we have four. David drives down to bring Frau Weber as midwife, and the baby comes without mishap. The next day Frau Weber sends her eldest girl, Amelia, with sweet rolls, a dressed chicken, and egg noodles cut almost as thin as thread. All these things are placed neatly in a dish pan and tied with a clean white tea towel. She has instructed the twelve-year-old girl to cook chicken noodle soup, to set the house in order, and to wash my children's faces and hands, and comb and braid their hair. What a good girl she is. Good, like her mother who is expecting.

I can stay in bed only two days. There is so much work to be done. At least Leah and I can have the chores done by the time David comes from the field. Maybe crops will be good. There is always that hope.

There is also hope that our two oldest girls, Leah and Mia, will do well at school. When we first moved here, David took them that same week and had them enrolled. The prairie school house is only three miles from here and they can walk. The teacher is very nice. Since David and I do not know the language, it is hard to say if the girls are learning anything. Still, they seem to try very hard. David, too, is trying to learn. He has bought himself a double service dictionary, German-English and English-German. So whatever word it is he wants to interpret, he can either look it up in German, or English. This way he can help the girls, and they can help him, especially by making him curious about certain words. "Papa, what is arithmetic?" Mia asks, feeling big.

Or Leah will say, "What is geography?" Then, the two laugh together, because he cannot imagine what they are until they write the words for him and he looks them up in the dictionary.

"Ah, so that's what they mean," David says. "That's good. Thank you. I will remember that."

Because there was no winter wheat planted, David has to content himself by putting out barley, oats, and cane besides corn. At least we can look forward to plenty of feed and straw for the winter.

Up to the middle of May the fields have taken on an earnest look of waving green, ankle deep and growing. David, inspecting the fields, says the roots are drawing the moisture from the sub-soil, and that rain had better come fast for added growth.

But the rains hold off. The sun hangs like a copper disc in the bleak, dry sky. The never ending winds from the south blow their searing breath over the land by day and night. The tender blades turn yellow, and little by little the fields wilt. "If rain comes, will they revive?" I ask, worried.

"Yes, some will, but rain must come soon," David says in anguish.

"Perhaps, we had better pray in more earnest," I suggest, feeling guilty for not having prayed before. David is quick to agree. Together, we kneel among the suffering blades and ask for help.

"Oh, God, Thou who art our every source of help, be merciful to us, and to our fields that are thirsting. If it pleases Thee, O Lord, send the rain."

Nights, before David goes to bed, and again in the early hours of the morning, he steps out into the yard barefoot. He stands looking into the great Kansas sky that will not fill.

Then, one night, fleecy clouds, like sheep, invade the heavens. And when David comes in he is no longer worried. "At last, God is sending us rain," he announces. "It will rain before the week is out. The feel of the earth under foot and the air hold a promise."

David's words bring hope to me. Happily, I go about setting the bread sponge for the night. "Tomorrow, we will have fresh baked bread," I say, and my thoughts go back to withered old *Grossmutter* Volz who would have said it this way. Tonight is the first time in weeks that David sleeps without tossing.

True enough, the weather is changing. No longer is the prairie sky pale and dry. No longer are the clouds fluffs of white riding the high winds. The sky is near and heavy with moisture. The clouds are dark and promising. Then comes the rumble of thunder and rain falls in cool showers upon the suffering earth.

And even though the grain fields yield only a half-crop, the corn, shoulder high, is in its glory. We cannot complain. Next year will be better. There is always next year.

Besides the potato patch, across a narrow strip of pasture land, not too far from the windmill, I have a vegetable garden. I hoe the rows and carry water from the stock tank. Leah and Mia help me. We do this in the early evening when the sun has withdrawn its fire. I have tomato plants, beans, onions, cucumbers, melons, carrots and cabbage. David has put a woven wire fence around it to keep the chickens out.

One day while I am in the garden staking up tomato vines I hear the wild pummeling of horses' hoofs, and hear the jangle of harness.

"O, God," I cry. "What is happening to David? Are the horses dragging him to death?" I can't see the roadway because of the cottonwoods, so I run from the garden toward the road where the noise is coming from. My children hear it too. They come running from the granary where they have been playing, shouting:

"Mama, a runaway! Mama!"

My legs are so weak I can hardly run. Then, I see it all. It isn't David. Thank God! It is a team of fast horses hitched to a light spring buggy coming down the slight decline of the roadway. The driver has given them their head. Their manes are tossing in the wind.

I think it is some stranger.Then I see that it is my brother Fritz. I can't imagine what dreadful thing has happened in his household, to bring him so fast. Terrible thoughts race through my mind and I can't move.

Turning into the yard, he half raises from the seat and draws on the reins. "Whoa. Whoa, there, my fine beauties. So-o, so-o," he soothes the lathered team to a stop. "A new team, Evaliz, I'm trying them out for speed," he announces, laughing, while we all stand there wide-eyed, expecting the worst.

"*Na*, what a fool you are," I scold, half mad at him. "You are like Otto, with his crazy Cossack riding."

"No," he says, "I'm better than Otto. I did that last mile in three minutes"

"Three minutes, to put me in my grave," I say, and we laugh together.

"Speaking of Otto," Fritz says, reaching for his pocket, "I have a letter."

"Has something happened to him?" I ask, fear taking hold of me.

"No. Nothing. He is coming to America. Mariesophie and he are in Hamburg, Germany already. And so are the others."

"The others who?" I ask, my heart racing.

"Our sisters, Malia and Marik and their families, that's who."

"*Ach!*" I can hardly believe it.

Fritz reads the letter and I am both sad and glad; tears well in my eyes and fall down my cheeks. I am glad, because so many dear ones are coming; sad, because my father and stepmother, and our eldest sister, Katrinliz, are staying behind. The letter says that Lydia, my stepsister, is married, and Jakor, her brother, is almost old enough for compulsory military service.

Fritz finishes the letter and says, "I have already leased a farm for Otto. The place a mile below me was empty, so I took it. I will find a place somehow for the others. Just leave it to me." Sure, Friederich is dependable. If he says so, that is the way it will be.

There are already thirty-some Russian-German families living in our farming community, enough to fill our German Lutheran church to overflowing. Almost every month someone else arrives, creating more farms out on the far-flung prairie. David has written letters telling of this country's opportunities, its freedom from oppression, its peace and security.

154

When Friederich is gone it is time to think of evening chores. I look at Leah, now ten, tall, and dependable. "Take little Maria in the house, wash her clean and put her down for a nap," I say. "Build a fire and peel potatoes, while I go and finish in the garden."

She goes immediately, carrying Maria over her hip. I turn to Mia, long-legged and gaunt in her calico dress, her golden braids half undone. "Have you gathered the eggs?"

"No, not yet," she says sheepishly, her eyes cast down, grinding her big toe into the soft dirt.

"Then go, do it. After that get the cows, so we can milk early. Watch out for rattlesnakes," I admonish.

"Yes, Mama," she pipes and runs for a pail to gather the eggs.

"Hester, you come with me, out of harm's way," I say, taking my four-year-old curly head by the hand.

She asks a question, "Why does Uncle Fritz have a beard?"

"Because his smooth brown-red beard makes him look handsome."

"Oh." She accepts my word as final.

# CHAPTER 12

## The Tears

Tears are our plowshares as a plague sweeps over our prairie land: jack rabbits! Young and old. Large and small. There are rabbits everywhere with a hunger twice as great as their teeming masses. Never before, in the memory of Old-Timers, have there been so many. They leave utter ruin in their wake.

The great masses have invaded every corn field for miles around. They are stripping the corn stalks as far up as they can reach, until the fields look light and sparse, like clean-stemmed trees that have have been shorn of their bottom branches. When the marauders can no longer reach the blades they rise on their long hind legs and gnaw into the young tender ears of corn. Surely, their lust for destruction has a boldness. The jacks have no fear of man or dog. Made bold by their great numbers they invade the yard and eat last year's corn left in the corn cribs, unmindful of surly dogs who have grown weary of the endless chase.

This year the settlers do not get rid of their unwanted dogs for lack of food, as in other years. With three or more dogs and with the help of children brandishing clubs the farmers go out to drive the grey devils out of their fields. We, too, must do something.

In desperation David mixes a poison of Paris-green, bran, and water. Then with a bowl or tin can for each of us, including the older children, we drive out to our fields and sprinkle the damp poison on the corn stalks, each of us taking a row at a time. The poison kills many rabbits, but it doesn't save our crop since the surrounding fields are full of thousands more jackrabbits.

Coming in from the field one day David is very upset. "Something bigger and mightier must be done," he says in a terrible voice.

"What *can* we do?" I ask, seeing no hope whatsoever and not knowing what idea is already brewing in David's mind.

"Maybe nothing, but we can sure try," David says, and makes ready to go see Christian Weber, our neighbor.

I see him go and I think to myself, "Now what can David and Christian do about a million rabbits? I cannot even guess."

But the two have a plan, not their own for it has been tried before, even before we came to America. And, so it is, that on a clear morning in the early fall of 1911, after a week of preparation and planning, all agreeing with one accord, the farmers gather from miles around for a rabbit drive, starting on the east hill over-looking our land and spreading far and wide. I see the great beginning from my doorstep. And I must marvel at man's power when desperation goads him to strike back.

The settlers are pouring in in all manner of wagons, buggies, and carts, bringing coils of rope and wire strung with tin cans and bright strips of rag. Every man and boy has brought his own weapon, a gun, a club, a pitchfork. One spritely fellow brings nothing but a concertina to play a lively tune as he leads the rollicking, noisy procession.

"Make it sweet and tuneful, Hansel," one hardy farmer calls after him as he rumbles past, headed for the hill.

"That I will, Georg. That I will! The *Pfeifer* with all the mice will have nothing on me, haw, haw," he calls back, his wagon rattling on.

Like a mighty army on wheels they maneuver into postion, swelling and growing in great numbers, spreading a dark line against the hill. And still the roads from north and west give signs of more. Others are coming across the open prairie singing songs, stirring up clouds of dust in their haste to join the masses.

As the vehicles file past the command post, all linked together with wire and rope on which jangle all manner of cans, buckets and kettles, the tremendous chain almost reaches across a mile and a half of field and prairie. Now, at last, all is in readiness. All are waiting for the opening shot.

My children and I are there too, filled with excitement, as are other farm wives and their brood, the children grimacing and holding their ears shut against the expected gun blasts.

158

The guns are up in the air, pointing skyward. Then comes a mighty din. Bang! Bang! It sounds like the mighty Volga breaking her ice barriers in the early spring, cracking, booming, roaring, surging forward, over-flowing the hill. The brigade moves forward, driving the marauders from their hiding place, scattering them in wild panic. Before this relentless charge the jacks try to flee, leaping, dodging, but they are driven back into the melee, helpless and lost.

Never have I heard such shouting, yelping, shooting and clubbing. And as the long chain of wagons, surreys, and the like, moves slowly forward they form a semi-circle closing ever tighter until the center arena fills and swarms with frenzied creatures, several coyotes among them. Children by the score follow behind the wagons and pick up the dead rabbits and toss them into the wagon beds.

The rabbit drives are carried on anew, day after day, throughout the county, until all farmers are benefited. When the drives are over the town newspaper states that 120,000 jackrabbits have been killed in the county. A bounty of five cents per pair of ears is being paid.

We cut the ears off the rabbits and string them together in pairs for the bounty and feed the flesh to our hogs and chickens; others are buried to prevent a stench. Even the dogs for once have their fill, so that they turn their heads and walk away, as though sick in their bellies at the sight of them.

The hogs, on the other hand, have gone wild for the taste of blood. It hasn't been a good idea to feed some of the carcasses to them. They rise up, squealing beasts trying to scale their pens, whenever we walk through the yard. I admonish my children to stay away, especially the little ones. In fact it is even too dangerous for David to feed them, and he has decided to bury the rest of the carcasses in the field.

Lean, indeed, are our crops this year. And although the jackrabbit horde has been greatly lessened, all our hopes have been dashed to the ground. This year nothing can be paid on our debts. David tosses and turns in his sleep at night, and I cannot sleep for worry. Not to pay our lagging debts gives me great shame.

Even though our crops are lost, my vegetable garden has been saved from the marauders. Like an oasis, strongly guarded by a woven wire fence, it sits in the midst of desolate waste. These days I store away many things for the long winter that is to come. We have dug our potatoes and stored them in the yard cellar. Cucumbers with dill are in salt brine. Onions with their tops attached are braided into long ropes and hung up to dry in the upstairs sleeping attic, later to be stored in the cellar under straw.

Some watermelons are buried deep within our haystack, safe from the winter frost, if they should last that long. Others I have cooked into *Schlecksel*, watermelon syrup, rich and russet colored, to be used with *Streusel* when baking coffee bread, or *Pfeffernüsse*. The turnips and carrots I have stored away in clean creek sand, also in the cellar. Peas have been dried in the sun. Green beans fill a stone crock, salted away, and of sauerkraut I have a barrel full. Surely, my garden has been filled with abundance, our reward for toil. With the help of my family I gather in the harvest, singing hymns of praise. This storehouse shall be our livelihood until crops come again. Crops will come!

And again, as if the failing crop had never been, David sets his fall land in order, plowing and drilling next year's wheat crop. Hard winter wheat, the Kubanka, will sprout and grow in the late autumn months, sleep through the long winter and waken again to spring and summer rain and sun.

While David is busy planting wheat I take my children out to the pasture to gather cow chips for winter fuel. When we are finished we take the wagon and haul the chips home and make a stack in the yard. This year we cannot depend on corncobs for cooking.

We live in an isolated world. Frost, and in some cases hunger, stalks the land. This is a winter short of feed and grain. There is also a fuel shortage, for unlike other years, there are no tall cribs of corncobs to feed the winter fires. Cash resources are short and very few settlers have laid by coal. And if one wanted to go and get coal now, the snow-blocked roads and fields would prevent it. There is misery and suffering among the people and among their livestock as well.

The cow chips I have laid by will see us through the winter. Though there are not enough for keeping our house warm, there are enough for baking bread and boiling soups. But next year David and I will make *Mischt*, heavy manure blocks, like our people made in Russia. They are the best fuel for winter. They burn hot and hold long-lasting coals. David has already hauled the manure out onto a smooth spot next to the corral, for it to season and rot throughout the wet winter snows.

David has cut the wild hay in the badlands beyond our pasture and brought it home to make a stack by the barn, and another stack in the pasture nearby for easy winter feeding. He has built a tight barbwire fence around it to keep the livestock away. There is a gate to drive in and out of with a hayrack. David is a resourceful man.

160

Everything is planned and arranged for convenience. He needs no sleigh to haul hay to either barn or cattle.

This winter of 1911 and 1912 is by far the most severe of all our Kansas winters the old settlers say. Snow, up to ten feet in depth, lies everywhere. The roads are blocked. And still the snow is coming down, down, carried on the high March winds as they sweep down to gather blinding snow clouds and swirl them skyward, only to blast them down again as though shot from guns. Dry, needle sharp flakes sting the face like fire.

The wind drives the powdery snow through every warped shingle and board siding, around windows and under doors. Snow is packed high inside our barn and poorly-built cowshed, making life miserable for our livestock. The cows, in their discomfort, give forth mournful sounds, sounds which even the howling winds cannot drown, sounds that live and haunt me in my sleep at night, cutting me to the heart.

And our poor chickens roosting on the top roost have their claws in the snow. There is no getting down for them. We cannot even enter to feed them. And surely, we cannot throw the snow out, for there is no place left in this world to throw it. Our hogs are completely snowed under and it is good that they are, or they would surely freeze. They are covered ten feet deep under snow, with only a tiny round hole their breathing has made marking the presence of each one. Here again, we must leave them. Where would we put them? They are better off, even without food, sleeping where they are. It is difficult to go outside, and when we do, we grope blindly by the help of rope and wire stretched from house to barn to pen and house again.

And so the days drag slowly by, day after day and night after night. Both sky and ground blizzards pause only long enough to gather more strength, lashing frigid, merciless blasts across the land, only to return and repeat themselves, pelting, moaning, wailing, with neither beginning nor end.

Endlessly the winds drift the sugar-like snow across our floors and over our beds. It sifts like icy mist upon my face through the long sleepless hours of the nights, settling on my hair, making it pure white.

On bitter days like this Leah and Mia miss out on school, for the school house is isolated, three miles away. Their learning is meager this year and the language is difficult for them. Again, I feel utterly helpless. It is true, as I have always said, I am a "know-nothing." I am one who can add nothing to the mental needs of my children. But I can work, for in this I have no failing; being willing and obedient is all I know.

On these cold days I hang quilts close to the kitchen stove to hold in the meager heat, and place my children in the enclosure. I bring little Maria's crib and also make room for David who is mending shoes and harness; the smell of worn leather and *Pech* stings our nostrils. And because my children's lips, at times, are blue with cold I chip frozen chunks of milk out of the earthenware crock and set it on the stove to steam, to keep them warm.

When the children tire of writing their ABC's on slates and reading them in German, because David is not sure of the English, he lays aside his work and makes rabbits and birds out of his red handkerchief. He nestles them in the palm of his hand, stroking them fondly, chanting a chain of magic words in Russian and, suddenly, the frisky little things leap out of his hand. The children shout with surprise and glee begging for more and David varies the length between jumps each time. Or again he takes time to trot Hester or Maria, now going on two years, on his knee singing a little ditty to the tune of hoof beats. But, as is the case, the prancing pony misses its footing and the little rider nearly topples from her perch.

> *Do not scorn me 'cause I'm poor*
> *You ne'er can tell! You ne'er can tell!*
> *The world keeps turning like a wheel...*
> *And yesterday a tower fell!*

Boom! And the rider falls. Not really, for David merely lengthens out his leg and the rider slumps. We all laugh.

"What words you choose!" I say, looking at David. "What kind of song is that?"

"Gypsy," David says, gaily. "Words are words, Evaliz. They make sense."

"*Ja*, sure," I challenge him. "Then why don't you say 'Snow go away' and see what happens?"

"There you have me! What words could do that?" he says, smiling.

"More, *Baba*. More," the children plead.

"All right. '*Die Drei Zigeuner*,' The Three Gypsies?"

"Yes. Yes."

"So shall it be. Now listen closely."

> *I saw three Gypsy men, one day,*
> *Camped in a field together,*
> *As my wagon went on its weary way,*
> *All over the sand and heather.*

*And one of the three whom I saw there,*
*Had his fiddle just before him,*
*And played for himself a stormy air,*
*While the evening-red shone o'er him.*

*And the second puffed his pipe again,*
*Serenely and undaunted,*
*As if he at least of earthly men,*
*Had all the luck that he wanted.*

*In sleep and comfort the last one laid,*
*In a tree his cymbal lying,*
*O'er its strings the breezes played,*
*O'er his heart a dream went flying.*

"Me, me, *Baba*! I'm next," cries Hester.

"Come, *mein Kind*." And David sings again, while another little rider gallops down a Gypsy lane, laughing and big-eyed, waiting for the jolt.

*Ragged enough were all the three,*
*Their garments in holes and tatters,*
*But they seemed to defy right sturdily,*
*The world and all worldly matters.*

**Thrice** *to the soul they seemed to say,*
*When earthly trouble tries it,*
*How to fiddle, sleep it, and smoke it away,*
*And so in three ways despise it.*

*And ever anon I look around,*
*As my wagon onward presses,*
*At the Gypsy faces darkly browned,*
*And the long black flying tresses.* *

Sure, David has a fluent tongue. His natural and book learning in Russia was wide and varied. I am very proud of him. Would that I could do only part of it.

On other days, with slates in hand, Leah and Mia copy letters from the salt and pepper cartons on the kitchen shelf. Then in all seriousness they try to read the words, agreeing and disagreeing on the pronunciation. And I am so unschooled I do not know if they are right or wrong. Seeing them struggle, that old tightening feeling closes in on my heart. How will the children ever learn to be Americans so far out here on the prairie?

*"*Die Drei Zigeuner*" — by Nikolaus Lenau, Austrian poet (1802-50).

David is of more help. When he isn't bringing in cow chips for fuel, or feeding the stock, or milking, he helps them read, using his German-English dictionary. While the family absorbs book-learning I am busy providing for their bodily need: sewing underclothes from bleached flour sacks, knitting woolen stockings, making kvass to drink, like we did in the old country. I start with a large loaf of dry, dark rye bread broken into pieces and tied into a clean white cloth. I place the bundle in a three gallon crock and pour about one and one-half gallons of boiling water over it. When it is lukewarm I add two heaping cups of sugar and a cake of yeast, then two handsful of raisins. I cover the crock with a clean cloth and let all ferment for three or more days, depending on the warmth. A good place for the crock is behind the kitchen stove. The bundle of bread can then be taken out and squeezed dry. After this I strain the brew several times through a clean tea towel. When the drink is ready it is bright yellow and clear, and sour to the taste.

Sometimes, I bake Russian *blini*. The recipe is based on bread sponge set the night before. I take out a measure sufficient for my family, add three eggs, salt, two tablespoons of sugar, enough warm milk with one teaspoon soda added to make a very smooth, thin batter that will spread quickly in a hot, greased skillet as I tip and rotate it. I make one large pancake at a time, turning it once so that both sides are golden brown. Quickly I sprinkle each with sugar and roll it tight and hand it piping hot to one of the family.

On other days I dip spoonsful of thick cream onto individual plates and make a nest in it, filling the dent with molasses or homemade watermelon syrup, then I break large chunks of fresh-baked bread to dunk in it. This makes a complete supper. I am thankful that we have a winter supply of flour stored in the attic.

Sometimes I cook chicken soup with egg noodles, adding a bay leaf, the princely aroma filling the whole house. I make my own noodles, rolling them very thin and cutting them as fine as I can with a very sharp butcher knife. Then I lay them out on clean white tea towels to dry. When they are cooked into soup David lifts a spoonful of steaming noodles high out of his bowl, pretending he has to reach clear to the ceiling before they come out of the broth, smiling and saying to the children, "*Na, sicher*, there is no one who can make noodles as long, and cut them as fine as your *matuska!*"

"*Ja*, slender as thread," Leah says.

"As long as a buggy whip, *ech, Baba?*" says Mia, sipping one off her spoon and drawing it slithering into her mouth, her blue eyes beaming mischief.

"*Ach*, go on," I say. "These are nothing. Wait until Alexander's Marieliz is in her *Kindbett*,* by then I will bring her noodles cut fine as silk, along with a dressed chicken. They will be thinner and longer than any other woman can bring her."

"That will be the test of all tests. The poor woman will receive enough dry noodles to fill a mattress, and enough dressed-out fat hens to feed a harvest crew," David says. He winks at the children and they all laugh at their *Baba's* silly talk.

On certain days, I bake *Kaffee-Kuchen* spread thick on top with russet colored watermelon syrup and sprinkled with *Struesel* made of butter, sugar and flour. It goes well with *Süssholz* tea, made from wild licorice root, brewed on the back of the stove.

So the days run by. When our kerosene is gone we sit in darkness, or go to bed as everyone else must be doing out here on the stormy plains.

When at last the winter storms have blown themselves out, they leave death and destruction among livestock throughout the plains. We, along with our neighbors, lost much-needed livestock and flocks of chickens. Yet, it could have been worse. Rumors have it that further out west where the land is still more open, one farmer alone lost fifty head of cattle. And it is no rumor that not just one, but three, railroad locomotives lie wrecked east of town, blocking all rail transportation. The town is crowded with farmers, all demanding hay. Lucky the family that had no need for a doctor. One doctor walked ten miles through heavy drifts where no team could have gotten through. It took him more than four hours.

And so, remembering the long, sad days and nights we go among our shaggy stock, calling them by name, and stroking them fondly, glad that so many of them survived the terrible ordeal.

When the hard frost has finally left the ground I dig up the cold earth and fill two shallow wooden boxes and bring them inside. I set them by the kitchen window for the soil to mellow. Later I plant tomato and cabbage seed, watering them when need be, growing seedlings for my spring garden.

With a light heart I go about my many tasks. I bleach empty flour sacks and make pillow cases and dresses and underwear for my children. I wash the sacks clean and dye them blue for the dresses.

When the weather is warmer and the wind milder, I build a good fire under the iron kettle out in the yard and I cook soap from used lard I have saved. It takes lye and buckets of water and much hard work stirring, watching, adding more fuel. But when I am through I

---

*\*Kindbett* — (German) Child-bed, the period of confinement after childbirth.

have two gunny sacks full of creamy white soap. I set them in the upstairs attic where the children sleep. We use the soap for everything, washing, bathing, dishwashing.

On Saturdays I clean the house from top to bottom. I make sure that my girls learn how to scrub out the corners; they are never too young to learn. I also bake *Kaffee-Kuchen*, custard pies, and sometimes a tall white cake with even whiter egg icing sprinkled over with store-bought red sugar. This is a special cake to serve on Sunday, but I can hardly keep my family away from it on Saturday. David is as bad as the children. Our Saturdays are days of cleanliness, and preparing good food. Sundays are days of worship.

We rise before sun-up on these chill March Sundays in order to get the milking and other chores done in time. I make breakfast and also prepare the noonday meal of boiled chicken or beef so that dinner will be ready when we return from the six mile drive from church and Sunday school.

While David, Leah, and Mia are milking, I wash the breakfast dishes, make the beds and put the rooms in order. Then I set out a long line of polished shoes, looking much like a line of sparrows sitting on a fence...little sparrows...bigger sparrows...and yet more bigger. And soon there will be another pair added. Maybe a son?

I wash little Maria and Hester clean and plait their long hair, sleeking it down with water, and I dress them in their Sunday best. And I set them at the table to keep them out of mischief. As the others come from the barn I help Leah separate so that I can wash the separator while they get themselves cleaned and dressed. At last I spread a white tablecloth made from flour sacks and edged with handmade lace on the table. "It may be that someone will come to dinner," I say to Leah who is at hand to smooth the corners.

"Yes, maybe Papa will ask three families, like he did the last time," she says laughing, glad to have company.

It is a custom among our people to ask a family or two home for dinner after church. Not one single Volga-German woman would be unprepared to have a houseful of guests; she sees to that. And, should they all be asked out, then the food she prepared can always be eaten on the morrow.

David comes from the bedroom fully dressed. "Hurry, Evaliz," he says. "The minister is gone today. I must give the sermon. We cannot be late."

"*Ach*, sure, I will not make you late," I say.

David goes out to hitch the horses to the one-seated spring buggy. He has hay in the back for the children to sit on. I run fast, my heels clicking hard on the clean-scrubbed floor. I carry heavy quilts outside and spread one over the hay; the other is to cover up with. The third quilt I place on the seat for David and me. Quickly I add noodles to the boiling meat.

I still have to dress. When I get my dress on I wrap my heavy shawl around me for the March wind is chill. There is no time to finish. I tuck my good shoes under my arm and reach for my head scarf and the comb on my way out. I must finish dressing on the way. Never have I been so late.

"The books!" David reminds us. "Have you the song books and catechism?"

"*Ach, Gott,* the books! Leah — Mia, the books!"

"It's all right, Mama," Leah calls from the back of the buggy. "I have them tied in a clean tea-towel."

"Good," says David. "Let's start."

At last, we drive out of the yard onto the long road to church. My head feels light after the cessation of hurry and clatter, and my body quivers all over. I sit on the seat beside David and comb my hair. I pull the comb straight through the long strands without any nonsense, twisting a bun in back, while the chill winds blow icy blasts over my feverish brow and neck where the hair is lifted. Quickly I tie my head scarf tight about my throat. Then short of breath, because of my body thickness, I lean down to change my shoes under the warmth of the cover. My last task of the busy morning! But it is a happy tiredness, for I can rest on the way to church, content for once that the road is long. It won't be long before my child is born.

The morning is beautiful. The rolling prairie is moist and sweet smelling. All along the roadway are the young green blades of awakening spring. White piled-high clouds stand like fairy castles against the blue sky. And over all the meadowlarks and orioles are singing. As I sit on the swaying seat with the hoof beats, and whirring of wheels soft on my ears, the now tempering wind on my face, my mind spins a web of dreams.

The people are seated in church in quiet reverence, the women and children on one side, the men and older boys on the other. The melodious tones of the organ, played by Friederich, *der Junge*, the younger, rise and fall; the people blend their voices in song.

David has chosen his text well. It describes sundry blessings which follow them that fear God: Psalm 128.

*Blessed is every one that feareth the Lord; that walketh in His ways.*

*For thou shalt eat the labour of thine hands: happy shalt thou be, and it shall be well with thee.*

*Thy wife shall be as a fruitful vine by the sides of thine house: thy children like olive plants round about thy table.*

*Behold, that thus shall the man be blessed that feareth the Lord....*

April. At last, we have a son. A son! After a houseful of girls. What a joy! What happiness! The arch of heaven soars. A million suns shine by day, troops of stars by night, and the great moon rides the glittering prairie sky, catching for a brief moment as a silken web in the tops of the greening cottonwoods on its westward flight.

"At last, we have a farmer," David laughs and I laugh with him. And even the yellow flicker of the lamp light joins in.

"He's not much good this size," I say, unfolding the covers and showing his scrawny little arms and legs. He is very tiny, but very precious. We name him David Phillip, in honor of David's father and grandfather who both were renowned *Schulmeisters* in the Old Country. I hold the babe in my arms and my heart sings with the words David is now reading from the one-hundred and twenty-seventh Psalm:

*"...Lo, children are an heritage of the Lord: and the fruit of the womb is his reward.*

*As arrows are in the hand of the mighty man; so are children of the youth.*

*Happy is the man that hath his quiver full of them...."*

How true, how true.

I am glad that my son was born in the middle of the night while my children slept, so that David had no need to bundle them up to take to the neighbors. David was not much good as a midwife, but he did bring me the scissors and other things I needed.

Here, from my bed, I watch the morning gild the sky. I gaze out over the tender wheat field and see the green rills run straight to the horizon. The year has a good beginning! In its freshness the dust and ashes of other years are forgotten, blown away by the odorous breezes of a new spring.

Presently, the morning sun creeps to my window and lays its golden sheen bright across my best patchwork quilt--which I am using because company will be coming before the day is out--warming and soothing my hands that are relaxed for a short space of time.

From upstairs comes the sound of my children waking. I hear Leah coaxing Mia to get up for the milking, and urging the younger

168

ones to stay in bed a while longer. Listening to her I realize what a regular little mother she is. Now I'm anxious to know what she will say when she sees her baby brother.

The stairwell door is at an angle with our bedroom door. And when I look again I see Leah peeking shy and shame-faced around the doorframe at me in bed. Mia, pressing close behind her, will not so much as look at me.

"*Na*, what is with the two of you?" I ask them. "Other times we had a baby in the house, you played with it like a doll. Why not now?" Still they make no response. Awakening shame is locked inside of them.

"*Ach!*" Suddenly, a tender feeling toward my children overtakes me. They have arrived at the sensitive age, not understanding entirely -- nor letting themselves understand lest they be shamed even more.

"Come, child," I coax Leah. "Did you know, you are a blessing to this house like the Psalmist says. All children are a blessing." I say it kindly, but she continues to stare at me.

"*Ach*, come, see your little brother. Come, Mia," I beg, holding my hand out to them. "Leah, will you not come to me?"

"No, Mama," she cries with an alarming voice, and like a frightened animal she flees from the house. Mia follows after her.

Tears wash down my face, but I wipe them away. This is no nonsense; it is the way of life! It has been this way ever since the world began. I decide I will get up and prepare the breakfast, and I will wash the faces of the little ones and comb and braid their hair when they get up. And when the others come in from milking life will be the same again.

And, so, the days march swiftly by. A shimmering green engulfs the land. Buttercups and yellow-blossomed sorrel color the slopes of the pasturelands. Meadowlarks lift their wings and rise straight up into the sky letting their three clear notes fall like silver rain in the sunlight.

And because the winter has been so severe, intense eagerness and renewed hope, among our people, rises even higher than before. Everywhere, spring seeds are put in the ground with all the hustle man and beast can put forth. In our own field there is singing as David works the ground, sowing summer crops. His favorite hymn, as well as mine, is "*Nun danket alle Gott*":

> *Now thank we all our God,*
> *With hearts and hands and voices.*
> *Who wondrous things hath done,*
> *In whom the world rejoices.*

How glad I am at last to have Wilhelm, my older brother, living close by. Even though his house is a mile away, one of his fields touches ours. I often see him plowing. He and Anna came to America long ago, when David and I were still building our house in Russia. At first they settled in a different part of the state. Now they have moved, and have been our neighbors for some time.

Today as I walk over our fields with light steps and glory in their greenness I see Wilhelm in his own field and I hail him. He stops his work team and crosses our boundary. And I say to him that surely *this year* we will all have a good crop. Wilhelm still has his old habit of calling me "child," as he did in my youth.

"*Ja, Ja, Kind.* With God's will. The soil is rich enough," he says, crumbling the dark loam through knowing fingers. But his wind-seared eyes are on the fine dust that trickles to the ground, dry as threshing chaff. And I feel a twinge of pain as I recall that last year, his first in our area, brought him absolutely nothing.

"*Na*, sure, Wilhelm," I say in all confidence. "This crop will be a good one. You will see!"

Wilhelm only smiles kindly at my unshakable faith in this land, and goes back to his team. Well, I think, up to now it has been good. It is hard for me to give up.

In my garden, the peas and beans begin to curl their tendrils, ready to put on fruit as the summer heat comes on, mounting higher and hotter day after day.

The morning milk begins to sour in the early hours of the day. Even the cellar coolness is of little help. The sun in the high heavens is almost without color, clear and hot, sending heat shimmers over the land. The winds blow in unending flight, powder-dry and sap-absorbing.

Billowing clouds draw their shadows across the prairie, linger and darken, then pass away with the winds that are never still, leaving only enough moisture to settle the stifling dust. The night stars quiver constantly in the heat, and in the morning the wind funnels the heat earthward. I walk our fields, my heart filled with silent dread.

June. The wheat has begun to form its kernels. But the stalk is dwarfed and lax, giving little sap to the new heads. It's true. This year's wheat crop will be nothing! Wilhelm can bank on that! In weariness, I leave the fields. I almost lose my faith in this land. But I will not let myself. Yet, as the days go by without change the questions pound at my brain like fist blows: Will the weather never be tamed? Will it never? Never . . . . .? Common sense tells me that it is not enough to tame the soil alone.

"Why, oh why, does it not rain?" Together David and I ask each other the question. Together we see the outer edge of our wheat

170

field turn yellow. Then the entire acreage begins to look wilted. The hot winds dry the milk in the kernel all too quickly, leaving shrivelled grain that is hard to chew. Five bushel to the acre is all we can look for this year.

Strange unseasonable winds blow out of the south and out of the west, blustering hot winds that claw and suck at the powdery earth, tearing it up until the air is filled with it. It pelts sand pebbles against the sparse corn stalks until they rattle and bend before its wild force. It drives a steady clatter of sand across the window panes, like rain.

The storms are like the snow blizzards of winter, only these are dark, leaving grit and grime in every crevice of field and building, piling it high against thistle-packed fences and filling draws and furrows. It sifts into the food until every bite is an aggravation. It sifts into the beds. It coats the water in the drinking pail. It muddies the milk. The chickens seldom leave their roost. The cattle stand in miserable huddles, eyes half shut. They would be better off out in the open than next to or in the barn, but it seems that this is their choice

Everywhere, throughout the country horses and cattle are becoming lean and ravaged by the lack of good pasture and clean drinking water. But, surely, even these dust blizzards, devilish as they are, must come to an end. They will, won't they? I do not know.

Then something strange happens. On a clear day with sultry clouds lying on the far horizon, the wind suddenly ceases to blow. The sun casts a weird, yellowish light, like the flame of a smoking lamp. I run out of the house and see a wall of reddish-brown dust rolling out of the south-west, out-racing the billowing clouds that have suddenly invaded the heavens. The ominous wall is circling from south to east, from west to north with onrushing speed, tumbling and lengthening until it forms a half circle on the far horizon. The air around me is still as death!

Fearful for David's safety, I look to the field and see him rushing home with the disc, urging the horses on with the whip. Quickly I gather the children and put them in the cellar next to the house. I take the kerosene lamp and matches, and go back for several loaves of bread. Leah and Mia are bringing quilts and pillows, and drinking water.

I leave the children there and go to fasten the windows in the house, and put out the fire in the stove. Then I shut the door, praying that the house will stay.

Before I am through, David has turned the gaunt horses loose, free of their harness. The chickens out in the far pasture sense the

171

danger and come running helter-skelter, as from out of a blustery rain. Rover cowers around my skirts, sensing the alarm.

"Don't worry, Rover," I say to him. "When I am ready I will take you with me." He understands and wags his tail. At the cellar door, I say, "Down you go!" and he scampers down the steps.

Together, David and I stand by the flat cellar door and watch the storm come. The wall of dust is almost full-circle, rising higher and higher, closing in, covering the clouds. All about us is a stillness, sinister and stifling. The sun, ruddy in color, swims in middle heaven, casting an eerie light.

"*Ach!*" A faint breeze stirs my hair! The circle is complete.

Suddenly, the wind becomes stronger, gathering more speed. Wind-devils swirl across the yard and to me it seems there is a faint roaring, like wind blowing into a bottle. Yes! It is a roaring, growing louder, ever louder. The dust wall is on us, the sun is blotted out, and sudden, fierce wind is everywhere!

It tears the cellar door out of both our hands and nearly rips it off its hinges. David and I are barely able to pull the door down over our heads, for all the blinding pressure of wind and sand.

In our earth cellar we have found a haven, but it is far from quiet. Our frightened children cling to us in the dark and wail aloud. But their crying is nothing compared to the howl of the wind in the ventilating pipes of the cellar roof. The shrillness drowns out all human sound, leaving us only the sense of touch. With great relief I light the lamp and bring ease and a sense of safety to my little ones.

For the rest of the day we are like Noah and his family locked in the ark. But, finally, the dove of testing tells us the storm has blown over. We go back to our house for a good night's rest, thankful, because the damage to some of the outbuildings could have been worse. We learn later that the red dust came from the state of Oklahoma.

❧

The dust storms have gone as surely as they came, but they have left a plague in their wake. Because of the dusty feed, and perhaps other reasons unknown, a very great number of horses are afflicted with a strange and terrible disease.

Bewildered, the settlers go among their stricken stock, dreading what losses they may find, not knowing where the cause or remedy lies. The illness is acute and terrible to see. When a spindle-legged animal finally gets down, it can never rise again. It writhes and struggles, its head and legs never still, carving deep furrows in the hard earth with weaving hoofs and flailing head until death ends it all.

Some men claim the disease is caused by a minute worm, or bug, that has eaten its way to the brain. Others say it is malnutrition. Still others say it is a germ carried in the dust. Even the animal doctor from town does not know, neither can he help. Therefore throughout the plagued area many remedies are used, professional and otherwise, all to no avail.

Our prairie people are hit hard. Many have lost one to five horses. And day by day the plague grows more severe. Town officials have posted strict orders that people must bury their dead animals on the same day they die. The people accept it willingly, for many believe that a pestilence will engulf the area if the stench is left.

David is worried about his six horses. Although they are greatly weakened, so far there has been no sign of illness. Still he cannot sleep for worry. He gets up at night, lights the lantern and goes out to check. And it almost looks as if it will pass us by. David has brought our horses in from the dust-laden pasture and has locked the corral gate. He will not let them eat dusty forage. Very carefully, he washes the dry hay before he places it in the manger, then he sprinkles it with lime and water-diluted molasses. Also, each day, he allots them a small measure of oats or corn, even though we can ill afford it. Washing the hay may not help in this case, but David remembers the method used by a rich bourgeois in Russia.

Our luck does not hold. This morning, one mare cannot get up. She is lying in her stall struggling with might, kicking the boards with a terrible clatter. David cannot leave her there. He calls me to come quickly to help. With rope and pieces of harness he fashions a cradle about her under-belly, and with a pulley attached to a cross-beam we pull her to her legs.

"Now, Evaliz, when I say the word slap her rump and push with all your might. Maybe, by pulling on the halter rope, I can keep her on her feet until we get her out the door."

David unbuckles the sling and cries, "Now!" I slap her with the broad side of a thin board and she lunges in terrible anguish, bumping here and there. Finally we get her out the door. She falls again and David puts chicken wire under her and with another horse drags her out in the pasture. With great concern he works over her. He pours medicine down her throat, but it does no good.

Resigned at his loss, David lets himself down on a chair and I pour him a cup of brewed *Süssholz* tea.

"This disease is as bad as the *Rinderpest** of Russia and Central Asia -- if, indeed, it isn't the same thing," he says, dropping his hands helplessly to his side.

*Rinderpest* — (German) a rare cattle plague.

I look at him and see how utterly exhausted he is. Perspiration is dripping from his blond hair and trickling down his face. "The mare wasn't even paid for," he says, and the trickles may as well have been tears falling from his eyes.

"*Ach*, sure. Drink your tea," I say, the words hurting my throat. I go to get a towel to wipe his face.

Soon we hear disheartening news from a friend of ours. When a horse he owned died he used two other horses to drag the carcass to an abandoned well out in his field. In the process the near horse stepped too close to the edge, the earth crumbled, and he started to slip. A panic ensued, and when the ordeal was over the weight of the dead horse had pulled the two healthy horses down with it. The trapped team squealed and struggled but before the farmer could get help, they, too, were dead. The whole community mourns with him and his family.

Then, finally, even this plague is gone. And the sun, moon, and stars shine bright and clear and promising from the high heavens.

# CHAPTER 13

# *The Prairie Fire*

Darkness is rising from the land. The September day has been hot and dry. David, standing out in the yard, looks up at the stars. He hears me on the threshold and says, pointing to the Kansas heavens, "Look, Evaliz, how clear! So thin and far!"

I walk to his side and look up to see the whole sky. The stars, like jewels, are burning brightly from one rim of the world to the other, washed clean of dust and wind.

"*Ach*, yes. So thin and so far. Maybe it even reaches to *Russland*," I say and a tear trickles down my cheek.

Quickly, David turns his eyes from the heavens and detects the tear. "Tomorrow will be a good day to thresh the cane," he says in all kindness.

I do not answer him. I think the half-matured cane is not worth the threshing, but we must have some kind of grain to feed to our chickens.

"*Ach*, look, Evaliz, it is no good to pine for *Russland*. We are finished with that land. Good things shall yet rise out of the dust and ashes of the past years." David still has faith in the land.

"You have me wrong. I do not pine for *Russland*. I pine for those in my family who have been left behind. But it will always be

175

America for me!" My throat tightens as I say it, for it is true. This is our home and a haven for our children.

I turn and look at the house outlined against the sky. The kitchen door is open and the yellow lamp light brightens the door step and reveals Rover lying there, looking up at us, his chin buried between two outstretched front legs. When I step into the lamp light he wags his tail in friendship.

"Come wash, David," I say. "Supper is cold. The children have eaten and are asleep at the table."

The wash bench stands outside the door, next to the water barrel. David dips the basin quickly to avoid gnats floating on the water and sets it dripping on the bench. He rolls his sleeves up and thrusts his hands into the sun-tepid water and brings it loudly to his face, spluttering and blowing, making a special effort to work it through his hair. Sure, what can be more soothing than the laving of water in the cool of the evening, when work is done?

"I hooked the chicken house door, on my way in from the barn," he says, the rinse water running from his face.

"Good," I say. "With so many skunks and even coyotes coming into the yard, poor Rover gets very little sleep nights."

David flings the rinse water out on the smooth, rock-like ground where it splatters hard.

I hand him the towel from the nail on the kitchen door. He wipes his face and tousles his wet hair then stops. "I'm hungry," he says. "What's for supper?"

"Smoked sausage and fried potatoes with onions, the way you like them. Now, come sit," I say and turn to Mia and Leah. "Hurry, girls, gather up the dirty dishes and start washing while I carry the little ones upstairs to bed. I'll be down in a minute to help."

Long after supper while David is reading from the *Friedens-Boten* and I am busy knitting, a strong, south wind blows up seemingly from nowhere. And presently, Rover lets out a wailing cry that cuts through the stillness of the house . "It's coyotes early tonight," I say, feeling the strangeness.

"Not coyotes," David says with alarm. He pushes back his chair, drops the book on the table, and jumps to his feet. He runs out into the yard. "That's fire!" he shouts. "Fire in the south. All the huge prairie is on fire!" David's voice is shrill like that of Rover's.

I run out after him. The sky in the south is red from the glow and glare of the great grassland. Only one family lives between us and the fire.

"Thank God, the fire is on the other side of the Smoky Hill River," I say, but David cuts me short.

"What is that, in a fire like this? It can jump the river in a hundred places." David states a fact, and I know it. The fire is more than ten miles away, but the flames are so high they look as if they are upon us. The acrid wind is full upon our faces.

David makes a quick decision. "Find gunny sacks and the shovel," he shouts, while he is off to harness the horses. He brings the team out on the run and hitches them to the wagon. He loads on the hand plow and I throw in the gunny sacks and shovel. David is ready to go fight the fire.

"I will pick up Ernst on the way. Maybe he hasn't seen it. Take care, Evaliz, you know what to do — do what you must," he calls back. The wagon rumbles loudly out of the yard, heading into the fire.

"Yes, I know what to do," I cry to myself. "Always, I do what I must. Always I know." But, for once, I do not know.

Sure, it is a terrible thing, a fire in this great grassland of Kansas. The leaping flames are as high as mountain tops.

I stand on the doorstep, dazed, too numb to move. The fire is ten miles away but what is that with the heat-swirling wind in a sea of hip-high grass? I pray that David can get to the river before the fire does. But he must go fast. The river is his only hope. And the only hope for us are the back-fires they are able to make on the other side of the river. Our own pasture land which follows comes all the way to our chicken house and granary. "God, protect the men and make them strong," I pray.

I can only guess that a railroad locomotive twenty miles to the south of us has set the fire. They have started fires before, but none as large as this.

"*Ach!*" Great onrushing flames leap into the sky, bursting with fragments of fire and shadow that might well be men swinging dampened gunny sacks, tossing them in fantastic shapes against the blazing sky. Setting more fires, eating ever closer, closer.

"*Grosser Gott in Himmel*, help us little insignificant beings."

I hear the rumble of a wagon to the west and I know it is my brother Wilhelm and his older boy rushing to the fire. Then, on our own road, I hear another wagon. It is our neighbor Christian Weber and his son, driving in terrible haste. Soon they are close enough to see, as they head for the lighted sky.

"Go to my place, Evaliz," he shouts, without slacking his pace.

"Yes," I cry, focusing my eyes on the moving shadow that is now taking on a crimson lining, quivering as a floating object in a heat-wave. Then, I cannot see them for the tears that fill my eyes. These are brave, courageous men who would give their lives to help tame this land!

Suddenly, all is quiet, and I am afraid of the stillness. Always, I've known what to do, but tonight it is as if my hands are tied. In my quaking I am a child again in *Russland*. I hear my father's voice,

177

like he used to say, "Evaliz, God in heaven sees you. He knows you are in need. Be strong."

"*Ach*, yes, God is everywhere! I will be strong."

A stillness comes over me and I go swiftly about my work. I am glad my children are asleep. I have only Rover underfoot and I try to be brave, for even the stars have left us. They are hidden by the high smoke that has spread over our world.

I look across the road, to the west, where my brother Wilhelm's freshly-plowed land lies in the shadowed night. And I feel blessed to have a raw field so close. When the time comes I will take my children and Rover and go deep into the field and be saved from this hellish fire. But first, I have things to do; I cannot leave our worldly goods, nor much less leave our livestock if the fire is not stopped.

Rover follows me as I carry the lamp into the other room, and he must wonder why I do not first go upstairs to get the children. His dark eyes watch me as I pull the wooden clothes boxes from under the bed, and while I pile other things on top, David's Sunday suit--I cannot leave that--my one good dress, wine red, like my wedding dress; I may not have another one like it. Besides, it frightens me to think of the fire eating into it and crumbling it to black ashes. I gather it quickly and put it on the box along with my head shawl. Now I have all the family clothes. Quickly I carry them out onto the black land. My feet stumble over the rough ground, and all the while I think my heart will fly out of me.

Nice Rover, he is so sorry. He runs back and forth faithfully with me. I sit down and cry for I am so tired from carrying my featherbed and pillows out onto the land. And I cannot leave the heavy quilt we brought from *Russland*. But Rover will not let me rest. His teeth take hold and pull at the hem of my skirt. There is such a terrifying look in his eyes as he watches the door to the upstairs attic where the children are asleep.

"*Ach*, Rover. Do not worry! I'll not forget my children!" At my words he becomes quiet and his eyes look into mine, content that I know. And because he is such a friend I say, "Rover, when the time comes I will waken the older ones, and they will help me carry the young ones out on the land. It will be good to put them on the featherbed. Now, come quickly, we cannot forget the cattle."

I run out in the yard and see that the wall of fire isn't nearly as tall. That is bad; it means that now the on-rushing fire has reached the river bottom, almost out of sight. The orange glow to the south is like a full moon rising, lighting the trembling grasses of our pasture land in its glare. A blackness is closing in all about us. And all the while Rover and I drive the cattle and horses into the corral, I pray for David. "*Lieber Herr Gott*, protect him . . . . . "

Rover jumps against the cows, barking and nipping at their heels and tails. "Get them, Rover. Don't leave a one of them asleep in the pasture," I shout.

After we have all the cows and horses corralled, I hook the wire loop over the gate post. Then I make sure that none are inside the cow shed or barn and shut those doors also. Now, should the fire come, I need only to open the outer gate and turn the livestock out to safety.

I look at the sky with terrible concern for David. I make myself sick with worry. In the surging night wind it seems I hear him cry out in pain. "David. David!" I cry out. And of a sudden, I think I can hear the roaring of the fire, can feel its hot breath against my face.

Quickly, I prepare to tie chickens together in pairs. I do this by using binder twine on their legs. Nothing is as non-resisting as a sleepy chicken. The job is easy. But I know the persistency of a stupid chicken when it wakes up and makes up its mind. By the time the fire would have gotten here and the danger would have been at its worst, they would have left the plowed field, and all would be back in the chicken house again.

It isn't the roar of the fire that I hear. It is the whir of grasshopper wings and the flight of birds. The night air is filled with them. Grasshoppers hit against the house; they drop off until the ground is swarming with them.

Mysterious, running things go swishing through the dry grasses in the dark, some tangle momentarily in the barb-wire fencing. Rover stays close to me now, his tail drawn between his legs. And I am not so brave, myself.

The fire has eaten its way down into the hollow of the far prairie. I cannot know if the river and the men have stopped it. A pain, swift as an arrow, stings my heart. "*Ach, Gott*," I cry. Perhaps the fire is on this side of the river and will come bolting over the horizon any minute to engulf us.

I race upstairs to get the children. I can see well because of the fire light coming through the south window. Then I see that there is not one fire burning, but two. I shout for joy. I wake my children, I shout so loudly. I call to Rover who is here. "See, Rover, the backfires, the backfires! *Gott sei Dank!*"

Rover keeps jumping against me, barking loudly. The children cry from the fright it gives them. "There. There," I say, stroking their heads. "Go back to sleep. God is in His heaven!"

It takes some time to undo all the things I have put in order. I go and set the livestock free and snip the binder twine from the chickens' legs. I lug the boxes of clothing and my bedding in from the plowed field. And still I wait for David's return. When he comes, at last, I run out to meet the wagons coming slowly down the road. The horses have had a bad night of it breaking sod. Soon David's wagon comes by. He sees me and stops. I climb up over the wheel and I can hardly speak his name, my lips quaver so. He hardly looks like David, seared black as a Tartar. Silent, he puts his hand on mine.

We turn into the yard and take leave of the men and young lads who came to fight fire. The men say, "Thank you and adieu," in heavy voices that only those with deep gratitude can understand.

Once inside the house, by lamplight, I take a good look at David and I want to cry. His clothes have holes burned in them. His flesh is seared. I cannot wash his wounds. I can only salve over the burned area with pure, unsalted lard to hold the sting of air out.

In bed, at last, I listen to David's heavy groaning, the morning hours already close at hand. Far out in the pasture I hear the mournful lament of coyotes and I am aware how much closer the fire has driven them. But I have no fear. My chickens are all locked up. And David is here beside me, safe from the hellish fire.

Once again it is late September. The cottonwoods by the windmill are pure gold. A whole year has gone by. And I have added yet another girl to the fold. Theolinda, David calls her, after a beautiful princess he once read about.

Much fall preparation has been made, but much more must yet be done before winter closes in. With joy in my heart I go to my wire-enclosed garden near the windmill. I gather the plump heads of cabbages and carry them to the house, and peel off the outer leaves. Some people have store-bought shredders, but I have to shred the cabbage with a butcher knife.

The large wooden barrel and salt are ready. A mountain of shredded cabbage is waiting. I scrub my two older girls very clean. *Ach*, so clean. I dress them in clean clothes. Then, with their bare feet they tramp down the new-cut cabbage in the tall barrel. This is Old Country sauerkraut, the very best.

The American people make a face and say, "Ugh, those terrible Roosians, with their children's dirty feet they stump down their kraut, such filth!" But they come and sit at my table and say, "Oh, Mrs. Becker, how thin the shreds, how good. So good!"

I just smile and nod, and know in my heart it is good. Later, when I give them kraut to take home, they put their arms around me with all respect. Sometimes I even give them a piece of fresh pork to go with it. I am always glad to share the goodness we possess. "*Ach*, please, no thanks," I say. "I give it gladly." When they are gone, I say, "It is clean kraut." Emotion runs through me. Yet I say it without ire. My voice is even. I do not hate.

After this, when I walk the town main streets, I look at food being displayed openly in front of the mercantile store. My attention is especially drawn to the open cask displaying long, dried-out salt fish. To me they look more like dead, dry snakes whose eyes, if any, are either white blindness, or bulging. But no matter how ugly, the flies do not care. They buzz all about them and hide in the crevices, leaving their specks there. And the street dust and tobacco spit of congregated menfolk blows all around them. Then my mind goes to the soiled looking cheeses kept under store counters, where rats play and leave their dirt, and I say to myself, What is filthy? Not my kraut!

While David plants the fall wheat, I take my six children by horse and wagon and go to Ernst Reyer's large pasture to pick cow chips. This man has great herds grazing over a far-reaching range along the Smoky Hill River. The cattle are so wild and ferocious that my children are afraid of them. Even I must be careful of them. We try to stay away from where they graze. But there are times when certain steers get curious and move slowly toward us, seemingly not sure of themselves, holding their heads high, sniffing the air. The mother cows with calves also do this. But a bull takes a firmer stand. He bellows, head down, totally enraged, and with strong hoofs chops up great volumes of grass and dirt, threatening to drive us from the place.

This work may last a week or two, depending on the supply, for surely we can use all the fuel we can get. I leave my young son and the baby, Theolinda, on a quilt in the wagon. My older girls, Leah, Mia, Hester, and Maria pick chips close to the wagon, where the horses are tied to the back. We use gunny sacks and two wash tubs with halter ropes attached, to pull as sleds. My children are good at this work; they have done it before. "Be mindful of the babies in the wagon," I admonish each one. "And be careful of the cattle, and look out for rattlesnakes."

"Yes, Mama," they all answer.

Tears smart my eyes and choke my throat as I think about my children. They should be in school, learning the language. But we must first gather the fuel for the winter. It will not take too much longer.

Leah is a good, fast worker. She fills her wash tub quickly and pours it out on the ground, then fills it with chips again and again, making a neat pile. Then she moves further out and makes yet another, and another. She will not be idle, for she yearns to get back to school.

For her sake, that is why I hurry too. I go far out from the wagon, making mound after mound, until the pasture looks like a field of shocked grain. Depending on the nearby supply an ordinary pile consists of five to six sacks of chips. I finish out each mound by laying the chips carefully to keep out the rain. For it may be a month or more before we can haul all of them home.

Every evening I fill the high wagon box full of chips using the broad wheat shovel and we drive home, all sitting on top of the load, surrounded by tubs, frayed sacks, shovel, lunch kettle and water jugs, empty and otherwise.

Soon I will have a stack of chips as large as the chicken house, a good supply right here in the yard. Each evening as I unload the chips I do what I must, laying the outer edges of the stack straight and packing them solid inside. When the stack is finally finished it will stand as solid as a sod-house, and as grey. All the snows of winter, and all the rains of summer cannot soak them all. Always, there will be some dry ones, whatever the weather.

Once again out in the far pasture, with my children around me, the sun is hot, and the untamed wind is strong. The dry, harsh grass sways all around us with a constant sound. All day our backs bend, unbend, and bend again; the fingers strain. It is not easy to pull the chips loose from the tall, sharp blades of grass that are ingrained in them. Sometimes, when the cow chips are old and decaying there are snakes under them.

This noon, when the sun stands high in the heavens, I come back to the wagon for lunch. The children also come, gathering around me. I have brought bread, fried pork, and buttermilk. But first I hand the children a bar of soap and pour water over their hands. It is then that I see that Leah's fingers are bleeding. The sharp grass and jagged chips have done this. Leah is crying.

"*Ach, liebes Kind,* dear child, do not cry. Tomorrow you stay home." I pour the sun-tepid water over her hands, to wash out the smart of sweat and dirt.

Mia is pressing close. "Look, Leah," she cries. "Look, Mama's hands are bleeding too."

"It is nothing," I say lightly, thinking how warm we will be when winter comes. "Now, come, eat. We will go home early tonight."

While we eat, I hear the wild birds in the prairie sky. "Look, children," I say, pointing, "already the geese are flying south." They look up and laugh at the honking wedge cleaving a path through the pale blue Kansas skies. Soon, the winter snows will be upon us.

# CHAPTER 14

# The Wedding Dress

Autumn passes, and after bleak, cold winter days come the
boisterous storms of spring. I walk over the land that is
steeped in the strong perfume of wild buttercups and
moist earth, and I thank the Lord that spring has come
again.

While the spring drives the sap up from the earth all around me
and the meadowlarks warble from the fence posts, I plant my
garden. The sun shines bright, and the white clouds drift lazily over
the sky. And my heart sings a glad refrain because I am in
America. Truly, this year it will be different.

My four oldest girls, Leah so good, Mia so fair, and Hester and
Maria so sweet in their look-alike dresses and smooth pig-tails, are
going to school learning the language. At last, they are beginning
to grasp the meaning. My happiness knows no bounds. They will
learn! I have waited a long time for this.

My little ones, David Phillip, three now, and Theolinda, one and
one-half, are around me as I work in my garden. They are happy
chasing butterflies with their tiny hands stretched out. How soon
we all forgot the long winter when snows drifted white across our
beds!

Later, my two little ones and I laugh while we walk in the
pasture and gather the first wild garlics that bloom at our feet. It is

a good country, America. Like a stepmother she may rant and rave, but when she smiles it melts the tears.

These days I wash down the walls and make all things clean after the long winter. David takes down the boards and old oil-cloth from the north windows and lets the sunlight in. There is peace in my heart. Crops will come. David works the fields.

This morning while I am watering the garden I notice the straight rows of green onions, standing alert like disciplined soldiers before their *Kapitän*, and I am reminded of Anna, my brother Wilhelm's wife. She stands straight, like these young onions. I hold a fondness for Anna, with the strong hands and the warm smile, remembering the day, so long ago, when her first child was born in Russia. How frightened we both were!

Now, it is good to have her as a neighbor in a house only a mile across the field from us. I look in that direction, thinking maybe she will come to see me, as she often does. But I see nothing. Then, when I look again, I see her white figure against the dark soil. She has come halfway already. Then I notice her hurried steps.

Fear takes hold of me. Always she has been lithe and quick, but never has she come this fast. Quickly I go to meet her. But it isn't Anna at all. It is Emma, her daughter, home from the far city where she does housework for a rich family. Emma is tall and straight like her mother, and swift, with an easy flowing voice, a beautiful girl, with black hair. She is carrying something tied up in a clean white tea towel.

Emma is happy to see me. Anna's children have always been so reverent toward me, so kind.

"Hello, Aunt Evaliz!" she cries, squeezing my hand, then she puts her loving arms around me, bundle and all.

"Where is your mama?" I ask, puzzled.

"Home, baking bread," Emma smiles.

"Is she coming later?"

"No," she says glibly. "Mama and I quarreled. We are mad at each other."

Pain stings my heart. This is so unusual. I can't imagine what has happened. "Emma, you are not working for the fine lady any more?" I ask, shocked that she should take the quarrel with her mother so lightly. By all appearances Emma feels nothing.

"*Ach*, no, Aunt Evaliz, I do not like her anymore." Emma is defensive. "That old fussy dame! I left her flat. I told her, 'You're not so good. You cannot preach to me that an oily rag is cleaner on a table top than soap and water.' " Emma's voice is sassy and bitter.

"Oh, Emma, Emma." I say. "You should not talk like this." It shames me that she should do this to a fine lady whose shining table

184

top does not need soap to scour it clean as do our mean farm tables. But Emma will not be corrected. I look on her young, sharp face, her naughty eyes and they quickly smile on me. *Ach*, such a girl! She can be mad and happy, all in one breath.

"I am going to be a bride, Aunt Evaliz," she announces, as if nothing else had happened. "See," she holds out the bundle, "here are the wedding goods. You will make my bridal dress."

This is news to me, a complete surprise. Who is she marrying? Before I can ask she tells me that Herr Merkle and Herr Witman had come to their house to make a marriage offer for Herr Merkle's son, Herman. At her words, a sense of dread fills me. I know him well. Herman is a nice lad, but low in spirit, with halting speech. He is no match for Emma.

"Better you wait, Emma," I say. My voice is sad, for she is making a big mistake. "Listen to me, marriage is more than just the marriage-bed, or an escape from things hateful."

But Emma is stubborn and will not listen. She holds out the bundle and discloses part of the material inside, as if both of us were enjoying the situation immensely.

"See, silk! His people have bought it for a wedding dress. There is also a bridal veil with pink roses all around. *Ach*, so sheer, so transparent -- like morning mist!" Emma cannot say it all fast enough; she gushes on. "That sister of mine will cry tears of madness when she sees the dress and veil together. She might have had them. But, no! Not her!" Emma isn't through yet. She goes on. "But I took them. I'm tired of doing people's housework. They get so mad. 'No, Miss Emma, soap and hot water is not good for dining room chairs and table,' they shout. 'Oh, good heavens! My precious furniture! It is ruined!' they cry and wring their hands, and say you are fired, before supper, even. And all for keeping their house clean. It is dirt they want, Aunt Evaliz, not cleanliness," Emma storms.

I listen to the youthful smartness of her voice and I think of the man she will marry, and I know it is not good. "Hush, Emma. Hush," I say. "Maybe it is better to shine the table tops with oil, like they say."

The angry lights are still burning in her black eyes. She has a firm chin. When she says no, I think the only thing I can do is agree to make the dress. In this matter Wilhelm and Anna can do nothing with her. Coaxing does no good with Emma, even from me, in my own house. She does not, and will not listen.

There is a feeling of sickness inside of me as I cut into the bridal material. So pure and white it is, and once cut it never can be put back together again. The sharp shears shish-h through the brocade neatly, severing it once and for all. While I cut, I think how Anna is home crying great tears, glad to be baking bread.

Emma's countenance doesn't stay cloudy. She is like the sun coming out after the rain. "I want such a wedding picture as Olinda Meyer made," she confides. "*Ach*, Aunt Evaliz, so fancy she looks. Like this..." The happy girl stands before the mirror, twisting and turning, smiling on the shimmering stuff she holds lovingly to her heaving breasts. "*Ei*, Aunt Evaliz, it is good to be fancy once." She continues, "My father and mother do not like fanciness. But, maybe, for my wedding picture they will not mind. *Ach*, sure, but I am happy!" Her voice is free and high, and she hugs the rich white goods under her delicate chin. "May blessings fall rich upon your head, Aunt Evaliz, for all your goodness."

But I do not call it goodness. It is not good for me to make this dress for her. It would be far better if I never made it. A lump sits in my throat and nearly chokes me. A blinding mist drifts across my eyes. Emma sees it. "*Ach*, Aunt Evaliz!" she says, shocked at my tears. "Please, no silent tears. Can you not see how happy I am? So **very, very happy.** Only you, Aunt Evaliz, could make such a fine dress as I will wear on my wedding day!"

As always the springtime is gay, and the new crops make a good showing. Nevertheless, I do not like the tiny, minute grasshoppers that shy out of the grasses wherever I go. They are almost as small as flies and green as the grass beneath my feet. They cling to my skirts and hop onto my hands, bold and unafraid.

I am worried as I go about my new garden. I know, in order to save it, I must sew long strips of gunny sacking and stretch it over the rows, held up by wooden pegs. Then I must sprinkle poisoned bran on top, so that the hoppers will not eat the cloth itself. I complain to David, "I do not like so many hoppers, so early."

"Yes," he agrees, "it will not be good."

And, sure enough, even before the young corn out in the field is knee high, the hoppers are full grown and ravaging the land. Day after day there are more and more, coming from no one knows where. They fly on the wings of the wind, hopping over everything, clinging to the hapless corn stalks, eating, eating. Even the forceful winds cannot shake them from their savage hold.

Together we go out into our cornfields and sprinkle poisoned bran on the plants, as we did for the jackrabbits, but even this has no effect. Other fields and pastures are full of them. The chickens have their craws so full that when they catch and swallow another one, they vomit it right up again and it jumps away.

Will this, then, be as bad as all the other years? Years of only half crops? Years of plague upon plague? When will the cycle break? When will it end?

And, as in other years, the dry fluffy clouds scud high across the windswept skies, leaving no moisture. The hot winds scorch the remaining stalks until there is nothing left, nothing but a small stubble crop.

Bewildered, we search the sky for a promise of rain. Again and again, the roving clouds cast their fleeting shadows across the land, linger and darken, and mutter their insolence. Mocking! Rumbling! Flashing hellish fire in false pretence and false promise, they spill their wrath elsewhere, leaving us only light showers.

On days like these, when the clouds rumble and the air lanes twist and churn the gathering mass into frigid thunderheads, dark and foreboding, I do not run for shelter. Instead I am driven on eager feet to the suffering fields, to stand among the quivering grain, arms raised to the cooling winds, awaiting the rains. Waiting.

And I think, at last, of the admonishing words of our pastor in Russia: how he warned, and beseeched the people not to go to America, how he predicted no good would come of it! *Ach*, all of a sudden I feel wavering doubt. Could he have spoken the truth, after all? How could I have been so blind? How? How?

Even though I do not want to admit it, my strong faith in the land is broken. I am like a floundering ship caught on a rock, trying to right itself. Two voices inside of me are arguing right and wrong: one, believing that rains will come, the other, believing the words of the minister. Maybe he was right. No good can come of this land. *Ach*, no, no. I do not believe it! Not even now. It will rain. It will! Crops cannot suffer year after year without relief.

But, as always, I come back from the fields, beaten and full of despair. The clouds are gone. The sky is a windy blue. Hot belching winds blow in from the southwest with neither beginning nor end. The grass in the pasture curls to its roots. The brittle, yellowish leaves of weeds rattle in the wind like so many rasping, tinkling bells. And the small sorghum field amounts to almost nothing.

Even the grasshoppers find the heat unbearable. They clamor for the shade, sitting in a solid mass on the sides of buildings and even fence posts, creeping slowly round with the moving sun.

The smooth, hard ground in our yard breaks open in jagged rents, crying for thirst, its famished mouth open to the defiant winds. At first, the children delight in the dry rivulets, filling them with handsful of soft powdery dust, or carrying buckets of water to pour into the crags, only to have it vanish as though by magic. They laugh at the eager gurgling of the parched earth.

Finally, my children become frightened, as day by day the suffering earth gaps wider and wider. They say, "Mama, will it open up and swallow us?" Some of the crags are two inches wide, with a narrowing depth of six inches.

With a two-horse team and a flat board sleigh we haul barrels of water to our potato patch. In this way we keep the plants going. And because this year there is no wheat crop, David hires out to work in the harvest fields in the eastern part of the state. I am left alone with the children to do the work.

As soon as the potatoes are in bloom, long grey potato beetles and soft fuzzy squash bugs come in great numbers. They must be destroyed. With short sticks and tin cans into which I have poured some coal oil we go among the long row of plants and knock the poisonous beetles and bugs into the oil.

While we work, the beetles crawl over us and into our clothes. They bite and leave their poison blisters on our flesh. These watery blisters smart and ache and when they break the yellow fluid flows over our bodies and creates more blisters wherever it touches. In the night, my children cry because of the itch and pain. And I, myself, do not know how to lie anymore. My back and one side are covered with blisters that must not break. And the next day we must go again, and again. We must save our potatoes!

Nights I lie awake and think of many things. My dreams for my children are not shaping up as they should. It is all work and so little learning. Always, I have wanted something better for them. But, what can I do so far out here, away from town and the American people? Here, among our own, where the country school is filled with German-speaking children, they are not learning the English language as they should.

I am reminded of Leah's words, "We always speak German on the playground, and when we go in we have to learn everything over again. We forget everything we learned."

Something has to be done, I keep telling myself. Then, I have an idea, maybe cruel in a way, but good. When David comes home from the far harvest I will ask him to go to the school board -- David is a member -- and ask for a ruling: that the children speak only English while in school. Yes, that is the answer. How else will they learn?

In the afternoon heat, with my little ones, David Phillip and Theolinda, by my side, and the older ones, Leah, Mia, Hester and

Maria carrying hoes, we take the shortcut through the pasture to the potato patch. We are all going to pull and hoe weeds. The older ones run ahead to roll playfully in the "early day" buffalo wallow, now smooth and grass covered, until we catch up. My mind wanders and I look at the two stacks of wild hay David has made here in the pasture with a stout barbed wire fence around them to keep the livestock away. And I am glad that David did this before the summer drought set in.

The brassy sun casts its shimmering heat on us, and the searing winds blow past in their unending flight. Our hoes rasp and scrape over the obstinate, stony earth, until more force must be used to break the hard shell. And all about is the constant sound of parched fields, yellow and raspy as dry onion skins.

We are thankful for the piled-high clouds that have invaded the heavens. They cast dark shadows across the land and cool the wind. The children laugh and shout when a fast-moving shadow comes skimming along. When it reaches us, they flop down on the ground and say, "I'm going to rest until every bit is gone." And they do. For them the clouds and shadows can't come fast enough.

When I look up again, I am amazed at the change that has taken place. The massive clouds have taken on a grey, frigid look, churning, building, tumbling, taking on an under-lining of midnight blue. The heat in spite of everything is stifling.

Then, with odd suddenness, the clouds seem to stand still, immovable, sinister, yet breathing within. They grow thicker and thicker, and darker, and still more dark without any outward sign of movement. There is movement though. The clouds press closer to the earth, their shapes distorted. Where there were clear outlines, there are now layers of deadly grey and brown clouds building right before my eyes, wind driven and looking like long, twisting sausages. The brassy sun is gone. The winds are still as death itself. On the far horizon, wind-devils swirl skyward and blend with the muddy-colored clouds.

It all happened so fast. It is then that I become frightened. I gather my children and head for home, through the pasture. We are halfway there, when suddenly, the whole world becomes alive. A funnel cloud is reaching down toward us.

"Mama! A cyclone!" my children cry.

"*Ach, Gott*, give me strength. We cannot get home."

The sudden, swirling wind is in our hair; it tears at our clothes, hinders our speed. We fall and crawl and struggle to our feet again. We all try to stay together by holding onto each other's clothing. It is almost impossible. I try to reach the stacks with the barb-wire around them. Then I change my mind and think the old buffalo wallow would be best.

The funnel has already come up over the rim of the greater pasture, roaring toward us. It is tearing up great clumps of grass and dirt, sucking it skyward, roaring a deafening scream.

"*Ach, Gott, erbarme Dich!* Be merciful!"

I remove my apron and wrap my two little ones together as best as I can, and I lie on top of them, holding them down with my weight. The others lie flat to the ground around me, face down.

We lie in total darkness, eyes pressed tight, the roar of a thousand demons in our ears, the claws of a thousand winds in our hair and every fiber of our humble farm clothes. The ground trembles to its very core, shaking me loose from my frantic grasp until it seems I can feel no solidness beneath me.

Blindly, and with all my might, I hold my little ones down. I try to shout hope and courage to the others, and I try to pray. But a league of savage winds tears the words from my mouth and mangles them into groanings.

Then, suddenly, a calm settles all around us. I feel my solid weight again. It is over! We are safe! The cyclone is gone! Thank God! But I am afraid to look. Is our house still there? I must look. I cannot bear the thought of it all torn up any longer.

*Ach*, yes! The buildings are not even touched. How can that be? I turn and look at the hay stacks. The hay stacks are demolished! They are completely gone, scattered in a carpet over the pasture. The stout wire fence around them is torn up, twisted into grotesque strands, bristling with wisps of hay and splintered fence posts.

"*Ach*." I shudder and look away. Today God has surely held us in His hands! I hurry my children to our house.

I make up my mind that when David comes back from the harvest fields in the east, I will say to him that *we will move from this place.*

When David returns he gives me no time to state my ultimatum. He has seen the condition from the roadway. And for once he is filled with ire, so unlike David. He almost forgets to greet us.

"We cannot stay on this miserable place any longer. Other fields bear harvests, if these won't!" he thunders, failing to see that childish joy for his return has turned to dark fear of him. Silently, one by one, the children draw away to hide behind my skirts.

David isn't through. "I will find a new place, where crops grow! I am tired of looking at thistles and thorns and bitter gall! Before winter comes I will have a place, I swear it!"

I should be upset over David's harsh words. Surely it is not like him to storm so. But I can hardly keep my face with dignity. I ask myself, can I be dreaming these glorious words clothed in anger? David has said he will find us a new place! Will it be close to town? Close to school? Who knows? *Ach*, my head spins, just thinking about it.

Later, when I go into the bedroom to put David's clothes away, I find Leah standing behind the door crying because of her father's unpleasant homecoming. And Mia, who is David's right hand, has fled to the attic room, weeping hot tears into her pillow. "Hush. Hush," I say, nudging gently. "Good things will come out of your papa's angry words. You will see. You will see."

# CHAPTER 15

## *Good-bye Forever*

I t isn't easy to find a farm to rent. David has tried many times. He is gone even now.

Long before he arrives home, Rover, lying in the lamp light by the door, pricks up his ears and listens intently.

Watching him I can see that he has filtered out the sound of the wagon coming down the midnight road. Finally I hear the slow pace for myself.

When David drives in the yard I run out to meet him. "Hello," I call to him. "You have good news?"

"No," David says lightly from the high seat of the wagon. My heart stops. I cannot tell if he is joking or telling the truth.

David swings down to the ground, laughing. "Well, Evaliz," he says, "this time I did it!"

"My....my!" I search for other words but find none. Overhead a million stars are winking their joy. I wipe away a tear, and it is as if I am wiping a happy starlet from my face.

David has said, "Wait until you hear. Wait until you hear." *Ach,* such joy!

I help him unhitch the horses and we lead them to drink, and while David gives them feed, he tells me all about it. "It is only a mile out of town. The children will go to town school. The owner is a grain dealer from Kansas City. He came to look for a suitable

193

tenant and Mr. Walker recommended me. What do you think of that?"

"It is marvelous!" I say, feeling proud that such an eminent man as Mr. Walker would think so highly of us.

"The land has gone to weed, and the house is dirty as a sty," David explains.

"*Ach*, that is nothing," I say quickly. "We have handled all that before. It won't kill us."

"Oh, I forgot to tell you, Evaliz. The man speaks German. He has leased the farm to me for a year. After that, if he is satisfied, we can have it as long as we like."

I can hardly believe it. I ask myself, is it really so? My children will go to town school?

When we get to the house I set food out for David, and start planning for tomorrow. I will dye the bleached flour sacks I have been saving and make my girls dresses to wear to school. I am so happy. At last my children will be among the American people, to gain new knowledge that is so necessary, and to make something of their lives.

We are actually moving. We are saying goodbye to this prairie home forever. It hurts for some of our life stays with it.

We are like a band of Gypsies trailing down the road, singing gay songs, laughing and shouting to each other. My ·brothers Wilhelm and Friederich, and their boys, each driving a hayrack or wagon loaded with machinery and farm tools lead the way. One wagon holds the hogs; the spring buggy is tied on behind. Next follows David with a load of hay, chicken crates fastened on top, and the extra horses tied on. After that, Leah and Mia follow on foot, driving the cattle. Rover, a busy third, yips and snips when one or another gets out of line.

I bring up the rear driving our own wagon loaded with household goods. My little ones, Davie and Linda, are on the seat beside me; Hester and Maria rock gayly on the featherbed tucked inside the upturned table on top of the load.

Whenever the cattle move along nicely, Leah and Mia can catch a ride. But, now and then, I get off the wagon and take my turn at driving the cattle. The girls need to rest often, for it is sixteen miles to the new place near town.

The fall day is calm and mild. The brown grasses sway lightly in the breeze, whispering and rasping the chronicles of the plains. "Wheels of **progress**," David calls the sound. "Grasses have a way of predicting," he says, explaining.

Mia, walking along the roadway, spots a procession of ants. She calls to us and I stop the wagon. We all get down and watch the sight. The number of ants is legion, moving steadily onward, up and over whatever lies in their path. The chain could be a half mile long for all we know.

"Look, Mama, a string of legs," Davie calls out, all excited.

We all laugh at the priceless remark. But Mia is quick to correct him. "No, *Brüderchen*, not a string of legs. Say, marching ants. A caravan of progress!"

*Ach*, that Mia; she is just like her father ! With both of them everything must be said proper. Everything is a sign of good.

Davie repeats the words, "marching ants," after her and adds, "I still think they are a string of legs." He pokes a little closer.

"Better not get in their way," Hester warns, pulling him back. "They'll march up your body and over the top of your head."

"*Ja*," Maria puts in, "and if you open your mouth to yell, they will march over your tongue and out again."

We leave the ants and get back on the wagon. "A caravan of progress," Mia had called them. I wanted to say, "Maybe, also, it means a winter of privation, and these ants know it." But, knowing Mia's sensitive nature I am glad now that I didn't say it.

The new farm has everything: a two-story five-room house, a wagon shed, a blacksmith shop, a chicken house, hog pens, a cyclone cellar, an outhouse, a windmill with large stock tanks, and a huge barn with separate cow sheds and two granaries all under one roof. It has a large hayloft and on its roof stand two winged horses, lightning rods. There is also a cupola, like a doll house, on top that lets in light and air, and creates a castle paradise for pigeons and sparrows.

More than that, all the buildings were recently painted a light grey. There is no mistaking, the place belongs to a rich man. If one could only say that much for the weed-choked fields and the inside of the house. But David and I will soon take care of that.

First the fields must be put in order, the tangle of sunflower stalks and thistles burned off and the dry waste ploughed under. Mr. Winkler, himself, will provide his choice of seed wheat, a strain of hard winter wheat -- either Kubanka or Turkey Red.

The farm consists of 320 acres, 120 acres of which are pastureland. David is anxious to get the neglected ground in order. Out of an eight-foot pipe he fashions himself a kerosene fire lighter. The end holding the rag wick is slightly bent upward to ride on the ground easily; the other end has a cork. With this handy tool David walks along the edge of his fields, setting small fires first along the fence lines and roadway. He moves inward only on windless days, after first ploughing fire guards. When, at last, the burned strips are wide enough it is safe to light the center fields.

I see it all from the house and yard: Leah and Mia with shovels throwing dirt against smouldering fence posts, putting out the fire, David with the team. All their energy is strained to get the fall-planting ground in order before school begins.

In order to keep two double-share ploughs and a harrow going, David needs to break in two frisky colts, and he, himself, must run one plough, Mia, the other. That means Leah must walk behind the harrow.

At first, David tried to make a platform for Leah to stand on, but the added weight made the harrow bog down. Poor Leah, she is so tired in the evening. She cries because her ankles hurt after wobbling on uneven clumps of earth all day. "Better that you ride old Buckskin after this," I suggest. And she does, for the most part.

Days when I can get away from my work I take Leah's place in the field, even though I am with child again.

In the evening, David and I sit by the lamplight. I do my mending and David reads from the Bible, and when he has it, he reads the *Dakota Freie Presse*. Our house is quiet, save for the heavy sleeping of our children. I can hear Leah's breathing even from upstairs. *Ach*, it draws a soul-burdening sigh from me. I look up and see that David isn't reading. He, too, has heard. He sits in stony silence and stares at the dark window that mirrors his image back to him, his reading limp in his hands, his shoulders drooped.

When he speaks his voice is filled with self-rebuke. "That I should do this to my children," he says angrily. "They should be in school."

"Sure, we both know it. But what can we do? The sowing must be done."

"If only there was a way, I would borrow money and hire someone." David shrugs his shoulders painfully, as if the weight of the whole world rested on him.

The American people driving past our place see the children working and chide us for it. "These children should be in school. Instead, you work them in the field, like beasts!" they shout. The men shake their fists; the women say nothing but look prim and disgusted.

David tries to explain, but gets nowhere with them. Either they do not understand his English, or do not care to. They simply resign themselves to defeat, saying, "Bah! What's the use! These foreigners have no feelings."

If only they knew. Our hearts are completely broken. We are filled with shame.

And yet, not all Ameicans are rude, far from it. Some stop their vehicles just to sit and marvel at the work already done. Their faces show only kindness. They bid us the time of day and say, "How wonderful. How wonderful!"

Each day David and I tell each other that this will be the last time we keep our girls out of school. Just this once, until the wheat is sown. After that they will never miss. But that is still two weeks away.

Then, even this is changed by a knock on the door. I go to see who it is, and there stands a young man, a stranger, begging for work. He tells me, "I am Andreas, new in *Amerika*. My home is Warsaw, Poland."

"*Guten Tag*," I say. "I am Frau Becker." And we are both surprised that we are German. He is eager to find work in order to send for his *Schatz*, his sweetheart, Betta.

Andreas has walked from town, a meager bundle strapped to his back, a frayed violin case in his arms, held as tenderly as a mother holds her babe. He has the warmth of goodness stamped upon his face, and the growl of hunger within his slender frame.

"May I give you something to eat?" I ask.

"*Bitte*." He bows his head in humility.

I bid him come in and set large slices of brown bread and thick sweet cream before him.

"Supper will be when the family comes home," I tell him.

And so it is that on the following day Leah and Mia go to school in town. There is peace and joy in our hearts, and a forlorn boy has laid his gnawing hunger to rest. We all owe him much, this gentle twenty-one-year-old German lad who does not mind the stifling dust of our fields that chokes his lungs and covers his gold-blond hair with grey siftings.

Evenings, washed clean of all dirt and toil, he sits outside, violin in hand, his chair leaning back against the house, his smooth-shaven face tilted back and glowing in the moonlight. He is unmindful of the adoration of my children sitting on the bare ground around him.

And sitting so, his eyes gazing into the starry sky, he plays strains of music, sweet and sad and tender, thinking, no doubt, of Betta, yearning for a letter from his *Schatz*. He has sent her his address.

Sure, Andreas is not a mere farm hand. He could find better work if he knew the language. He has a genteel fineness that shows in his every movement. There is genteelness in his hands, in his long slim fingers. It is in the carriage of his shoulders, in his fine temples. It wings from the music he plays: Schubert, Bach, Liszt.

We cannot pay him much. Neither can we keep him on for winter. But, already, he has a job waiting for him, feeding cattle for our neighbor, Mr Haldeman, who can pay him well. We rejoice with him when we hear it.

"My, my , Andreas," we say. "Almost before you know it you will have Betta with you."

"*Danke*. Yes, thank you!"

It is late October and light green rills of winter wheat are running in straight lines across the clean face of the land, growing thicker and thicker until the whole field looks like a green carpet. David says the growth is heavy enough to winter the cattle on between snows.

Our girls, Leah, Mia, Hester, and Maria are in school learning the language. They are finding many treasures in their books. Eagerly they bring the tidings home to me. Eagerly, I listen. How their eyes sparkle! How my heart thrills at their new-found knowledge!

Surprised, I learn that America's freedom was born out of revolution. I can understand that it is a land dedicated to the belief that all men are created equal, like the history book says. Surely, learning is a treasure and an adventure. More than that, it is a gift of God!

Leah tells me of the nobleness of George Washington whom the people call "the Father of our Country." She tells of the greatness and humbleness of Abraham Lincoln, who as a child lived in a rough-hewn log cabin, desolately poor. She brings the book to show me. "See, Mama, it was without chimney or fireplace, entirely open on one side."

I look and see the wintry picture with my own eyes. "*Ja*, this is real poverty," I say, shaking my head.

Eagerness leads her on. "Would you believe it, Mama? The family lived like this for a year before the fourth wall was added."

I know it must be true or her lesson would not teach it. I see a picture of the tall lad in awkward dress, his homespun shirt and deerskin trousers several inches too short for him. And I am amazed that he became President of the United States.

Evenings when David sits at the table, studying the Constitution of the United States for his final citizenship papers, our children flock to the lamplight on either side of him. Together they study and learn about Washington and Lincoln. They make it clear that while each differed in class and rank, one man was as great as the other. But for the sake of debate, David takes the side of Washington while Leah and Mia defend Lincoln. I sit with my mending and listen with admiration to their earnest wrangling on matters I know nothing about.

Although David defends General Washington most nobly, stressing the greatness of the man who, barefoot like his soldiers at Valley Forge, stained the snows with blood, Leah will not give up. Leah rises to her feet. "Yes, Papa, I agree. Without Washington we would not have won the right to govern ourselves. But Lincoln severed the bondage of slavery. Is that not as important?"

"Yes, I must admit that Lincoln, weighed down under principle, gave himself to do God's will," David says easily.

"Good. Then let me recite Lincoln's Gettysburg Address," she says. "Fourscore and seven years ago our fathers brought forth on this continent a new nation, conceived in liberty, and dedicated to the proposition that all men are created equal . . . ."

It is plain to see that before such words David must bend. Slowly I let down my mending and listen. And though I do not understand I know it must be a speech of great renown. Leah does not falter. Her voice is firm. In this one thing, she has no shyness before her elders.

"Now we are engaged in a great civil war, testing whether that nation, or any nation so conceived and so dedicated, can long endure. We are met on a great battlefield of that war. We have come to dedicate . . ."

*Ei, Ei!* This is our Leah, now past thirteen years, and I hardly know her. Proudly she recites the whole speech. She stands erect, her gaze far beyond this humble room. And I know, this night she is no longer a child. David's eyes fill with mist as Leah continues, and I do not show that I notice, hiding my own tears.

Leah's voice becomes stronger, " . . . that this nation, under God, shall have a new birth of freedom, and that government of the people, by the people, for the people, shall not perish from the earth."

Silence fills the room. A lump sits in my throat, nearly choking me. Surely, I can tell by the mere tone of it that it is an immortal tale. No one needs to translate it. This, Lincoln has done for America! We in our house are all agreed.

In the cold of winter, his livestock taken care of, David undertakes the time-consuming job of drawing a picture of George Washington on the ample wall of our eating room. He copies it from a colored post card, in full detail even to the gilded frame, the red, white, and blue flag draped across the top of the oval, the screaming eagle sitting on its golden dome, its beak open and wings raised in defiance and threat, guarding the safety of man and flag alike. While the children are in school he accomplishes much.

When David isn't working on the wall picture, he writes names in fancy letters on the flyleaves of books. Every Bible, catechism, song, and prayer book in the house has the individual child's name written in it, the letters colored in ink. When our church people see our song books, they, too, want their names inscribed. Every Sunday after church he brings more and more books home with him until I think there can be no more Bibles, confirmation, and old Volga-German song books left to write in.

From fancy name writing David goes to wooden name plates to hang over house gates. The carved boards come complete with hanging chains and when the name is finished they are a sight to behold. The colorful arched plaque hanging over my brother Friederich's picket gate takes one's breath away. It took David a month to make the star and crescent signboard and design the name with winged swallows, prancing horses, dancing fish, laughing gnomes, and capering donkeys all under a garland of roses and trailing vine.

Surely, there isn't anyone like David, full of happy ways. His stubby, work-worn fingers do not lessen his skill, because the will to do comes from his heart.

While David is painting the George Washington picture I have a project going also. I bring in the old wooden box from the barn and put legs on it. I don't blame David for trying to stop me, because it has one board kicked out on one side, but I scrub it clean. I need something to display the Bible and maybe a vase holding a paper rose. This side table is meant to be like Frau Shuster's, only hers is a store-bought one, made of fine-grained wood polished to a mirror-like golden sheen. When the children come home from school they eye it with disdain. "Ugh, what is that?" Hester asks.

"A show table," I say, feeling proud of myself.

"What is a show table?" Maria wants to know.

"It is a parlor table," Mia explains. "Only we do not have a parlor. Besides, it doesn't look so good."

"*Ja*," says Hester, "I would be ashamed to let anyone see it."

"*Ach*, children, do not mind. When I am finished, it will look fine," I assure them, knowing how I have planned it in my mind.

When the table is finished, sitting stout and smooth on its four legs, I cover it from top to bottom with a linen cloth that has deep insertions and a wide crochet lace border around the hem, hiding the broken side and ill-matched legs completely. The table goes in the corner, under the clock shelf, here in our large eating room. On its pure white cover I lay our gild-edged Bible and a red crepe paper rose that David brought from town. We can't afford a vase just yet.

"My! How pretty!" The children exclaim and smile with joy. They are so proud of it, they wouldn't think of cluttering it with their school books. "Now, we are becoming stylish, like the town people," they say. Even David must stop and pay his respect to the table, but only after the table cloth has hidden all its defects.

On other days while David paints the stars and stripes on the wall picture, I crochet a lace scarf for the wall shelf to compliment the ornate clock. The clock panels are pretty with faint gold roses, and winged starlings darting across a field of glass, behind which swings a bright pendulum.

Next I crochet a lace hanging with tassels on each scallop for the glass door leading to the front porch. Sure, but it all goes nice with the clean sky-blue walls, the crisp white curtains on tall windows, and David's gild and flag-draped picture, glowing in the midst of it.

What, I think to myself, will our friends say when they stop in on their way to town and see all this? Most of all I wonder what Frau Shuster, my neighbor, will say. She has no kith or kin, yet she cannot find time to make this or that or the other thing, much less make a fancy sugar bread, though her fat stomach craves for thos I make.

It isn't too long before friends come to see the picture. All of them praise David for his accomplishments. Even some town people, having heard of such a patriotic picture in a foreigner's house come and ask to see it. David shows it gladly, with a measure of pride, assured that he is being accepted as a citizen.

But before his guests arrive, I place the table I made directly beneath the painting and lay the Bible and red rose just so. I smooth out the cloth so that the lace hem falls in even folds close to the floor that is scrubbed clean until the boards look white.

I am so proud of my room. Boldly, before I close the door to keep out the children with their snowy shoes, I steal another look, to picture in my own mind how striking it will look to a stranger glimpsing it for the first time. Then I hurry to my kitchen stove to make coffee, and I cut fresh baked *Kaffee-Kuchen* onto plain white plates. Then I set out thick sweet cream and new churned butter so that our guests do not go away hungry.

And they do come, talking friendly talk to David, smiling and bowing to me as if I were a queen, and patting the shoulders of our children, lovingly. *Ach*, how good it is to be accepted!

As the days go on a winter storm rages. The stock tank freezes over. The pastures are blanketed with snow and David must halt his shoe mending to feed and water his stock. When the snow gets deep, he meets the school children at the edge of town with the sleigh and brings them home all snug and warm under heavy quilts.

On cleaning days when the scrub water freezes on the floor of the upstairs sleeping rooms before it can be wiped up, I tell my girls to take buckets of snow and spill it on the floor and scrub it about with the broom to make the floor fresh and clean. I tell them to be careful and sweep out all the cracks between the boards, and to move the beds away from the wall to get the corners clean. There are many winter tasks I must teach my young girls so that they will be good housewives in years to come. This is a mother's duty.

We also get our winter quilt-making done, tying the soft thickness with bright woolen yarns. My new baby clothes are ready and waiting, too. And David completes his harness and shoe mending. All hands in our household are busy.

Together with our children we sing away the winter evenings, lilting new songs, reciting new poems, setting to memory Bible verses and Luther's Catechism, telling new tales.

Then, spring comes onto the land again, swift as the shimmering wings of swallows. Spring, lush and green, and beautiful!

# CHAPTER 16

# *Wheels of Progress*

This year is truly different. New life is everywhere — in the rain clouds, on the land, in the hearts and souls of prairie men. Even in our cradle there is new life, for my Kathi is born. She is my tenth child. Ten, like the fingers on my strong hands. But my three eldest lie buried in Russian soil.

Surely, this year the rains come when they should and the ground holds the sub-moisture. The untamed winds, for once, forget their fiery breath. And the tall blades of growing wheat go rollicking in waves across the broad face of the land, growing, growing.

Deep within the grooves of new-listed corn, green rills run true and straight up the gentle rise of the land to where the horizon meets the pale blue sky. Sorghum, milo, kafir and millet fields make square, newly-green and brown patches across the earth's bed — like a mammoth quilt spread far and wide.

And the cattle rise from their night's rest at daybreak, to trail off into the lush pastures, before we milk them. We must bring them back and shut the corral gate, so that they do not walk away and leave us sitting with a half-filled pail.

Buttercups and violets are thick in the prairie hollows buzzing with bees. The children gather flowers and wild garlic and yellow-blossomed sorrel that is sour and good to eat. I clean and chop the sorrel and fold it into cool chunks of clabber milk to which I have added slices of hard boiled egg and seasonings. "*Sauerampfer*" we call it, or "*Sauer-Rumbel*," as my children say.

Later on, the children pick and eat the prickly red pears of cactus which grow in the pasture. I keep busy picking stickers from their tongues; if that fails I give them a hard piece of bread to chew on.

Meadowlarks perch on fence posts, the morning sun in their yellow breasts, thrilling their three clear notes like silver bells. And in the pasture the grass-lined pools of yesterday's rain reflect feather-light clouds sailing a sky of blue. In the barn yard our ducks begin to pair off and trail out to the fairy-clear pools or into the open fields lush with green shelter, to nest their eggs.

In my garden plot there is merriment and spring riot. Stout potato shoots lift bonnets of brown earth and peek joyfully into the shimmering light.

Surely, this is the year we have been waiting for. At last, faith has tamed the prairies, and plowed them, and sowed them. *Ach!* All things look to the good. Destiny has decreed that we should move to this place....

Now is the time when school lets out for the summer and my children bring home their report cards. I meet them by the mail box as they come hurrying down the road from town.

"Here, Mama! See?" they call, all running forward to give me the cards that tell whether they passed, or not. Only eleven-year-old Mia is in no special hurry. I gather the cards from their out-stretched hands, an envelope for each. *Ach*, and though I cannot read them or understand the marks, my fingers tremble with excitement.

"What does yours say, Leah?" I ask. Leah, nearly fourteen, is my best learned. In her lie my greatest hopes.

Leah's face dimples. "It says I passed to the sixth grade. See, Mama? Here, it says it in the teacher's handwriting." And she points it out to me.

"My! My! The sixth grade! And only a few years in school, with so many interruptions." I can hardly believe it. Pride overwhelms me.

The other children clamor about me, asking that I see their cards also. And I say, "Wait, wait, I will get to you. I can see only one at a time. We have not finished with Leah's card."

Leah reads me her grades. "E for reading," she says, all eager and proud, taking the card from me. "See, M is my grade for arithmetic. That is because Papa insists on teaching us to do the problems the Russian way."

204

Surprised, I say, "Is there another way? Your papa always knows the answers."

"Oh sure, Mama, the answers are always the same, but the method he works out is what the teacher objects to."

"I have heard your papa say his way is shorter. Is that not better?" I cannot see why the teacher should object. But Leah explains.

"Mama, you do not understand. The teacher wants no short-cuts. She wants the problem worked out the long way so that in later years we can build understanding on it."

"Oh, so," I say. "Now go on with the other grades."

She continues. "The others are G for spelling, E for geography, and E for deportment. Now, do you see, Mama?"

"No, child, I don't. What is all this E and G?"

She answers proudly. "E stands for excellent; G for good; M for medium and F, which I have none of, is for failure."

The moment Leah mentions the word "failure," I have a fight on my hands.

"Mia has an F," nine-year-old Hester tattles, not able to keep the secret any longer. A smile wreaths her face at such a joke.

But Mia, instantly fiery with rage at such snitching shouts back boldly, "Yes, and Hester has all M's even in her deportment and I have excellent -- so there!" She sticks her tongue out to Hester, to even the score.

*Ach*, such actions! Here on the public roadway! "Mia -- Hester. Hush!" I say, shaking them for silence. But it is no use. The shouting goes on:

"Yes, and that is the *only* excellent you have -- so there, too!" Hester yells, making for a violent yank at Mia's pig-tails, her own sailing through the air. But Mia beats her to it. And there is immediately a cat fight.

I look around quickly, afraid that one of those new-fangled, fast-moving automobiles may be coming down the road and find us in disgrace. There is none.

"*Pfui*, shame. Stop!" I cry. But I must pull them apart by force. They are like two bantam roosters clawing at each other.

When I have them apart I wedge myself between them. "Now, Mia, answer me. Did you pass?"

"Yes, I passed to the fourth grade," she sulks, looking sourly at Hester.

"Then, what is this about a failure mark?" I ask sternly.

"Spelling," she says, still mad, as if the word itself were a slap for Hester. But her eyes lift to mine and she calms down to obedience. She explains further:

"Well, it is like this. My friend Edith and I have been proud of getting 100 in spelling. So, last week, after our big test I was sure I had all the words correct, and because I couldn't wait to see my grade the following day, I took out my speller and checked for myself -- and the teacher saw me."

"Mia, you didn't cheat?" My breath catches in my throat.

"No, Mama. Believe me. I didn't cheat. But the teacher says for all she knows I have been cheating all year. Nothing else I can say will convince her. 'For, how else then,' she says, 'can you account for all E's in spelling and low marks in all other subjects?' "

I study Mia's face intently, and I see only truth. "After this, you had better let the teacher check your words," I say, and add quickly, "Say you are sorry to Hester and take her hand in forgiveness."

Now that the argument is over, I have time to see Hester's card. Hester's grades are neither good, nor overly bad. Beginning this evening, Leah will have to make an effort to help her, I think. But quiet, brown-eyed Maria, past seven, has nothing to say about the goodness or badness of her grades. Already she has fled to her play. She is concerned only about her corn-husk doll who needs a new crisp dress. She is off to the barn, with her precious Sara, in search of a new corn-husk garment, our dogs, Brill and Rover, trotting joyfully at her side, glad to give their understanding support.

I hurry to the house, satisfied in my children's accomplishments. All have passed to higher grades. Next year Davie will go to school also. Theolinda will soon follow. Then, there is Kathi, too. This is what I have dreamed of: book learning for my children!

I lay the report cards on the lace-covered shelf, next to the clock, to show David when he comes in from the field. He, also, will be proud of our good scholars.

~~~

Though it is summer and Andreas is still working for Mr. Haldeman only a mile away across our pastureland, the letters from his sweetheart Betta still come in our mail box. He leaves the letters until evening when he comes to make us a long visit. It is always something special to wait for.

Then as the evening insects pipe their shrill notes, and the pale golden moon invades the starlit sky, dimming the tiny lanterns of the fireflies, we hear him coming, playing his violin. The announcement of his coming sets the children shouting with glee, though he is still far off.

Walking the well-trodden path across the pastureland, he serenades the cool of the evening: his feet light, his eyes bright with a starry light, his glad music dancing on the shimmering moonbeams -- filling the outside world complete, and filling the house, at last, with his lilting strains even before he comes through the corral gate. Maria, Davie and 'Linda have thrown it wide open by now, and are sitting on the top rail like three sparrows, waiting.

"Hurry, quick, with the dishes," I say to Leah and Mia. "Maybe, he will stay and play a lively tune, if his word from Betta is good."

I turn to Hester. "Quick, child, the broom. And mind you sweep out the corners and under the chairs, too, and watch how you sweep out the door sill; leave no dirt there as you usually do," I admonish, washing the supper plates fast enough to keep both Mia and Leah busy.

It is best, I think, that I teach my girls to keep the door sill clean. It is a necessary quality to have when they marry. If the door sill is clean the rest of good housekeeping follows. I remember it was the first thing my mother taught me as a child. Later, my stepmother held me to it.

"Now, Mia, leave the dishes to Leah. Go, quick, put a clean table cloth on the table where Andreas will sit. Be careful to make the corners straight. Put a chair close to the hanging lamp."

"Yes, Mama," she pipes, running for the cloth which is neatly folded on the cupboard shelf.

I call to David to bring his newspaper out to the kitchen light, so that Andreas can have the dining room to himself to read his letter in solitude.

Quickly we go about our evening cleaning up, for this is a special occasion.

Then, Andreas is at the door, bowing politely, his clean-shaven face beaming.

"*Guten Abend, Andreas. Komme herein.* Come in." David is out of his chair to meet him.

"*Schönen Dank, Herr Becker. Guten Abend, Frau Becker.*" Andreas reaches out his hand in hearty handshakes.

"Quick now, Andreas' letter," David and I say in unison to the children. But we need not have bothered. They have brought it to him already, their eyes gleaming as if it were a priceless gift of their own making. They draw back politely, yet not willing to withdraw entirely. Still, politeness is the first order.

"*Bitte*, go in the eating room to read your letter Andreas," I say to him.

I shoo the children away from the door and make them sit on the floor. They sit quietly, waiting for him to finish, their eyes wide-eyed with questions. "Mama, will she come soon?" they come to whisper in my ear where I am mending stockings at the kitchen table.

"Quiet, he will hear you," I caution and nod my head. "Yes, she will come as soon as he earns enough money."

"What makes him so still? What takes him so long?" Davie wants to know. And I lay a shushing finger against his lips. He settles back on the floor again, next to his sisters.

Andreas sits by the table near the hanging light, his back turned to us, reading and rereading his letter in silence. Miracle of all papers! It has traveled so far over far-flung oceans, over hills and plains, to the rightful owner.

I can only imagine that he hangs onto each word as a precious jewel to be captured and sealed into a filigree setting, or as a fine instrument strumming melodious strains across his heart, full of yearning, living secret thoughts, dreaming dreams.

He sits by the lamplight, quiet and unmoving, forgetting time and place. Betta's letters always have the same effect on him.

And then, as is his old habit with us, he goes to sit in the dark night, leaning against the house, looking far off into the glittering sky, playing his violin — serenading his true love far across the sea with Franz Liszt's "*Liebestraum*," soft and sad, and beautiful. Almost like breaking your heart....

At last, the wheat is ripening! There will be a full crop this time, not a half-crop, nor a stubble crop seared by wind and sun, as in former years. How very long we have waited for this. In exaltation David and I walk our fields, glorying in their richness, almost afraid it is a dream that will vanish in a twinkling of an eye. But it is real. Real!

The wheat stands higher than our waists. The greenish gold tops are rough with plump wheat-heads, bent with the weight of ripening grain. Swaying. Swaying as ocean waves before the gentle wind.

With laughing eyes, David says, "The field is thick enough, Evaliz, to spread and dry your wash on." To prove it, he sails his hat out onto the waving heads and it rides light as a cork.

David reaches out and gathers in two fat wheat-heads and husks them into his hand. "*Gott sei Dank!*" he says, with uncontrollable joy. "Look, Evaliz, see the liquid gold washing to our waistline, drowning us with riches!"

I stand silently and look, as he bids. And I see the whole field bowing and rising, and bowing again. *Ach!* Such homage and salutation from our ripening field calls only for mute silence.

All about us the ripening heads sigh in their lifting and falling, whispering in a thousand voices. Saying, "This is your reward for faithful toil!" Saying, "This is your bread. Your meat. Your peace of mind. Your night's rest. Gather it in with thankful hearts."

"*Ach*, yes, David," I say at last. "Our wheat crop."

And because I am reminded of a time in Russia when I was sixteen, standing in a field of golden grain, such as this, with no way forward and no way back, a glad hurt comes to my throat and I say no more.

When we get back home David starts setting things in order. On the prospect of a good harvest he has already bought a new header. He has built a new header barge and rimmed an old set of wagon wheels for it in his blacksmith shop. He has bought a team of horses. Surely, he has borrowed too much money from the bank. This harvest cannot fail now. It must not fail!

All stands in readiness and waiting. Old harnesses are riveted and smeared with oil. A new set of harness, gleaming with shining metal, hangs on smooth pegs by the new team's stall. They are sleek looking bays, Tom and King by name.

For days now, David has fed grain to our horses getting them primed for the great task ahead. And before he turns them out to pasture he curries them until their coats shine. In all, we have twelve head of horses, filling our large barn to the limit. "It will take eight stout, grain-fed horses to go through that stand of wheat," David says, a smile playing across his face.

In the evening, reassured by the day's inspection, David brings in the tines of two broken pitch forks, stained and rusted with age, and puts new handles in them by our lamplight, rubbing and polishing them with wax. And he sands the prongs to new shininess. "By the looks of things I will need these. Ten forks cannot be too many. Who knows how many that 'pure gold' will break," he says, winking at the children, turning the new made forks this way and that, filled with pride.

"I will take the one with the shiny tines and the pink marker on the handle," says Mia.

"No, I will take that one," Leah laughs.

Our girls play-argue among themselves, knowing that they will have to help in the harvest. They are as eager as we are to begin. Harvest will find them in the header barges and possibly on the stack.

Time weighs heavy. Never have I known four days to be so long. Each night the wind dies with the sunset. The stars hang low and bright. And in the field just outside our window the drying, rasping wheat heads talk in hoarse whispers, waking me from my light sleep. I rise quietly so as not to wake David, and stand by the tall window to gaze in awe at our moon-drenched field. Bright as moon-gold, it wears a radiant halo, blackening to ebony the other fields by its brightness.

"Strange how one forgets the glorious brightness of a ripening field, eh, Evaliz?" David asks pleasantly from his white pillow. He hasn't been sleeping at all, but keeping watch over his field, the same as I.

And though the nights are a thing of beauty, the days are hot and dry. Each morning, with the sun's return, the wind blows over the searing plains, washing the wheat with golden fire, drying the full-ripe milk in the grain just right.

Heat is everywhere — even in the deepest shade, where our dogs pant with racing breath. The thin, high sky is too hot to look at. And shimmering heat-waves rise from the whole land, as from a hot stove. The heat-waves play tricks along the roadway in the distance. It seems to be flooded with blue lapping water, running over, spilling into our fields, drowning the crops, washing blue oceans over the pasturelands.

Diligently we watch the skies, praying that no rain or hail comes to destroy our crop. Heat is all we want. And heat is what we get.

It is so hot that the morning milk sours before the noon hour, even in the cellar. And the boards inside the buggy shed ooze yellow beads of sap that both tempt and repel the chickens who have taken shelter there from the terrible heat. Even meadow-larks, tamed by the intense heat, share the shelter with our hens, standing with panting breath and wings cupped.

David can neither eat or sleep. The weather is too perfect. Nights he goes outside to see that no thunderhead comes riding out of the north-western sky. Days, he waits for the night to come, and I am as bad as he.

One by one the days drop away and nothing happens. Nothing, save the steady ripening of the grain. This indeed, is a miracle! I cannot account for it.

On the last evening before harvest David comes home from town with a load of groceries and a large barrel of bottled beer. The Kansas City and Milwaukee Breweries have a way of packing bottled beer in layers inside of wooden barrels and banding them in metal. It is much cheaper to buy these than smaller lots. Our people always serve cold beer to harvest hands, and David for one would not forget. Also with him in the wagon are three harvest hands, college youths from the city. They are all he can get. Mr. Haldeman will not give up Andreas. It is better so, for Haldeman can pay more than David could.

All stands in readiness. Only one long night of sleep remains.

210

And then, even this long night is ended. In the early morning hours of July 4, with the sun rising, we move out into our field just east of the house to cut our golden wheat.

Never has there been such a jubilant day. Dogs bark. Children frolic. David, grinning like an over-grown boy, drives his span of eight horses hitched to the new header. He has pushed the height-controlling lever down to the last notch, to lift the cutting blades high above the ground so that nothing can mar them. The canvassed elevator on one end stands at a rakish angle, lurching and swaying, its bright red and yellow paint gleaming in the morning sun. Two header barges follow, driven by Leah and Mia. One hired man stands in each, balancing himself by the handle of a pitch fork. The other young man, who is to make stacks, walks in long strides after them.

And though I am a grown woman thirty-seven years of age, nothing can keep me in the house this morning. There are no forces strong enough to hold me. Along with our frolicking children and capering dogs I follow the glad procession to the field, leaving my little Kathi asleep in the cradle. "Run to the house every little bit and see after the baby," I tell Hester.

"Yes, Mama," she says. I can always depend on Hester with little ones.

Excitement beats like a drum through my veins when finally the knives whirr-r-r shrill as a locust call, and I see the wheat stalks fall as if by magic. They drop neatly backward onto the cradle-bed of the header and are carried away in a steady, shimmering ribbon up the elevator into the accompanying barge.

As the machine and barge move steadily forward they leave behind them a smooth, yellow strip of close-cropped stubble. In glee, my little ones run barefoot down the new-cropped run way, lifting their feet high, shouting laughter as the prickly stems stub their tough little feet, leaving slim scratches, red as red silk, on their bare legs higher up where the skin is more tender.

Leah's wagon is first to follow beneath the spewing elevator. And the young man in her wagon, unaccustomed to the work as he is, has to hustle with all his might to clear away the wheat that is coming in on him like an ocean wave. Even so, it piles up and starts spilling back on the ground. The young fellow panics. Smiling confidence to him, David slows down, giving him time to learn. In the meanwhile, Mia is following behind, driving on the new-crushed wagon trail, ready to take her turn the minute Leah's barge is full.

Leah does a fine job driving. She holds her team to the same pace as the header, keeping the elevator gliding at the center section of the barge. But when the barge is almost full and the

211

wheat is difficult to handle — the young man sinking hip deep at every step he takes — she pays too much attention to him. Her horses lose the pace and the elevator moves forward covering the man completely, then her, and after that piling wheat on top of the horses.

David sees what is happening and stops. We all laugh, even the young man who by now has clambered back to daylight, looking like a scarecrow. Straw is sticking from his ears, hair, and clothes. He even spits pieces of it out of his mouth. He has lost his pitchfork. His hat is gone, too. Surely, who could get mad on a morning such as this?

Laughing, David says that they better go now to start a stack. He cuts a wide circle into the thick stand on which to place the first stack. For now, all they have to do is unload; there will be more.

Mia's barge comes next. She gets showered right at the beginning. Her team doesn't move in time. She sees the elevator coming at her, and she screams in terror. She shouts until her mouth fills with straw and she can shout no more. David stops quickly. All this takes only a twinkling of an eye. This time, David lets her get her horses into motion first. And so they move steadliy down the field and I stay behind.

The loads soon pile up, as our crew cuts ever deeper into the field. Before I walk to where they are outlining the first stack, I send Hester home to look after the baby and to set the house in order. At ten years she is old enough to be of great help. "Scrub the eating room floor, Child," I say to her. "After that, swat all the flies and shut the room dark. I'll be home soon to start the dinner."

"All right, Mama," she says. "If I do, can I have some dried prunes from the top shelf of your closet?"

"Yes, yes, have some," I nod her on her way, smiling to myself, not a bit surprised that they have already found my latest hiding place. Next time I will have to find a more difficult place to hide my prunes and raisins, I think.

Because none of these college men has ever made a stack before, and David cannot stay to do it himself, I help the fair youth named Tom start the first stack. We keep it straight and firm at the corners and on all sides, interlacing each forkful in a manner so that the edges will not crumble and slide away. And because the barges are filling up too fast, Leah and Mia must help unload, in order to keep the header going. Sometimes when they get bogged down, David comes to do his share of the work. And all the while we have an eye on the weather.

"Better that you go to town every night until you get more capable help," I say to David as he comes around the field. "You will

212

need two men to each barge besides the girls, and another man for the stacks."

"Yes, I know all that. And I need another barge and team, as well," he says, hurrying back to the header.

The July heat is intense. The searing winds are like oven blasts, eddying up from the hot stubble until their fire stings the innermost part of the nostrils, and one must keep his head bent when walking into the wind.

Our clothes cling wet and dark to our backs as the sun climbs higher into the heat-hazed sky. Froth falls in puffs from the horses' bits as they labor past. Foam lays in a thick lather on their hides, drying to crusty salt crystals, and wetting again; their stomachs heave with heavy breath. Surely, this is weather to kill man and beast alike.

Because Tom has been at school in the city and is not used to being outside, his fair skin burns to a fiery red. His light blue eyes stand out in his livid face like two orbs of winter ice. His hands welt into blisters, even under his gloves. But he is a brave lad. He suffers patiently, and will not quit.

I am filled with compassion because of his tortured hands. I bring the oil can from the header when next David comes around the field and I pour machine oil on his open palms to soften the flesh and lighten the pain. It takes only two quick pumps of the thumb to spurt enough oil, but it is time enough to see the pulse, fluttering like a wounded bird, on his blue-white wrists, slim as a girl's. Suddenly, admiration wells within me. Any other lad would have flung the pitchfork aside and walked back to town. Surely, his people, whoever they are, should be proud of such a son.

Tom's hands taken care of, I hurry home to prepare the noon-day meal, a big meal. I have everything in readiness, having gotten up at four o'clock in the morning to bake five pies and a cake. I had plucked eight young roosters and have them ready to fry. I have many loaves of bread. Amber tomato preserves, pickled beets, and crisp dills sit in a neat row on my oilcloth-covered kitchen table, ready for opening. Only the best for our harvest hands, I say.

I call my youngsters. "Come, quick now, Maria, home with me. By the look of the sun, it must be nearly ten. Time to bring a pail of cool lemonade and doughnuts for Papa and the help. I need Hester at home. Come now, all — Davie, 'Linda, come out of harm's way."

The house feels cool as a shaded brook after the scorching wheat field. With great relief I pull the white head scarf from my head, but there is no time for rest.

213

"Maria, run quick to the cellar; get the lemons. Hester, pump me a pail of water," I order, while I place six cups, plus one for Maria in the bottom of the large soup kettle, and lay the doughnuts on top. I tie the whole thing up with a large, clean tea towel.

When the lemonade is made, I tie another towel over the top of the pail to keep dirt and grasshoppers out, and send Maria on her way. This I will do for the workers every morning at ten, and again at four in the afternoon.

I must not fail to take an armload of bottled beer to the cooling barrel, for the dinner hour. The barrel is an overflow from the windmill to the stock tank. The water in it is always fresh and cool. We also use it for a surplus dipping trough on wash days, and for other quick uses. It saves much pumping time and it is where the men will wash up, when they come in from the field.

And so, our harvest goes; days pile upon days; acre after acre falls away, shrinking our wheatlands, turning them into sunparched stubble. Heat and dryness is everywhere. And David brings home more help to speed the work on its way.

It keeps me busy baking many loaves of bread; baking pies, cakes; making egg noodles; boiling great kettles of this and that: fine soups, brown beef roasts, pork and sauerkraut, from our own salt-brine barrels; cooking doughnuts and pretzels; plucking chickens, ducks; peeling bushels of potatoes; doing the family wash; milking ten cows morning and night; turning the separator; washing dishes, and still more dishes — to say nothing of carrying large pails of water to our sweltering hogs.

Tired beyond words, I crawl into bed at night. Tired, I crawl out again in the wee hours of the morning.

It keeps Maria and Hester busy too, with scrubbing floors, making beds, fixing garden vegetables, churning butter, washing the cream separator, carrying the field lunches, for the stacks become further and further from the house. *Ach*, my poor little girls, doing so much!

It is hurry, hurry, bring in the cows for early milking, before the harvesters come home. While the evening meal is cooking we must get the milking done. How else can I do it? All must go in haste. The meal must be ready as soon as the men wash up. In this I am strict. At my table, no one waits.

After the blessing, David smiles and says, "Eat. Eat. When this is all, my Frau will bring more." David knows I will not let a bowl get half empty before I fill it again. He is like that, too. The men must eat to please him, with a glass of beer, whiskey, or wine to wash it down. Besides the beer, we buy wine and whiskey in wooden kegs shipped from the eastern breweries.

214

The wheat harvest is in full swing throughout the width and breadth of the land. A harvest such as this will not be forgotten by the State of Kansas, nor by the Kansas City and Chicago grain markets.

Everywhere one looks over the broad countryside one sees machinery and wagons moving over yellow ripened fields, like ants. Large, sturdy wheat stacks take their stand not in pairs, or even in four's, but in sets of eight and ten, side by side with just enough room between to drive a barge through. And this is duplicated every quarter mile or so from one end of the field to the other, from neighbor's field to neighbor's. From county to county, and even beyond.

Some farmers prefer to bind and shock their grain. Here one can say the fields are as checkered with sheaves as the forearm is dotted with pores. Where the shorn stubble fields leave off, the lush green corn plots rise to miniature forests running in broad belts over the fruitful land. Kansas is not Kansas this year, but a chalice filled with pure gold!

Our great prairie is no longer a barren plain. Stacks by the hundreds throw their dark shadows across the shorn earth, quivering, as one gazes, in rollicking heat-waves like hundreds of dark spiders on a shimmering web.

The roads leading into town are no longer lonely roadways, but streams of simmering dust, teeming with activity. The wheels of progress are truly rolling at last, engraving their livid wounds of advancement on the land.

Our little country town clatters with excitement. It racks and groans with the pain of new-birth. Provisions must be made to handle the bonanza crop! Grain elevators rear their grey hulks to the skies, challenging, at last, the unending winds of time. Lumber sheds to hold millions of feet of lumber spring up. For new houses! New barns! New granaries!

Implement sheds and wire enclosed storage yards cover the vacant town lots with new farm wagons and farm machinery of all kinds and colors, reds, yellows, dark green.

Buggies, light and springy, high priced carriages, with padded seats and fringed valances swaying from their tops, arrive to tempt the farmers. And for the single fellow there are glimmering black top-buggies with black, yellow-veined wheels and patent leather dash boards, equipped to a nobleman's taste, with slim buggy whips — the color of sleek garter snakes — from whose willowy tips dangle red silken tassels.

And most phenomenal of all is a new glass-front store on whose mirror-like floor automobiles are displayed. Automobiles are not entirely new; there have been a few on our town streets and country roads these past years, but I still marvel at them. Now they are the coming thing, for more and more people. Still, I think our Volga-Germans will hold to the horse and buggy — except perhaps my brother Friederich who always takes to new notions.

David will stick to horses. "Why should I buy an automobile," he says jokingly, "when my fleet pacers can climb into the back seat of any of them? You have seen while driving the long road to church, how we passed one of them and fed it our dust. No, horses will do me for a long time," he adds, closing the matter.

A new way of life is everywhere. The railroad is the main artery, pulsing new blood into the veins of our age-old prairie that will never again experience the drowsy days of yester-years.

The wheat at its best is averaging from forty to seventy and more bushels to the acre. "Think of it, Evaliz! " David exclaims. "That is better than a wagon load of grain to the acre, in some instances. It is no wonder men in the East do not believe it, and come to see for themselves."

Land sharks and brokers flock into town to buy waste tracts of outlying acreages — selling them again at three times the cost to city folk who have never seen a farm or a plow. Wheat prices stand at eighty cents a bushel. Rumors have it that it will rise to a dollar, or even a dollar and a quarter, before the year is out, because of the unrest in Europe.

Mr. Winkler, our rich landowner, arrives by train from the Kansas City grain exchange market. He takes a good look around and hurries back again. Seeing is believing! But, before he goes, he promises David the lease to the farm as long as he wants it.

Locomotives clatter into town from the east and leave empty grain cars on the sidings. Trains! And more trains! More empty grain cars going out to meet the western harvest beyond the horizon.

Other trains chug into town, leave new land-tilling machines on our sidings, fill their hissing boilers at the water tank, and head out West with the rest of their cargo. Puffing, straining, double-header locomotives pulling fifty to sixty flat cars loaded with bulky threshing outfits follow the long procession westward, leaving our county's share as they go.

Surely, it looks as if all the East is moving out West and nothing is coming back, save lone engines hurrying back for their next load. The threshing season has not yet begun. It will take the best part of a month before the grain moves through to the East.

For my children it is the show of the day to sit in the shade and count the rail cars coming out of town and going west. Most of the trains seem a mile long. And how the children laugh when they see one coming back with only three cars! "*Herr Gott!* Look at that little devil, Maria! I would like that one for a plaything," Davie shouts, and gets slapped by her, for swearing.

"You must not use God's name in vain," she scolds.

But Davie is undaunted by the quick flip of her wrist. "Well, I still would like that little fool train for my own."

"Children. Children," I admonish from the screened-in porch. "*Bitte*, no swearing. Davie, tell God you are sorry."

"All right, Mama. I will tell him," Davie says, submissively.

"....eighty-nine, ninety, ninety-three, ninety-five!" I hear him count yet again. "Maria, I counted ninety-five. That is the longest train I have ever seen. Where do you think they all come from? Huh, Maria? Do you know?" But he gets no answer. She is also counting.

Davie is still puzzled. "When I grow big, I shall go see where it is they keep them. It must be such a big barn. Only America could have such a big barn, huh, Maria, huh? Not *Russland* or *Deutschland* either, the way Mama talks."

Maria ignores his questions but says, "You are wrong, Davie; that train had one hundred and twenty-six cars. I count better than you."

Finally, the day comes when it seems there are no more cars left to trail out West. Now only double-header engines go scampering up the glimmering tracks to disappear over the horizon.

Now the trains return with their full cargo. They are shorter this time, going faster for all their heavy loads. They look more vicious, as though mindful of their precious lading of gold. Rumbling mightily, they hurry eastward only to return again and again. The same activity is going on in our town. Locomotives are shunting rail cars on the sidings every day.

There are not enough granaries in our farm communtiy to hold all the grain. Wheat is being piled temporarily in open fields, in farm yards, even near the elevators in town. And still it pours in steady streams from scores of threshing machines throughout the country. Everywhere one looks, there rise columns of black smoke from coal-burning threshing engines. They are everywhere! Moving out of one field into another.

And still there are impatient farmers awaiting their turn, goaded by rumors that this neighbor or the other is threshing 4,200 bushels of wheat in a single day.

Rumors have it that a certain threshing crew has broken the 1903 record of 4,071 bushel. According to the rumor, this world record is held by a man we all know who lives no more than eleven miles from here. Still I can't believe it. "*Ach*, go on! How can that be?" I say to David. "More than 4,000 bushel a day? That is an awful lot. Anyway, some people talk too much. They sully that fine gentleman's name, with such a lie."

"So you don't believe it, eh, Evaliz?" David says, laughing. "Go, Leah, bring me this week's paper. I will read your doubting mama a reprint of it. It happened before we came to America."

David reads the account out loud, and I must believe. In his broken English, and with Leah's help, he goes through the whole article:

### BREAKING WORLD'S THRESHING RECORD
#### September 26, 1903

Frank A. Krhut, with his big Avery thresher and Trego county, Kansas, with her monster wheat crop, broke the world's record for fast threshing last Saturday, September 19, 1903.

He threshed in one day, on his farm in Collyer township, 4,071 bushels of wheat, and that was only a part of his crop. This immense quanity of grain was threshed from 33 stacks and it was necessary to reset the machine 19 times during the day.

The Avery Machine company offered a cash price of $500 to the owner of one of their rigs who should thresh the greatest number of bushels in one day out here in Kansas this year of 1903. A representative of the company was present all day to observe the test, keep time and tally and scan the measure.

The conditions of the test allowed for one continuous run from sun to sun of one day, only; not parts of days. By some unaccountable accident a ball of binding twine found its way into the cylinder, breaking two concaves and causing a delay of 66 minutes. Mr. Krhut threshed 45 minutes after sun down and it being almost dark and having broken all former records to pieces, he did not care to use the remaining 21 minutes.

The former Kansas record was 3,090 bushels, made near Russell earlier in the season when the days were about 30 minutes longer! The world's record was 4,002 bushels.

His rig is one of the largest and heaviest made; a 30-horse power engine, driving a 42-inch cylinder and 72-inch separator.*

The country roads are crowded with wagons. Even though wheat prices havn't risen more than a cent or two, farm families,

*Printed in the *Western Kansas World*. WaKeeney, Trego County, Kansas, September 26, 1903.

nevertheless, are hauling their surplus grain to town. They have no space to store it.

Little children, tied to high wagon seats to prevent their toppling off if they should fall asleep, follow after their elders. Three, four, and sometimes five wagons represent a single family. If the family is large enough and their neighbors can spare a wagon or two they borrow them also. They fill the town grain elevators and granaries to over-flowing; they fill train cars, waiting on the railroad sidings, and finally end up by dumping the grain on the ground then and there, or selling it to speculators dealing with them on the premises. But they are selling, selling. The prairie people are not prepared for such a harvest.

David and I are lucky that we have two very large granaries. Even so we will have to pile some on the ground before we are through. There are still a hundred stacks in the fields. Four large lumber wagons are hardly enough to keep the threshing outfit boss from running the grain onto the ground. The wagon crew must hurry and get back in time. The man has an eye only for business. Already, he has his cap set for Mr. Haldeman's lease, since his harvest was even greater than ours. The man works his crew of twelve pitchers very hard. There are six men to each stack, and it is a sight to watch them dwindle down two stacks, in no time at all.

David climbs up the side of the wagon and lets the golden kernels flow through his fingers. "This is the start of paying our debts," he says happily.

"Yes," I agree. "But it will take more than your share, to set you free. Better that we have more crops like this."

The grain flows out of the separator so fast that David must station another man at the granaries to help unload. And as the threshing crew moves further out, the wagon teams must bring in the heavy loads at a trot. It is very hard on our horses; the ground is so soft; the wagon wheels cut so deep. It is equally as hard on Mia and Leah who must help with the hauling. Throughout the day I go out to the granaries to help them throw back the wheat, while the men shovel it in, in heaps through the window. All must hurry, then drive back to the field at a gallop, passing two incoming wagons at different stages along the way. Sometimes, a load of coal must be taken for the engine, for it must not stop.

*Ach*, such a deep road is cut through our stubble land. At first, it is soft and difficult to travel, causing our horses to strain desperately with the heavy loads. In the end, it is a solid road, packed tight and naked.

The family and I had it hard at harvest time, but threshing has no comparison. The threshing crew consists of eighteen hungry men, besides my own family of ten. I am not as lucky as some farm women, who have threshing outfits complete with cook shacks. The food I must cook and bake would fill a hundred washtubs. To complete the work, I must press every child into duty. Even my little Kathi must do her share of fussing, unattended.

It is also during the threshing season that war breaks out in Europe. Germany declares war on Russia! David is so upset when he brings the latest news home from town. When I ask him what it is all about, David tries to explain:

"It is a very complicated affair according to what I have read in my German papers, the Dakota and Fresno *Freie Presse*. First of all, Serbia has hindered Austria's supremacy in the Balkans. Then a Serbian rebel assassinated Austria's Arch-Duke Francis Ferdinand, and Serbia objected to Austria's ultimatium of search and arrest."

I am completely puzzled. "What has that to do with Germany declaring war on Russia?" I want to know.

"I am coming to that, just give me time," David says, continuing. "Germany sided with Austria. And Russia, in order to keep the straits open so that her shipping trade would not get bottled up in the Black Sea, agreed with Serbia and began to mobilize. Now, get this, Evaliz. Germany, in turn objected to Russian troops on her border and declared war on Russia. So there, you have it."

"Yes, I have it," I say, and must sit down. My legs are shaky. "What is to become of our Volga-Germans now?"

"They will have to serve in the military," David says, shrugging his shoulders, all life going out of him.

We have hundreds of relatives left in Russia, uncles, aunts, cousins, and some family, on both David's and my side. I have my sister Katrinliz and my stepbrother and stepsister, Jakor and Lydia. The others, Otto, Malia, and Marik are now here.

Our German Lutheran friends on their way to and from town stop in and ask David to help write letters for them to their people in Russia. Others come as far as fifteen miles by horse and buggy to ask this favor. David can translate the difficult addresses of Russian provinces and villages as they should be written. David does it gladly. He brings out pen and ink and writes heart-felt words, as directed. And tears flow freely from the eyes of strong men and women, for we all know and remember fond ones so far away. Some letters are addressed to a widowed mother, or an aged father, or some other dear one, whom they can never hope to see again in this lifetime. Some of our farmers send money for passage over, though that is a foolhardy thing in time of war.

Andreas comes to our house, stark anguish in his eyes, seeking answers, worried sick over Betta in Warsaw. He asks people in our house, "What think you, friends? If Warsaw is an open city, as they say it is, will actual warfare come to her streets?"

The answer is always the same. "Sure, how can it fail? With Russia holding Poland and Germany and Austria marching toward Warsaw, how can it stay forever free?"

After this, wretched waiting overtakes Andreas.

Surely, it is a sad time in our lives and in the lives of our people. But here on the western plains, the troubles of Europe are only fat in the fire of industry. The tremendous grain crop of our "Wheat Belt" creates a high fever among our farm people, grain buyers, and speculators, alike. Immediately following the war news, rumors of rising grain prices sweep the country, like prairie fire. Those who can, hold onto as much grain as their bins will hold. Bolder ones dare to speculate and guess at future wheat prices — prices so high that they defy the imagination. Rumors!

"Who knows how much wheat this boundless prairie could produce, if it were set to the plow?" some people say.

Others say, "My guess is, countless millions! Why, neighbor, the riches would be astounding! Yeah, with better and newer farm machinery it can be done. Think, man, what the price of wheat will be, with war raging in Europe! Think, man. Think...."

Others answer, "Yes, and what if rain doesn't come?"

"Oh, pooh, the cycle of draught is over. Can't you read the signs, man?"

"Indeed, listen to him. What better chance have we?"

And so the flame of adventure burns, fed by the boundless logs of disregard and greed of man. Then, almost over night, the people speak as with one voice, "Plow! Plow more land. Raise wheat and corn, and more wheat. Plow the Prairies! Plow! Plow!"

Soon, plow-wounds, true as a surgeon's knife, lie new and raw across the mute prairie. Pockmarks of fencepost holes, festering heaps of fresh earth, run in straight lines through buffalo and meadow grasses, checkering up the face of the land, making out of the whole, cubes, and triangles, diminishing the prairies! *Ach*! It pains mind and soul to see it happen.

Everywhere, unthinking landowners demand it of their tenants. Everywhere, pasturelands shrink back to ravines and hillsides. Cattle no longer roam the wide open ranges. Only on the lands of good thinking owners, who look into the future with clear, unspoiled vision, the virgin soil remains.

David shakes his head sadly. "Don't they know that the high prairie winds have blown before? And that they will blow again? Then, what will become of the land, in later years, when the top soil has mellowed and bad crops have left no stubble or roots to hold down the soil?"

David is right. The winds can take hold of an open field, and claw and suck the earth into rolling, pelting waves, that no power on earth can stop. How well he knows and remembers it from the old country, where he was over-seer for a rich boyar whose fields ran into a hundred *dessjatins*. *Ach*, yes, the people in their excitement cannot know, or cannot care, what they are striving for.

Then, there comes a letter from Mr. Winkler, our landlord, asking that twenty acres of our smooth pastureland be plowed under. And David sets about his task, with a heavy heart.

# CHAPTER 17

# Newfangled Gadgets

Over a wee span of life, our entire world has changed. The prairie land has cast off her dusty mantle of yester-year and has put on a shiny cloak of high exultation. One must thrill with the newness of it all — the growth of these times. Everywhere one looks things have changed: the town, the land, the homes, the people. Truly, the march of progress is on the land!

The town has a water tower, around whose high dome is a wreath of electric lights that can be seen for miles around. Many of the town homes have running water in steel pipes that work like magic. Just a slight turn of a spigot makes the water gush forth, and when one chooses, it can be shut off just as quickly. When I first came to America, I thought the windmills of Kansas were wonderful. But they are nothing compared to this. Even more marvelous than this are the electric lights in town homes and stores. The lights switch on and off with even less effort, and flood the room with dazzling brightness, or run washing machines with unseen power, taking all the work and drudgery off of the hands of those town women who can afford such luxury. Surely, my friends in *Russland* would not believe such magic possible. Some would judge me insane for even mentioning it.

But that is not all. The greatest wonder to me is the telephone up town, which carries the human voice from house to house, over miles of country roads and back again, even at a whisper. That, I would not have believed myself, if I had not seen it myself.

"Just wait, Evaliz," David says, "now that the farm people have had good crops, they, too, will have many new things. Soon, the roadway will be lined with telephone poles. When that happens, we will have a phone in our house, also."

His words take my breath away. I stare at him in unbelief. Such things are not for poor people like us, I think to myself. We must have many crops before we can pay our tremendous debts. And because David does not know what I am thinking, he smiles and says, "The phone will be right here." He points to the wall of our eating room, by the door leading into the kitchen.

*Ei*! Such a man! Already, he has a place for it, when the time comes. "Then only you will use it," I say, teasing. I cannot believe that we will ever have such a thing in our house. "I will never talk to it." I really mean it.

"And, why not?" he asks, quickly, surprised and put-out that I am so hard-headed.

"I could not say words to a dumb box with only a black spout sticking out. It would be like a grown woman talking to a doll."

David laughs at my foolishness and says, "We will see when the time comes."

I am sitting on the front porch, in the afternoon shade, sewing a dress for my 'Linda and watching the wagon loads of grain going into town. I am thinking about the new sewing machine Frau Shuster has bought. Frau Shuster, robust and stout, with a man's voice and hair on her upper lip, but a gentle smile, lives down the road about two miles. I am thinking of the words she used, telling me how she got her machine: "*Ach*, Mrs. Becker, it was so easy. You should try it sometime. A machine you should have once. *Ech*! Now there would be something, with all your girls!"

When I asked her how she did it, she said, big like, "*Na*, what do you think? I just took hold of the empty wagon with my bare hands and pulled it to the granary. Then I shoveled wheat into it until it was full. When my Reinhold came home from the field at noon, I said to him flat, 'No more stubble plowing today, man. I am sick sewing my fingers to the bone. Go, take that load of wheat to town. Get me that newfangled sewing machine I saw in Meyer's store.' And, he did it. See, little Evaliz? Easy, was it not?" She laughed in her deep bass voice and chuckled like a naughty girl — only not looking like one, one bit.

But I could see it was no joke with her. No, not with Frau Shuster! She is strong enough to pull a grain wagon if she chooses. And smart enough, that if she says "scat," through her heavy lips, her Reinhold leaps like a frightened cat. I can still see her clearly. "Ho, ho, ho," she chuckled from the deep depths of her, beaming on me with her small, bright eyes folded in her fat face. "And, watch you, Evaliz Becker, some day I will get me a telephone put in the same way, even if I have to plunk three miles of telephone poles myself. Just you wait!"

"Yes, it would be easy for her," I think, and sigh, stitching ever forward on the dress I'm making. "But, not easy for poor Reinhold, he who jumps like a puppet on the end of a string."

I could not do that to David. Even if it took me forever to make a dress, and I had no fingers left. Tired, she says she is of sewing her fingers to the bone. Sewing what? A tea towel, an apron? She, who has no kith nor kin. What would she do with a houseful of children to sew for, like I have?

Still, I cannot blame her. The new machines are a thing of beauty, and a miracle to look upon. I, too, without David's knowing, have dared to go in the store to look at them, without buying. But I fled in shame, soon enough, when the clerk could see that I had no money to pay for such a fine thing. Why should I take his time looking and not buy?

Down the road toward town I hear our dogs bark furiously, and long before it arrives I know it is an automobile. I stop sewing to look at it as it goes by and follow it with my eyes, until it is past the barn and out of sight. Our dogs will get killed this time sure, I think. They are always under the wheels, barking and snapping. I hold my breath. But they are not hurt. That is a wonder, for the wheels whir-r so fast, stirring up clouds of dust. Surely, they are a sight to behold. A miracle indeed, a metal creature, made by man, to do man's bidding. Where will these wonders end? I do not know.

A wagon trundles slowly past, and by comparison it seems to be standing still. It is Ludwig Steiner, one of our people. He calls hello to me from the top of his load of lumber, nodding politely. I wave back to him.

"A fine house your Marieliz will have, eh, Ludwig?" I call.

"*Ja*, fine, fine, Evaliz. Like yours once," he shouts above the clatter of the wagon.

"Only it doesn't belong to me," I call back not knowing if he heard right. I am glad they can move out of their half sod and half stone house that is always surrounded by rattlesnakes.

Other wagons follow on their homeward way, wagons piled high with fence posts and huge rolls of barbed wire swaying on top. For days and days now, this has been going on.

The people are fencing the prairie, shutting out the wilderness, taming, wantonly, the wild buffalo grasses under the milling hoofs of their teeming cattle. They are breaking the age-old sod, turning, forever, its smiling face from the sun; breaking the sensitive spirit of the prairie flowers, sweet with wild perfume, and crushing, without mercy, the timid souls of mothering herbs; scattering the bird throng; driving the tawny coyotes out of their age-old lair, taking their sad, primitive call with them. Stilling . . . stilling the voice of the prairie. *Ach*!

It is Saturday, when the children are home from school and David is plowing in the field, that a man drives into the yard with a mud-splattered buggy pulled by a lean, moth-eaten horse. He is a peddler, selling something. But the dogs will not let him get near the door. The man jumps from his buggy bravely enough, his face holding a bold look that defies man and beast alike.

Mia and Hester stand beside me here in the kitchen doorway, but the other children are crouched by the eating room window, peering through the edge of the curtain.

"What does he want?" I call out to Leah, who is standing in the yard.

"He says he has a sewing machine for you to use."

"Tell him no. People do not use sewing machines without buying."

"Mama says no," I hear Leah say. "Mama says --" It is like saying it to the wind, or to the wall of the house. She darts this way and that way, in front of him, waving her arms, saying, "Mama says no."

It does no good with this brash fellow. He disregards the barking dogs and Leah altogether and — as if he were a favored guest come to visit — he fastens the reins, unconcernedly, onto one of the front wheels.

"Mama," Leah calls, "he says he will bring it anyway. It is all free."

Dumbfounded, I don't know what to say. A sickening heat stirs my stomach. My legs become weak. Shame burns on my face. What kind of man is he? Has he no shame? If only David were home.

And though the dogs threaten to tear him limb from limb, he pays them no heed. Even his mousy horse, already hanging its head in blessed rest, disregards the yapping dogs flitting dangerously around the legs of his master. No doubt, long ago, through many brazen calls like this, he, too, has learned the futility of concern and anxiety — even as his self-assured master has.

The dogs tire of their unnoticed barking and lie prone on the ground, growling wrath and indignation, lifting an eye to me in question and back again to this intruder.

The man moves around to the back of his buggy with agile grace, busy untying the quilt padding that holds his valued treasure. The ropes slip their knots smooth as oil under his knowing fingers. There is no haste, no uncertainty, in his manner — only cocksuredness.

My children, braving the outdoors, all stand around watching his every move, holding back and yet half expectant.

"Tell him that I do not want a free machine that is not free, at all," I say severely to Leah from the screened-in porch, where I am now standing.

But he pays no attention to her as she again darts back and forth with gesturing arms, trying to keep in front of him to be seen and heard. It is of no avail.

Once the bundle is free, he sets it on the ground, and with princely mien he swishes the quilt cover from it. *Ach!* I catch my breath, at the beauty of it. The glowing wood shines as if an orange moon is rising from its depth, as the sunlight strikes it. My, it is even prettier than Frau Shuster's machine! I can see that, even from inside the porch. The thought comes to me that she had better not see this one, or she will be unhappy with her own.

The sight of it brings a surprised "Ah!" from the lips of my children. They move in closer now, as if it is quite all right and safe now.

Wise beyond words in the art of his work, the salesman idles eloquently, dusting here and dusting there, the better for us addle-brained ones to drink in the beauty. He has us bewitched, and he knows it.

Then he gathers it in his arms and with quick, wobbling steps he comes to the house carrying the heavy machine before him. All of us, with proper regard — nay, like dunces — step aside and let him in, holding the screen door wide. Mia even runs ahead and shows him where to set it in our eating room.

Abashed, Leah looks on my face, expecting me to come to my senses and show him out of the place, like he deserves. But I am speechless with embarrassment for myself and shame for him. Brazen, shameless fool that he is! Spineless fool that I am!

And yet, if he knows all that I am thinking, he shows no sign of it. Calmly he bides his time. He takes a soft cloth from one of the drawers and shines the already too smooth top — far too smooth, and too shiny to match anything that we have in this house. Surely, nothing as good as this could ever be ours.

Then, like the man of the house, he reaches for a chair and places it before the open machine. "Madam — for you!" he bows, extending one hand. And I am too dumb to move. I cannot see, nor hear, nor think.

"Mama, he says, have you something to be sewed?" Leah says. I say, "No," shaking my head. "No, nothing."

But, Mia adds quickly for me, "Yes, Mama, you have the basted hem of 'Linda's new flour sack material dress."

*Ach!* The cat is out of the bag. The flour sacking stamps me as a nobody, and besides, I have lied in the bargain.

Without waiting, Mia runs and gets the dress and lays it on the machine. And I have to be ashamed before this man. But I need not have wasted my pride, for this man does not recognize a lie when he hears one. He makes out as if nothing has happened, and as though this wad of a dress were of the finest silk.

"Now, Madam, will you try this beautiful machine?" he asks, half bowing and looking at me as if I were a queen being ushered to her throne, though he probably notices that I have rough, work-worn hands, more like a cinder maid's and unworthy of this attention.

Suddenly, a hot fire burns on my cheeks. That he dare shame me like this, in my own house. But, still, my tongue will not move. Like dry sand it lies in my mouth. I see the broom standing by the door, with a good, sound handle. But, my hands will not obey me. Never have I been rude to a guest in my house. I cannot begin now.

Determined, I shake my head, no. And Leah declines, also, ashamed of this situation. Even Mia, though not asked, for once does not make a move.

"Look, Madam," he begins again, standing by the machine and pedaling lightly with the toe of one shoe. "See, it is easy to run. One can use it standing up." He places the hem under the needle and gives me a fine demonstration of its smooth speed. "Why, even a child can run it, see?" He holds the hem in line just with the tip of his finger, while looking about the room. Then he spies Mia. "Why, this young lady can run it! Come," he says, smiling and holding the chair. Flattered, she sits down.

"Now, Miss, just pedal with your feet. So."

But something is wrong. Her foot rhythm is out of tune with the gear, and the machine rants and halts, and rants again, like a *Geis-bock*, a goat that has been given a staggering blow between the eyes.

"No, no smoothly." It is the first time his voice is raised. "No, Miss, all the way down with the treadle and up again, not just half way. So. Up-and-down. Up-and-down." His foot guides the way.

But no matter what, as soon as his foot comes off she can't find the rhythm. The machine starts, stops, and runs backward. The needle gets tangled in its own thread. Then, crash! Crunch! Clatter!

There is such a loud noise in this still house of ours. The needle is shattered, falling piece by piece through the machine and clinking on the metal foot pedal. Mia is too startled to move. Horrified, she looks at me, afraid to look on the man's face.

There is a sickness inside of me like I never knew before. Now, we have to buy the machine, I think with horror, and my legs will hardly hold me. I have to be ashamed for all of us. Ashamed before this man who has no shame for himself! What will David say?

But the salesman says quickly, "That's quite all right, Madam. Do not feel badly." He makes fine gestures with his woman-soft hands. "See, it can easily be fixed." He places a new needle in the machine. This time, placing his open pocket watch to one side, he runs up the seam himself.

"There!" he says, pleased with himself. "Eleven seconds, by my watch. What else, Madam, could do it so fast?"

"Sure," I have to admit, "nothing could do it so fast."

"Ah, ha! You are right, Madam!" he exclaims, smacking his hands together and rubbing them. At last, he has made me talk, just as he knew I would. "Tell you what, lady," he beams with satisfaction. "This machine doesn't go out of this house, until you have received some good from it. Yes, sir! A pert little woman, such as you, with a houseful of girls should have a machine."

All my no's cannot change it. He refuses to take it with him, no matter what I say.

On the day he finally comes back, David is at home. David greets him and says, simply, "We will take it." And I must go quickly to hide my secret joy.

So, in the end, I get my sewing machine, even as Frau Shuster got hers. David took a load of wheat to town to pay for it and I feel shame, even though he took it willingly, without my loading it first.

Before autumn is gone, a crew of men comes driving out of town by horse and wagon every morning to set up slim, tall telephone poles along our roadway, going further out into the country from day to day. My little ones watch with amazement from the front porch as the men dig holes past our house.

"It won't be long now before Frau Shuster gets her phone," I think. She is so impatient.

Every night, the men return with empty wagons, singing and harmonizing songs. The melody floats on the evening breeze, and I am reminded of my childhood in *Russland* — how the village people, young and old, man, woman, and child marched back into their villages, after the hard labors of their fields. Singing is a healing balm, like sunlight and prayer. It makes the heart light, and lagging feet nimble.

On the day that the men string the wire on the cross bars, Davie comes running into the house, his eyes wide with excitement, shouting, "Mama, a man is walking up a pole like a fly!"

We hurry out of the house fast. I can hardly believe it myself. With spikes on his shoes and a leather strap about his waist, the man makes his way up the pole.

"Mama, do men do this in *Russland*?" Davie asks, pulling at my skirts, asking the question ever again. "Do they, Mama?"

When I have finished looking, I say, "*Ach*, no, child. In the old country, around our little village, there was no such thing. There were no roads even, only the wagon trails that the people made themselves."

Davie is always comparing countries. "Nor wheat headers either, huh, Mama? Nor plows with seats for men to ride on, huh, Mama?"

"No, son," I answer him simply. "No, son, only here, in America, are miracles performed for rich and poor alike." And though all these things may in time also come to Russia, this great land holds a golden opportunity for my children. I shall never cease to be thankful for the blessing that has brought us to America. Suddenly, deep pride wells inside of me, and I add, "No, son, not even coal-oil stoves, nor windmills, nor cream separators, nor dust pans, nor flour sifters did we have in the old country."

And though he is only six years old, and his favorite play acting is to go drive the various farm implements sitting here in the yard, he ponders in silence, then he says flatly, "I would not leave this country, Mama." And he goes to sit on the plow seat, his face cupped in his hands, watching the man on top of the telephone pole.

It is Saturday, and because Frau Shuster cannot wait until the telephone crew reaches her house, she comes to make me a visit. *Ach*, what a woman! Already she has smelled this new thing coming, and must get close to it. On his way to town, Herr Shuster drives into our yard to let her off.

I am taking a large *Kaffee-Kuchen* from the oven when I hear their spring buggy pull up by the screen door. She has already seen me. Quickly I put my fine, sugared bread on the kitchen table, to cool.

"Hal-loo, Evaliz Becker," she calls in her lusty voice, and it fills my clean-scrubbed house completely. "Hal-looo."

With happy steps I hurry out into the yard, wiping my hands on my clean afternoon apron. Our dogs, Brill and Rover, wag around my legs, making small dog talk, announcing their joy at our neighbor's coming.

"Good-afternoon, Frau Shuster! Herr Shuster!" I say. "Welcome to our house."

From inside the house I hear my oldest girls come hurrying from the upstairs rooms, where they have been laying out their Sunday's best. Fast, yet softly, with womanly dignity they come.

"Good-afternoon, Frau Shuster. Good-afternoon Herr Shuster." They curtsy politely, smiling their joy.

"*Guten-Tag. Guten-Tag*, young *Madels. Ock*! Soon, you look out, one gets married," Frau Shuster booms at me, and winks with the eye of a bold man.

Leah flushes red all over her face. But her, "No, Frau. No," is drowned by the woman's laughter. One must make light, with this otherwise fine neighbor. There is no other way, even if it hurts.

"*Na*, why sit there on the seat like a bumpkin? Come, get down. Get down," I say happily, while the rest of my children come running from the header-barge where they have been playing house, their faces beaming joy.

Obediently, from long years of practice, Herr Shuster turns the horse team to one side, parting the wheels wide enough so that robust Frau Shuster can back out of the buggy, fat rump first, broad legs and feet bulging in high-top shoes tangling in her heavy skirts.

I am always helpless when it comes to watching her alight. I never know how to help, and it is always best to stand aside and wait for good results. A job it is, indeed, one worth moaning and wheezing over.

But, in this one thing, tiny Herr Shuster is serene. In this matter alone he is lord and master. He sits with nary a concern, bobbing like a milk puff on his high tilted seat, while she groans and moans and the buggy springs squeak in dismay, giving to the very shocks on one side and rising to their fullest on the other, tipping the buggy at a reckless angle.

Her man-like hands grasp the dash board and seat stoutly while her exploring foot flounders desperately under her many skirts, to find the one little metal step that will help her down to the ground. In awe and silence we stand about, awaiting this well-accustomed arrival.

At last, she is down on the solid earth wheezing like a sick chicken, reaching into the buggy for her bundle of sewing. I sigh a breath of relief at her safe landing. And, sighing, even as I, the buggy eases back into shape and complete silence. But unlike a wheezing chicken who is bound to croak, Frau Shuster recovers quickly.

Paying no heed to any of us, she says short and snappy, "*Na*, be on your way, Reinhold. What you sitting there for? Go. Gid-dap." She waves him out of the yard on his way to town. "Oh! Forget me not the red thread I want," she shouts after him. Since he makes no sign, it is hard to say if he has heard. Though hear he would if he were at the very edge of town, a mile away.

Only now, she turns and smiles her broad smile on me, like her usual self. "*Ock*, men! Like my Reinhold, can be so useless..." Before she completes what she started to say, she remembers the new telephone line; the pole is right by our mailbox. As her probing eyes find the top-most peak, her fat lips quit moving, dropping her Reinhold in mid air. Spellbound, at such final reality, she stands and gazes at the poles with their finished wires shining brilliantly in the afternoon sun.

"*Na*, Evaliz," she says elated, slapping her stout thigh. "Now, we can have phones put in and talk to each other a dozen times a day, even without stepping a foot outside the door."

"*Ach*, go on! A phone is not for people like us," I say, not believing even now that it is as easy as all that.

"*Na, Kissel*, why not?" she storms, in her big voice. "In this country everything is for everybody. Just pay, and you get it. The more who take, the cheaper the price."

And I think, what kind of talk is this?

Frau Shuster is quick to sober. She says, smiling, nudging me toward the house, "Leave it. However it may be, I shall be the first to ring you, when you do put one in. Now, I want you should help me with this sewing already. *Ech*! A velvet bonnet once I am trying to make me and I cannot get it right."

"Sure, sure, I'll help," I say, holding the screen door wide.

"There isn't anyone sews like you, little Evaliz, I always say to my Reinhold." She is as sweet as sugar. But always I must marvel at her fancy ideas. Frau Shuster tries to be first in everything. *Ja* first in everything but the making. Now it is a velvet hood, like all the fashionable town women are wearing, trimmed with net rushing about the face. That is Frau Shuster for you!

"Sure," I tell her. "I will help gladly, if I know how. Now, come inside."

Even before she lays down the bundle of sewing, she sniffs the air of my kitchen. "My, my , Evaliz! Always so good you smell. What is that you bake?" she asks, following her nose and forefinger. "*Kaffee-Kuchen*!" her voice explodes. "Like from the old country! *Ech*, nothing smells better than your *Kaffee-Kuchen*,

I always say to my Reinhold." She tests the delicacy of the buttery topping with her probing finger, smacking the sweet crumbs between her lips.

"*Ja*, neighbor, *Kaffee-Kuchen*, like from the old country," I say, helping her to a piece, proud that it turned out so nicely.

"Mm-Mmm--" she smacks with satisfaction while the rich crumbs fall from her fleshy lips onto the floor.

From the corner of my eye I see Leah eyeing the broom, eager to sweep the buttery crumbs before they mar her whitescrubbed floor. I shake my head because that would not be proper before company — grease spot, or no grease spot.

Frau Shuster is too engrossed in her pleasure to notice. "Tell me," she booms, her mighty voice cloaked in sweet flattery, puffing even more crumbs through the air, "how you get the time to do all this, Evaliz? How you find time for fancies, huh?"

"There is no time," I say, lightly. "I *make* time, Frau Shuster."

I must make time indeed. Even a busy housewife does not forget how to live. So it is that I also find time to fix her velvet hood before the day is out and she goes home. She looks like an over-grown baby with the peacock blue ribbon tied crisp under her many chins. But she is proud of the cap, thanking me without end. "Only you, little Evaliz, are so clever in everything," she flatters.

"*Ach*, no thanks. No praise," I say. "I do it gladly."

Before Frau Shuster leaves Leah pipes up and says, "Mama, why do you not cut a paper pattern for yourself?"

"No, child," I say. "For me it is the fascinator or *Halstuch*, like all our church women wear. I could never allow myself to be so stylish."

"Bosh!" Frau Shuster thunders, her eyes flashing quick fire. "Why shouldn't you have a velvet bonnet? If I went to your church, I would show your old country *Frauen* something — you can bet! Here," she adds, suddenly softening. "Put mine on once. Far better you will look in one than any town woman I have seen. See?" she clucks her tongue, as she ties the bow.

I look in the mirror, and I'm surprised at what I see. Frau Shuster is pleased, too. "*Ech!*" she says, "with a cap like this the *Frauen* will not even hear the preacher. Each one will scheme how to get to you, first, to ask if you will make them one also. Wuch! What a church day that would be." She chuckles deep down and smacks her fist against the door jam, so that the mirror shudders on the wall.

I feel shame for her sinful talk. That thought would never have entered my mind. Maybe it would be better if she went to church once, and not be such a heathen, I think.

I look in the mirror again. *Ach*, I hardly know myself in something so fine, so soft. The bonnet is a bit large, but it can be fitted down. I hold a pinch here and a pinch there. Frau Shuster stands, silent, with hands akimbo on her ample hips, while I turn from side to side feeling clumsy before the mirror — yet satisfied with what I see.

Suddenly, guilt overtakes me. I am no better than Frau Shuster. Do I really dare to be so stylish? Better that I forget such foolishness. Still, a velvet hood would be something to treasure. I worry only for an instant about what our church women will say when I lay aside my Russian babushka and wear a fashionable velvet bonnet. And then I am planning how it will look, when I get the money. It must be a deep wine color, with creamy-white net rushing about the face. Sure, I can see it in my mind's eye already.

Frau Shuster is silent all this time. "Evaliz, I tell you what I do," she says, with a bright new thought. "For making me this cap, I will get the goods for yours — any color you want."

"*Ach, net!*" I protest. "*Bitte*, no. I could not think of taking from you." But with Frau Shuster there is no such thing as no. With her, it's her own way, or hell-fire. Anyone knows that.

It isn't long after this that she comes and lays the deep wine colored velvet on my table to cut. And now, I am forced into this stylishness. Who can go against Frau Shuster? Surely, not I.

I keep busy at my new and marvelous sewing machine. No longer does it take weeks to make a dress or a coat. One or two days is usually sufficient. And it is like Frau Shuster said about the velvet bonnet. Every woman within twenty miles south of town must have one. The friends come to copy my patterns, and have me sew the things in the end, though they have machines themselves. They cover me with high praise, and I can charge them nothing, though many bring me a measure of cloth, or some other gift.

The task of cutting newspaper patterns for the overly stout, the large of hip and narrow-shouldered, the gaunt and long of limb is surely head-splitting. But they trust me with their valued yard goods and I must not fail. So they keep on using me to their advantage. I do not mind it too much.

It isn't long after this, that a wily horse trader drives into the yard. Tied to the back of his wagon are several shaggy horses. One is a spindle-legged mare with foal. The man is lank and lean-faced. Foam and spittle play at his mouth corners as he plies his trade.

At first I see David shaking his head. But the man keeps on. "She will bear you a thoroughbred, a descendant of none other than Dan Patch, himself."

And though David may not really believe him, he buys the mare. It irks me that he should be taken in for so useless a horse, though

234

she must have been a fine mare long before this monger laid hands on her. Even I can see the fine strain in her. Yet, it irks me.

"She will be no good before the plow, I can tell you that. Your money could have bought a better one," I say to David, as soon as the trader has left with his menagerie.

This one thing is strictly men's business and David is easily touched. He will not be badgered. "Now, Evaliz," he says. "Sewing is for women. Horses are for men. Let that be enough."

When I would say more, he stops me by saying, "A plow horse she will never make. But a colt I hope to have, like you will not find in these parts."

I recall how good David was to buy the sewing machine and shame fills me. I say no more. Later I am good to the mare. I bring her an extra measure of corn when David is out in the field.

On the day that her foal arrives and she nearly dies, there is no one to help her, except me. I try with desperate might. When it is over I am as tired, and weak of flesh, as she. But I save it, as beautiful a colt as ever I have seen. It is golden brown with four black stockings in shoes as slim and trim as any thoroughbred must have. We have never had a colt like this one before. David will be proud of it. He has planned to call it Danny Boy, if it is a he. And Dan it is.

One afternoon not long afterwards, David has a telephone put in. Now, at last, Frau Shuster can phone me, as she has threatened to do all these weeks. Still, I will not answer it! No. I will not touch the magic thing, to be shamed by it.

A man is busy fastening the brown box onto the wall of our eating room. David had picked the place long ago. Another man is outside stringing the wire from the telephone pole into the yard and fastening it onto the house, boring a hole through the wall, sifting plaster on the floor.

To see the new contraption makes me feel all queer inside, proud and bewildered, too. Carefully I scan the road, afraid that Frau Shuster will come snooping too soon. Relief is inside of me, but it will not last. That woman is like a mouse with a piece of cheese.

When the phone is all hooked up and the man has talked to "central" in town, he asks David if he wants to try it. The light that comes into David's eyes is something to remember. He has waited so long for this thing. He has read and understood the makings of a phone, yet in the face of reality, he is hesitant and awkward. This is something strange for David. He is always so sure.

"Who shall I call, Evaliz?" he asks, excited as a boy with a new toy. I, myself, am stunned; I cannot think of a single friend. My

235

mind is blank. All I can think of is Frau Shuster, and that I do not want.

We act dumb as sheep before this man who is waiting for us to decide such a simple question. David remembers Mr. Walker, the man who loaned the money for our trip to America. "I will call him," David says. "He will be glad to hear that we are getting more and more American." He turns the crank and tells the operator and gets an answer before he is ready for it.

Although I would like to stand boldly by and see how it is done, I have to back away, ashamed before this telephone man who has to say, "No, no, Mister, not that way. This way..." He has to show David how to hold the receiver to his ear, show him what to talk into. Even then, David does it wrong. His all-knowing mind and hands for once are as slow and awkward as a babe's in its first attempt with a spoon. With a great deal of effort, though the thing is light, he tries to hold the receiver to his ear, but fails in the attempt.

*Ach*, dumb Roosians, he must think we are. In shame I flee out to the barn to hide myself. I gather eggs in my apron, finding new nests in out-of-the-way places. I come back to the house only when the men are gone.

Embarrassed, I think I will not say anything to David. I will not hurt his feelings. But I need not have worried. When I come in he is standing back admiring this new thing, saying, joyfully, "*Ech*, Evaliz! Where else, but America, could a thing like this be possible for poor people? *Wahrhaftig!* Upon my word of honor, I am glad we have come!" He rubs his hands in satisfaction. He is so proud and pleased that tears of joy fill his eyes and burn there in their stillness.

"Yes. Great are our blessings," I say and hurry about my work, a lump hurting my own throat for a thousand reasons.

As soon as the children come home from school they want to call everyone. "Mama, I'm going to call Frau Shuster!" Leah shouts with glee. "She will roar with delight when she hears!" The children laugh in wild chorus at the thought of how Frau Shuster would roar with delight.

"*Ach, net!* Not her!" I call over their loud chatter. "No, Leah."

"It's all right, Mama," she pleads. "I will take only a minute." She smiles so sweetly, I cannot refuse.

Leah grinds out the party line ring. They talk a long time. That is, Frau Shuster talks and Leah can only say, "Yes... Yes... Yes..."

Better I go outside before Frau Shuster asks to speak to me, I think. Yet, all this yes, yes, yes, intrigues me. I wait, but can make nothing of their conversation. "What does she say?" I ask, when

Leah finally hangs up. Leah is tongue-tied for a moment, and that is strange for Leah.

"Frau Shuster says she cannot call you this evening, nor tomorrow, either. She is going away," Leah says guiltily, not looking me in the eye.

"So? That is strange!" I say, not knowing what to make of it. But there is joy in it, too, for me. Going away, is she? Maybe now I can get used to the newness first.

Sure, Leah is vague with her answers. I can make nothing of them, though I try many ways. Afterwards there are secrets running among my children. Secrets, that bring on pleasing snickers whenever they look at me, or quick feet and elusive shoulders whenever I try to catch one of them and demand a straight answer. Even David is taken into the secret scheme after supper.

I expect Frau Shuster to call anyway — any minute now — from the way my family acts. I sit on needles, waiting. Yet, not really waiting, at all. I hope she never rings.

At last, it is bedtime and she still has not phoned. I must believe what Leah says is true. Frau Shuster could not wait this long.

In the morning the children are eager to be on their way to school, taking their secret with them. David is out in the barn puttering about, moving this thing and that, making a terrible racket. Davie and little Kathi are playing in and out of the sliding barn doors. I have forgotten all about the telephone.

Suddenly, a shrill, drawn-out ring shatters the silence, followed by two shorter ones. Surprised and startled, my heart nearly flies out of me. My! Such modern ways I must get used to.

Burr-r-r-rrrr. Burr. Burr.

*Ach, Gott im Himmel!* That is our ring. A long and two short. "David . . . David," I call from the door. He is nowhere in sight, and though I hear nothing at first, the noise far back in the barn starts up again.

BURR-R-RR-R-R-RR-R-RRRR. BURRRR. BURRRR. The shrillness becomes more persistent, impatient, angry. It gives me no peace in its madness. My head is full of it. It is breaking my ears. My whole body is heavy with the noise.

I must answer it! But my feet will not obey. They seem frozen to the floor. Surely, everyone hearing the ring must know I am standing here — dumb as an ox — not answering it. Everywhere, along the party line, receivers must be clicking off waiting for Evaliz Becker to answer. Probably everyone is saying: "*Na,* can she still be out in the separator house washing the separator at this time of the morning?" Now, it's ashamed I must be even before my friends who are miles away.

A hotness is on my face, burning my ears. The palms of my hands grow cold and moist. Again and again the brown box calls its shrill voice through the house. Whoever is turning the crank is making her feeling known, in harsh plain words. Both Brill and Rover, lying on the cement step by the screen door, get up, at last, and walk away, eyeing me with disgust. I must answer it. My hand shakes as I take the receiver from the hook. Now, at last, I know how David felt. I cannot find my ear with it. Then, the thing in my hand starts to speak:

"HALLOO... HALLOOO-O..." It is Frau Shuster. Her mighty voice rumbles in its black walls and vibrates my fingers until I have to grasp it tighter to keep it from slipping out of my hand.

"HAL-LOOOO. Evaliz? Is that you?" She will not give up. "Is that you, Evaliz Becker? *Na, sacre!* Say something!"

*Grosser Gott im Himmel.* I have never known such strangeness. My name vibrates in my arm, even! I cannot help it. I am foolish, but I cannot make conversation with Frau Shuster who is now a black metal spout on my wall.

"Say something," she yells. "Say something!"

No matter what, my tongue will not move. My lips are of stone. Ashamed, I flee my house. I leave the thing dangling on its cord, shouting my name in the booming voice of Frau Shuster.

I stay out of the house a long time. I keep myself busy cleaning the chicken house that needs cleaning anyhow.

# CHAPTER 18

# *Love Weeps*

When the goldenrods are yellow, Andreas receives a long-awaited letter in our mailbox. The letter is from his sweetheart, Betta, who lives in Warsaw. Warsaw, according to what David reads in the papers, is now under military occupation.

I cannot account for the letter's safe arrival, nor how it made the long and hazardous journey. But here it is, worn and limp-cornered and the address faded almost beyond reading. Holding it in the strongest light, David cannot make out its European postmark. My, but Andreas will be pleased to hear.

"Go, quickly, phone the Haldeman's and say Andreas' letter has come," I say to David. He does it immediately.

After dark, when the evening work is done, we hear him coming along the visiting trail across our pastures. Andreas is playing his violin, glad, as if the gates of heaven had opened to him. His melodies wing their way before him, dancing on the evening breeze.

Music to him is like bread and wine, and meat, and love, all in one. Once, when I asked him why he plays always under the open sky, he answered simply, with a touch of impulse, "Music is not meant to be shut in the confines of unfeeling walls. Music has wings — even as the dove, Frau Becker."

Strange, that I have not thought of it before... "even as a dove"....

Then, he is here, almost before we know it, eager to take his letter.

Tonight, he sits by our table a long, long time. Longer than on any other night. I think he will never move. Sitting. Sitting, as if he were made of stone, holding the precious paper before unseeing eyes. As he sits there, time has found him, has stamped him, leaving her ravishing marks of weariness upon him. He seems hunched and far older than his years. And seeing him so, a bitterness beyond words fills me.

"Curse all wars!" I say almost out loud. For once I am not ashamed of swearing. Out of evil lust comes fighting and wars among men, consuming good people with the bad, the wheat with the tare as the Bible says.

David stirs, restless, with his reading here by the kitchen light. Our children sit quietly, some on the floor, looking frightened and questioning one another. Soon, they will ask me, "What is the matter?" And I sift, without seeing, the flour for tomorrow's baking. *Ach, Gott,* tonight there is no life or meaning in this house of ours!

Then, with a sudden harshness, Andreas rises from his chair and stalks out of the house, looking neither this way nor that, forgetting to smile on us. This is not like Andreas who is always so fine.

David's voice is full of feeling. "It is my guess, the war will not permit her passage," he says, looking up from his newspaper.

A sadness clutches my heart and hurts, and hurts. Would that we could mend his broken heart. Would that his Gethsemane would end! "God, grant him his Betta," I pray.

Andreas goes to sit outside in his accustomed place leaning weary, against the house, looking vacantly into the autumn night sky, to where the high heavens are glittering with silver stars that beckon him in vain. For once, I will not let the children follow him outside.

He sits silent, alone with his thoughts, his violin mute across his lap.

"Mama, will he play tonight?" Leah whispers, scarcely loud enough to be heard. All the doors and windows are open.

"Maybe, when he rests awhile," I answer.

All the other children are full of questions.

"S-sh now, let him not hear," I warn.

But Leah will not be quiet. "*Ach!*" she says, louder this time. "Maybe he will never play again. That would be an awful thing."

240

There is alarm in Leah's eyes. "Maybe she is dead, Mama!" With these words she spreads panic among the others.

"S-sh!" I say, and quickly rattle the large flour tin to drown out the chatter that would give away our dismal thoughts to Andreas.

Maria, so tender-hearted for her seven years, sits silent. Tears well in her soft eyes and glisten there, in the flickering lamplight winking, winking in her brimming eyes like a distant star, and I must look away, must busy myself with my bread mixing.

"*Ach*, s-sh," I say. "How could that be? Her handwriting is on the letter. Quiet now, so that he will not hear." The thought that her hand-writing was on her letter gives me hope.

I stir the yeast into the soft batter and think back, when other letters came more often, times, when Betta's letters seemed to irk him lightly with her seemingly impatient waiting. Those times, there was silent pain in his blue eyes. And he played flippant pieces, light and airy... scolding her... scolding the stars... scolding his impatient heart... scolding the slowness of his saving! His nimble fingers flitted and danced. His head bobbed, with his left shoulder holding the chirping, bickering violin in lively sway, the bow leaping in rapid strides over the taut strings, like silver beams leaping in the moonlight. Yes, he was scolding her, and entreating her, also, for her wavering trust in him. His words were simple:

> *Du, du, lieg'st mir im Herzen*
> *Du, du, lieg'st mir im Sinn*
> *Du, du, mach'st mir viel Schmerzen*
> *Weis't nicht wie qut ich dir bin.*

Then, his chiding done, his pardon given, he comes easily back to his fervent yearning, as must always be his way. His fingers quiver in all gentleness. And, as if by magic, the jerking, jarring bow loses its harshness and begins caressing the strings once more. His bleeding heart pours forth in Schubert's "*Ständchen*."

> *Leisse flehen meine Lieder*
> *Durch die Nacht zu Dir.*
>
> *Lass auch Dir die Brust*
> *bewegen----*
> *Fürchte Holde nicht.*
>
> *Softly my songs fly*
> *Through the night to you.*
>
> *Let your heart be*
> *Moved by them--*
> *Darling, be not afraid.*

"*Ach!*" I sigh deeply.

I think all this while I go about getting my bread dough ready, with my family around me. Andreas sits outside gazing into the lonely night. At last, as if he has read our thoughts, he lifts his violin and the music flows forth, soft and sweet, like breaking one's heart. He is playing Liszt's "*Liebestraum*" with soul-stirring tenderness. Surely, his heart must long for her, even as parched earth must yearn for life-giving rain.

Then, when the wild geese and ducks are winging south, their wings strumming in the chill fall breeze, and the frostblackened sunflowers bow their heads, quaking with their fear of grey winter winds, men speak of the possibility of world war.

Conditions in Europe have worsened. War is raging with ever increasing hate, consuming peoples of all nations. Russia, Serbia, France, Belgium, and England are already involved on one side, and Germany and Austria-Hungary are on the other. The big question is: Will it draw America into the frightful slaughter? Men, everywhere, are speculating as to its outcome. Rumors have it that America is divided in thought. Some say England will be to blame if we enter. Others swear that it is Germany and her threat of submarine warfare that will pull us in.

David pours over the happenings with great concern, clinging to his hopes that the United States can and will stay out, as President Wilson has promised.

When men are gathered in our house, the talk always goes to war. It will not lay its ugly head. Some men with quiet knowledge predict that America cannot stay out, that she cannot remain neutral for long, especially since her ships are carrying cargo to Germany and neutral countries round about, which Britain is even now seizing as contraband of war. It is the contention of most, that a leopard cannot change its spots. "Britain has ever ruled the seas with an iron hand. She will not break her strangling blockade on the German Reich. She will first starve her out."

"And what of the U-boats? Will Germany always heed the warning to keep them out? I think not!" Their words rise to a fevered pitch.

"If America insists on shipping to foe and neutral alike, how then can we stay unmolested? How then stay out of war?"

"Our president will demand neutral rights for our waterways," David answers them, in the argument.

But, they shout him down. "Bah! Neutral rights! Sink one ship by mistake, or even with wilful might, and where are your neutral rights?"

Fierce, indeed, are the words of those who visit in our house. It makes chills like ice run through my veins. I must make myself busy in my kitchen so that I do not hear. But, I do hear. How can one not hear?

A loud voice shouts, "They, the whole tribe, made this war. Let them cut their own throats. I will not send my son!"

"Nor I," shouts a dark-skinned Bohemian, long in this country. He squints his black eyes to glinting fire, and strikes his chest. "Me, I fled Old World strife to be rid of it forever!"

"Nor I, by damn!" shouts yet another, springing to his feet. He is an American, born in this country, who lives in an adjoining county. He strikes his fist on the table, causing the match sticks to leap from the smoking dish. This man has a houseful of girls and only one son. The son is old enough for the service. There is a flash of hatred in the man's wind-seared eyes, his flaring nostrils are ringed in white.

"Those damned Germans! Those damned Germans! They started this!" he swears, pacing the floor, looking not at all like the good man he is, but a madman, shaking his hard fist before the faces of all. His loud cursing makes the house ring. He stops before David, clenching his fist white.

"Wait, friend," David says, holding up his hand. "You forget, it all started with Serbia and Austria over the murder of Arch-Duke Francis Ferdinand."

"Yeah, well what about the damned Germans? They are in it, aren't they?"

*Ach!* The shame of it makes me sick in my stomach. That this should happen in my own house, here, where there have never been any unkind words among our guests before.

It is then that I notice my little three-year-old Kathi looking round-eyed from the stairway door, listening and watching the terrible goings-on.

I enter the room silently where the men are sitting and I bring her out to the kitchen. "*Liebchen*, go outside and play in the wagon shed," I say to her. "Here, Mama gives you a piece of *Kaffee-Kuchen*," I add quickly, bribing her away from the door where she is again listening. Gently, yet firmly, I push her on her way. "Run you, now, and climb up on the wagon seat and drive to *Lauterbach* and back." I make my voice light for my child's sake. But there is no lightness in my heart.

When I start cutting the coffee bread to set before the men my hands tremble so, I drop the butcher knife. A terrible thought crosses my mind. I had better hide it before someone runs amuck and kills. But I do not. I cut the bread all soft and sweet with buttery crumbs, my heart racing wildly. When the bread is piled high on the platter I take the large porcelain coffee pot also, and place it on the table before the men.

David has stayed calm through it all. "Now, friend," he says, rising and taking the unhappy man gently by the arm. "Come sit. Just sit. Our president will keep us out of the war, as I said before. Evaliz, pour the coffee."

Although the broken man calms down and does as David bids, it sets a new spark. Incensed at David's words the bolder ones shout him down. They rise up with hostile manners and shake their fingers in his face. "Like, hell-fire, the president will keep us out."

"Are you completely daft? If those filthy Germans lay one hand on one American ship, they deserve the brimstones of hell. And, by Jehosaphat, they'll get it!"

*Ach!* Their words become bitter. Bitter against David. Against our president. Against America, even! Ashamed I am, that it should happen in my house.

From here on out, I think to myself, things will not be good for those of us who speak German. A rising war-hate, and spite, for all Germans everywhere, is mounting day by day.

Nor are my fears ungrounded. When the long winter has spent itself and it is May again, David brings disturbing news from town. "A German submarine has sunk the British passenger liner, Lusitania. It had nearly twelve hundred persons aboard. One hundred and fourteen were Americans. All have drowned at sea, Evaliz," David says, letting himself down on a chair, his eyes moist. "I would not have believed it. But things are going from bad to worse," he adds, defeated.

A weakness comes over me at his words and I, too, must sit down, trembling all over.

"Now, what?" I ask, thinking to myself that feelings will run to a new high.

David can only sit and shake his head. "The sinking of the Lusitania will seriously impair our neutrality," he says, no longer sure that America can stay out of the war.

After this, when people sit in our house and talk of new threats of war, I feel a great sadness for those who have sons old enough for the service. Especially do I feel for Hanno Von Waldschmidt, a German from *Deutschland*, who sits shame-faced and hunched-shouldered, his eyes to the floor, rubbing his work-worn hands — unaware of their rasping sound.

Now here is a good American citizen, I think, who is willing in quiet obedience, if necessary, to send his three sons. But you don't see him stand up and shout, "What about me? Sons of mine would spill the blood of brother, cousin, and uncle."

244

And though I have compassion on some who sit in on the argument, I feel hatred for those whose only aim is to grow rich on war prices. They are the loud mouthed who show their true feelings by shouting, "Let'em fight! While they do we'll get rich on the spoils. It is war that makes wheat and corn prices go up... and steers, and hogs. Let those who have no business over there stay off the high seas."

I see their blazing eyes and I know they are carnal. "Lord, forgive them. They have no compassion on the suffering masses," I breathe, leaving the room and setting the coffee pot on the stove.

Deep as the hurt is, there is still one that goes deeper: it is knowing that my children will have to suffer even greater torment, the brunt of hostility against those of German descent.

To our great farming West comes another labor saving device, the gasoline tractor. Huge and massive, churning the earth with ease and canter, exposing it with speed never known before, they are a wonder to behold.

We are too poor to own a tractor, but in the great fields where they are being used the new loam rolls forth in magic strands of six, eight, or twelve. The tractors plow up more land in four hours than a man with six horses can do from morning to night, even though sweat and foam should stand out on the flanks of the stout horses. Will wonders never cease in America?

Every day now, one can hear the heavy pulsing of tractors far out on the plains, the wind carrying their busy song of progress. These iron steeds are the thing which eager farmers everywhere are buying with hard-earned crop money. Sure, the excitement of it runs like a fever among enraptured men — poor and rich alike.

Even on still nights when the white moon rides the wide open sky, flooding the stubble-land with mellow light, one can feel their heavy pulsing in the throat veins, drumming... drumming, deep sleep across one's brow. Even the night now is used to rout out the old call of the prairie. Never again will it find its wild, lilting song, anywhere...

I lie awake on my pillow and gaze at the moonbeams playing on the window screen. And it pains me that childhood's free laughter should be still, even in virgin soil. But that is as it should be, I say to myself, manhood ever comes after childhood. When it comes, it brushes all childishness aside with grave and somber strides.

The tractors drone on and on, humming a half tune in the far night. I can almost make out the music in my half sleep. A breeze stirs the drying sunflower stalks behind the house, rustling them

245

like tiny jingling bells. The soothing night wind lifts and blows the melody of a beloved hymn softly across my heart, and over my soul these words go lightly flying, "ponder anew what the Almighty can do, if with his love he befriend thee..."

David stirs. "I still prefer draft horses," he says from his moon-sprayed pillow, thinking thoughts of his own. "Evaliz, I could not bear to exchange the gentle understanding of a horse for the unresponsive touch of cold, hard steel, good and strong as it may be."

"Yes, I know," I say, understanding how he feels.

"Your brother Friederich likes feather-hooved Clydesdales. I would choose dappled Percherons, if I had the money he..." Sleepy, his words trail on into silence. Soon sleep comes to him in measured breath.

*Ach*, sure, Friederich likes Clydesdales, I say to myself. But like as not, he will get a tractor, or two. Friederich is like that.

In the end, David does not get his dappled grey Percherons, as he dreams he would. There are too many other things needed: a new wagon, another team of work horses, better farm machinery to work our increased acreage. We now have three girls old enough to handle work teams. Many other things are needed, too. But a bull calf of high breeding is a must with David, even though our share of the crop is nearly gone. Still, David is tormented with the thought of a new spring buggy to go with our fleet pacers. Danny Boy is grown now and has a fleet partner, Mike.

One day David says he will make spokes for the old wheels and tighten the iron rims in his blacksmith shop, assuring me that they will do just as well, but the next day he decides to buy a new buggy; he is eager and ready to go to town and order one. Then, he changes his mind again, satisfied, this time, in his work at making and reshaping new spokes. Sure, in this life's work, farming, common sense must be adhered to — first, last, and always.

On the day that our neighbor Haldeman, for whom Andreas works, gets one of these massive tractors, David and I drive out with one of our old work teams to see it. I must marvel at the sheer strength these iron beasts possess. It comes around the field with all the speed and clatter of a demon, turning great swaths of earth behind it, coming closer, purring ever louder, getting bigger as it comes. Andreas stands on the vibrating platform, proud as a peacock, dust blowing over him in a yellow mist.

When it comes abreast, Andreas smiles on us, his teeth gleaming like a white light in his dust-covered face. He salutes us with a pert hello, as befits a man who has mastered great things. And yet, he doesn't quite know how to act, cocky as a boy, or stately like a man. Now which? And Mr. Haldeman, standing on a plank across the plows, his gauntlet-gloved hands resting very importantly on the quavering levers, makes it no better.

Skittish, our old horses will not go near it, rearing in their harness, straining at their bits. They are afraid of this smoke snorting monster born from the minds of men. David must get out of the wagon and soothe them by standing in front of them, his hands on the check reins.

Mr. Haldeman does not stop work right away. He calls to us that he will demonstrate for us first, to show us what this thing can do.

"*Ja, ja,* go right ahead," David shouts. "We watch from here."

"Look, David!" I say, marveling, when it passes us by. "It not only pulls plows four times the size of ours but a sectional harrow, as well, leaving the ground ready for sowing."

Together we watch it go by, big-eyed as children. And David must clack his tongue at the sheer beauty of this performance. "Twenty horses haven't the strength of this iron machine, Evaliz," he tells me.

"Twenty horses!" Sure, I cannot know what wonders will come next.

Driving past our own field on our way home I think back on the year when Leah walked behind the harrow, and it seems like a dark dream to me, so far behind these new times. Yet, times have not changed for everyone. This year she must do it again, and this year we have one third more land to work. Our landlord has bought more land three miles away for David to work and plant to wheat.

"How much land does he think you and three little girls can farm?" I ask, angrily, since the deal has been made without our knowing. We received the letter in the mail, saying David should take over. "Does he think I can kill my children working his land? They will never get any schooling because of it!"

"He is the landlord, Evaliz," David answers, simply, without rancor. "He has the say-so to what amount of land he should own. You cannot blame him. These are great wheat years."

David is right, I know. A landlord is still a landlord. One cannot forget that. But I say stoutly, thinking also about my children, "Our girls will not miss school again this year because of field work."

"Tomorrow, Evaliz, I will go and get me a farm hand. No more school will they miss, I promise you that."

But our girls, Leah, Mia, and even Hester work doubly hard for all of David's promises, for there is no help to be found, except for a tender town youth who can neither understand the work, nor handle the horses to be of any help. He goes back to town before he has mastered the task. It grieves me deeply that the girls must miss the opening of school again.

David spends much time looking for someone to help with fall planting and husking corn. But, everywhere, among farm people the answer is no. Even among my brothers, Friederich and Wilhelm.

"Sorry, David," Wilhelm says, "I cannot spare one or the other of my boys. I need them. Even the girls are working in the field now."

"I know, I know," David says, "only asking I am."

"Go to Friederich; he will lend you one lad out of his many," Wilhelm assures him.

Surely out of six boys maybe the least of them could be spared. Here, indeed, is where we should have asked first, even though it is such a long trip out and it will not wait until Sunday. With hopes high, we drive the long lane into his fine yard, for with Friederich it has gone well. We survey with awe his nearby fields lying in apple-pie order. We see off in the distance six puffs of dust rising into the pale blue autumn sky, where his sons labor in the field.

Friederich comes out of his blacksmith shop, beaming with love and greetings. Gredel and the girls prepare us a sumptuous meal. But Friederich's answer is, "No, David, I need all my boys. We are planting a thousand acres into wheat now that I have bought a new farm for Georg, my eldest. It will take tractors and horses and sons, I can tell you, to complete the task." He shakes his head dolefully, having a bit of trouble looking us straight in the eye. "Too, I have three hundred and fifty acres of corn to husk," he adds. "But, if we finish the husking before you, I will send you help. Believe that."

"Sure, sure." We have Friederich's promise. Nothing more.

It is no use. David finds no one, just another promise. This one from our neighbor, Haldeman. He will send us Andreas as soon as his corn is husked, he says.

"But, that will not be until the end of November," I complain, thinking only of our girls and their schooling, yet knowing full well that it cannot be helped, and that it is still a good offer. One cannot blame people for keeping their help, I tell myself; we would hang onto them, too, if we had them. I resign myself to the matter. What is, has to be.

"You girls will have to help your *Baba*. School will have to come a little later this year. But only this year remember," I promise.

"You always promise," Leah says, streaking out of the room, to cry.

248

"Yeah, if Haldeman were not so selfish, he would give us back Andreas." Mia's voice is full of anger. I am shocked at her outspokenness before her parents.

"Mia!" David calls. "Quiet, this very minute."

Who can blame David for his touchiness, I think; these worries have weighed him low.

"Well, it is true, is it not?" Mia speaks up again though it would be safer to tread on snakes, when David gets angry. "He took Andreas from under our noses only to give us promises now. We cannot always be dumbbells in school."

"Mia! Consider you tongue!" David says sternly, reaching for the strap.

I stop him. A whipping she should have sure. But maybe an explanation is better.

"Now Mia, the school we cannot help," I say. "But Andreas' place is with Herr Haldeman who can pay him well, the sooner to send for his Betta. You know that."

"Yes, I know," she sulks.

"It would be far better to do without any help, than to do that to Andreas. If he knew, he would come to us in a minute. Right?"

"Yes, Mama. I mean no, Mama."

"Then say you are sorry to *Baba*, and off to bed with you. Don't forget your prayers."

So, in the end, David and the girls are in the field from morning till night, working fourteen horses, plowing, harrowing, disking, and drilling wheat. This time David who has great compassion for our girls has built a low two-wheeled cart with a seat for Leah to ride on behind the harrow. He worked on it late at night in his blacksmith shop.

I stop my house work long enough to look out of the window and see my children working in the field, slicing away furrow after furrow, a cloud of stifling dust following them wherever they go. The sight weighs heavily on my heart. David has left them here, on the home fields, while he has gone out to work the new land, three miles distant.

Then, with the wheat sowing done, Mia and Hester go to school, missing all of September. But Leah must yet stay to help with the corn-husking. Haldeman has kept his word and has sent us Andreas. With three wagons now, instead of two, they go out day after day. Leah takes her place, husking two rows while David and Andreas take four rows each. When their wagons fill up, they come to the yard to unload, adding to our ever-growing pile.

On quiet days one can hear the steady bang, bang of fat corn ears hitting the bang boards, as all three husk with persistent speed, working against time. The season is changing fast. The November winds are getting cold, and still they are deep within the field. The end of harvest is nowhere in sight. Already they have husked two thousand bushel. Surely, one who has not seen cannot imagine the enormity of this year's crop. As one drives through the countryside it is nothing to see, at each farm, anywhere from two thousand to ten thousand bushel of husked corn, either in bins or heaped on the bare ground in long stacks with no shelter around it whatsoever. This year no one has to pick cow chips, nor buy coal for that matter; there will be enough corncobs to keep the whole country warm all winter, and then some.

This winter, too, the cattle can graze in the husked-out corn fields, like never before. For once David is beside himself with joy.

"My, my, Evaliz!" he says. "What a year for cattle and hog raising!"

"Better you hurry," I remind him, happy, too, "before the snow flies and the cows have to do the husking and grow too fat."

David laughs. "That kind of fat cow I would like to see once."

Then, early one morning, after cold night rain has frozen a sheet of ice over the bowing corn stalks and ears in the field, and the ground is glazed with thin, crackling ice and I think that Leah's hands will surely freeze, my brothers, Friederich and Wilhelm, come driving into the yard. Each has come in his own wagon, ready to help. I cannot hold back the tears of gladness. Unashamed, and without sound, I let them roll down my cheeks.

"Hello, Brothers!" I call, running out into the yard to greet them, the cold, damp wind whipping my skirts about me.

"Hello, Evaliz! What field are they working in?" they call in glad greeting at the sight of me.

"Down there," I point to the south field and wave them on. "Down there. Go." My voice is out of control for the gladness that is in me. At last, salvation has come to Leah.

I hurry to dress another chicken to add to the noonday meal: baked chicken with onion and browned potatoes, *süsses* kraut, pickled beets, rice pudding, and apple pies.

Tomorrow Leah can go back to school, thanks to my brothers!

But, it is too late. Leah refuses to go back willingly after a week or so. "I won't go to be shamed by my classmates for not knowing my lessons," she sobs. Leah has grown over-sensitive.

"*Na*, what are you saying?" I question, both concerned and surprised. "You can go to school, Child. No more staying home. Think of it!"

Leah will not be comforted.

"Besides, Mama, they tease me for being a dumb German. They give me no peace."

250

"Leah! How can they?"

"No, Mama," she insists, "hear me out. The way they act, one would think I was to blame for Germany making this war."

A sickness goes through me. What I feared before has come true. My children are suffering because they are German. "Sure, you cannot help that! Germany, and we people are something else again. We make no wars," I force myself to set her straight. "You tell them we are good citizens of this country. And that Germany has nothing to do with us. We fled Russia because of Bolshevik revolution."

"No, Mama!" she says firmly for once, standing up to me. "I will not go again."

And, suddenly, my whole world falls apart. "Leah! Do not talk so! I have dreamed so long for your great learning. *Bitte*, do not throw it away now! Think, Child, would you be like me?" Gently, I take her tear-wet fingers from her face. "Leah," I plead, "this will soon blow over. Your lessons will come easier after this."

Half sad, she smiles on me, meaning not to hurt me but, saying like a woman grown, "If I am breaking your dream, Mama, I am truly sorry. I have loved learning. But, this, unjust humilation, I cannot stand!" She sobs deep down inside of her, the spasms racking her whole body. She says more: "They do all kinds of mean things to us. They spit in our faces. They pull our braids. They stick out their feet to trip us, calling us clumsy Huns, and the teachers do not seem to notice."

"*Ach, Liebchen*, do not cry like this," I soothe, wiping away her tears with my apron. I will not let myself believe that this could happen in my America, yet I feel an unknown anger, too, rising within me.

"Sure, the teachers would not let them mistreat you if they knew." I scold, angry, that Leah should throw away her chance for knowledge. But it does no good with Leah.

*Ach!* What now? What of my long-awaited dream? Bewildered, I grope for an answer. At last, anger tightens the walls of my heart, leaving me no peace.

Nights I lie awake scheming how to get Leah back to school, if only to finish out the last part of the term. I make her two new dresses of bright plaid gingham, with deep pleats and large pearl buttons, just as she wants them. And, out of my egg money I scrape together enough to buy the classics book she needs. And though I finally persuade her to go from December to closing day, she does not pass the grade. And in September, at the beginning of a new term, she will not go at all — to be shamed as the oldest girl in her class.

This, then, is the end of learning for my oldest one! What will it be for my others? Surely, the first part of my dream lies in ashes, at my feet. My spirit broken for the first time, I flee from the house, out into our autumn fields, to think, to lose the pain that is breaking the walls of my heart. I lift my eyes up to the skies, up there where cloud-castles are piled too high for me to reach. My stumbling feet worry the ground beneath me, and searing winds sting my uplifted face with bitter gall. There is great need within me to pray. "Oh God, this is not the way I have dreamed it. I would have knowledge for my children, unhindred by petty scorn...."

Grievously, the two powers within me, right and wrong, battle to overcome each other while I try to find the answer. And though I know that these are but childish taunts that are keeping Leah from school — and should be forgiven as such — I still cannot fight down the bitterness. For even children speak unwitting words that leave indelible marks. Idle words, yet strong enough to change the natural course of Leah's life, as truly as raging flood waters change the age-old beds of idling rivers.

All about me is the whisper of the grasses. The unending winds rasp and rattle the drying seed pods of the Kansas sunflowers, saying hist-t and hist-t to everything else but to itself, singing a flute song along the full hem of my fluttering skirts. And in their strumming, I recall one other time, in Russia, so long ago, when I had to flee to the wild steppes to find the answer to my young torment. I did not fear bold Cossacks, not fierce marauding Tartar bands, nor any other thing.

Oftentimes, if one listens to the sighing winds stirring through wild growth, one can find the answer to many things. I have known this from childhood. Soothing are the whispering grasses, for they are likened unto the voice of God. This I learned sitting at the feet of my father. "Listen, Child! Listen, with the ears of your heart."

"*Ach*, yes, I'm listening."

The grasses sway on, and on. "It may be that your dreams are far too big, Evaliz," they seem to be saying. "Wisdom ever follows tribulations, have you forgotten that? Learning does not end with the closing of a school book. It is here and now that life begins... begins... begins..."

At last, the sighing grasses bring me to my senses.

*Ach!* What am I doing? Where is my understanding? Where is my pride? My thanksgiving? Mine is a family rooted deep in this land, without book learning to be sure, yet sound with understanding. A calm comes over me and deep wisdom stands before my eyes. Sure, we are a people who need not be ashamed. We are by our own will true Americans! Our lives will be as we make them.

On glad feet I return to our house.

"Mia shall be the first to graduate from school," I announce calmly to my family, who have been wondering where I have been. "Today I have renewed my pledge that from Mia on all shall go through school, even down to the littlest one."

The children stand and look at me, as if they cannot make out what has gotten into me.

"Hurry now, Leah," I say, "go to the cellar and get the yeast starter. I will set bread tonight. Tomorrow's fine dinner will be *berok* and *Steppe Tea*. And you, Leah will help me. You will learn how to cook."

# CHAPTER 19

# *World War I*

T his is a year of great trial for everyone. President Wilson has not been able to keep the United States out of war. David's hopes that he could have gone to naught.

Besides, all crops are still-born in the tortured earth, except for the Russian-thistle, and the tall spiked fox-tail that are ripening before their time. The pasturelands lie seared and brown under the broiling sun, showing false greenness only in the prickly cactus, growing and spreading their thorny mats.

Day by day, cyclone clouds ride the murky, wind-torn skies, looking for new gains to plunder. Hogs swelter in their hard-packed pens, grateful for a fresh bed of mud to wallow in. And over on the railway fleet troop trains go hissing by, trailing smoke through our tree-filled town, and out again, fading into the eastern sun-scorched horizon; followed by still others, with others yet to come.

This year our nation is harvesting her noblest sons. Only the prime are good enough to swell her bumper war crop! *Ach*, it leaves a deep hurt within me to see it so. Already the young men from our vicinity, ranging from ages twenty-one to thirty, have registered for the service. The local members of the Kansas National Guard have been called to headquarters at Lawrence and Junction City.

But, regardless of how mothers and fathers feel about giving up their sons, the troop trains passing through our town are filled with happy youths leaning smiling from open windows, shouting hello and goodbye to all strangers alike, joking, laughing, singing songs of going overseas — calling themselves Yanks.

I cannot understand their eagerness and willingness to go. It was not so in Russia! How well I remember those who maimed themselves, in limb and eye, to avoid compulsory conscription.

In our weed-choked fields, where almost no tame blade grew that was planted, my family is busy gathering a make-shift fodder, the green, still immature thistle. In its tender stage the thistle is not a mean fodder and the cattle eat it willingly. But even these are ripening into a multitude of stickers before their time. And before my family can gather enough to carry our cattle through the winter they must suffer from the prickly thorns.

David takes the torture of reaping the thistles in silence, a grim look on his wind-burned face. But the children come into the house between loads, crying, showing me their scratched and blood-streaked arms and legs.

Hester's complaints are pitiful. "Mama, I cannot stand it in the hayrack tramping them down. The thistles stick me every step I take, every move I make. Not once but a thousand times I sink down into the thorny mass, and a thousand times I must pull myself out again with the help of the pitchfork, only to sink again. Oh, Mama, my hands," she sobs.

"Please do not cry," I beg, trying to take the deep stickers out of her hands. "I will go to town and buy you girls rawhide gloves and stout coveralls. Then it will be easy, you will see." I smile, but only with my lips. Obedient, they return to the field again, content that I will make the task better.

But the hurt goes with me while I buy the heavier clothing. I know they will not help much. David wears coveralls and still the work is almost unbearable.

The first day they wear their new coveralls — looking like the boys we should have had — they work without complaining. But after the newness wears off they come crying again.

The thistles are maturing fast in this dry weather. The color is a deeper red, the barbs sharper than ever. It isn't any wonder that the mouths of cattle, tough as they are, will bleed on winter forage such as this. Yet, it is far better than old straw left over from the year before.

Sick at heart, David views his dour fields and says, "To rid this plague from the land, I must deal with fire and deep plowing or next year will be no better."

And viewing the lands with him, I must admit that it looks hopeless. No wonder the thistle has become a swear word on the lips of the people. "Roosian thistles. Those damn Roosian thistles!" It is fast becoming the name we Germans are known by. Some Americans look down on us with scorn because of them. They swear loud and long as they gather and stump down the thorny fodder in their hayracks.

"You damn Roosians brought this plague to America," says a man from down on the creek bottom, poking his finger at David. "It is you who ought to eat them, rather than our cattle."

David says nothing. He knows it would only lead to strife. Surely, some men mince no words, placing the blame on our people.

It is true, Russian thistles have thrived in Kansas long before this. But in this year of total crop failure, world strife, and racial discrimination, the native farmers have grown angry and blame our people for it. They are aware, of course, that long ago the Mennonites from the Ukraine — as well as our early Russian-Germans from the Don and Volga steppes — brought to America the first sacks of the hard winter wheats which also contained the seed of the thistle.

And so the farmers complain, "Bah! What else but thistles can this country expect when they let all them foreigners in here. If I had my way, I'd send them all back. Or, better yet, give them to the damn Germans over there to fight their battles. They claim to be Germans, and not Roosians."

Oh, how it pains me to hear it said of us. All we are trying to do is to be good citizens. Sometimes I think there is no way to prove it.

Indeed, these are the times when thorns pierce the hearts of men. No one, it seems, is exempt. Today a letter bearing a strange handwriting, addressed to Andreas, arrives in our mailbox. Soon, if I am not mistaken, he, too, will suffer. I have learned to recognize Betta's neat handwriting. But this is not it.

I glance at the clock and see that it is high noon and I say to Leah, "The Haldeman's are in from the field. Go, phone Andreas. But do not tell him it is a strange letter," I warn.

Andreas has not seen fit to change his address from ours. "It would only make for confusion," he said from the beginning, not knowing how long he would stay at the Haldeman's. So the address has always remained, bringing all of Betta's letters here, and now, this strange one. I dread the evening when Andreas will come to read it, for I fear a dreadful thing has happened. Then, all of a sudden, he is here, standing dark and mute on our doorstep.

"Oh, it is you, Andreas," I say surprised, washing the evening dishes. "We did not hear you come as always."

"I did not play," he says, looking down at his violin until the house echoes with silence waiting for him to speak further.

*Ach, Gott,* I think he has guessed the awfulness of it. But, I say quickly, "Your letter is in the eating room on the shelf by the clock. Go, sit by the lamplight. The children studying their catechism will not disturb you."

I busy myself washing dishes so that I cannot think while he reads, and Leah and Mia must hustle to keep up with me, wiping and putting the dishes in the cupboard. David is still out in the barn working by lantern light. It isn't long before Hester slips silently from the other room.

"Mama, what is wrong with Andreas?" she asks in a low whisper. "He stares glassy-eyed at the floor."

I wipe my hands quickly to go and see. He sits lifeless, his arms hanging by his side, the letter fallen to the floor.

"Mama, is he dead?" the children cry, crowding around us.

"No. Go," I say and shoo them away. "Andreas, what is it? Are you ill?" I ask. But he sits in stony silence.

"Leah, get me a damp cloth! Mia, run, get Papa, quick!"

So fast, my older girls obey me. The younger ones all run after Mia, shouting, "Papa! Papa! Come." The screen door bangs open and shut again and again.

"Andreas, look at me. What is wrong?" I ask, shaking him by the shoulders.

At last, when I have bathed his brow with the cool, damp cloth, he speaks. His voice is heavy in his throat.

"Betta will never come. She is dead."

"Oh, Andreas," I cry, the tears smarting in my eyes. "Oh, Andreas, it pains me to hear it."

Then because he is so like a motherless child sitting here in deep sorrow, having no one of his own, I clasp him to me and he gives himself over to loud weeping.

When quietness comes to him again he says, "Oh, Frau Becker, I cannot live without her. I need her, as I need the earth beneath my feet."

"Sure, sure, Andreas," I soothe. Then David is standing beside us, offering Andreas a glass of *Branntwein.*

"Here, lad," he says, "drink all of it. It will strengthen you."

258

When Andreas' grief has abated somewhat, he rises to his feet and goes outside to sit on the hard ground, leaning against the house, as is his custom. But he is not the same. He just sits and sits.

At long last, he stirs himself. He lifts his violin and plays — but tonight the strains are of prayer and supplication, *"Ew'ger Felsen"* — "Rock of Ages."

> *Arm und schuldig, wie ich bin,*
> *Werf' ich vor dem Kreuz mich*
> *hin; .... Schwach, die Kraft*
> *komt nur von dir; O mein Fels,*
> *dann bitte ich, Thu' dich auf*
> *und birg du mich.*

Once again it is the school season, and it isn't long before Mia comes home from the town's grade school with a worried look. When I question her, she draws away. That is strange I think; Mia is always so confiding. I look at her and realize how very unhappy all my children have been since the war started. They have had to bear many things because we are German. The Germans are hated so!

It gets the children nowhere when they say they care nothing for Germany, that they know nothing about the land, except what they learn in their text books — the same as other children. But, it doesn't help.

Mia puts her dinner pail on the kitchen table listlessly and does not go to change her dress, as the others do.

"Are you sick, Child?" I ask, and look closely on her sad face.

"No," she says barely shaking her head, her eyes cast to the floor. Her chin starts to pucker and her lips quiver, and I know it is not a light thing.

"What has happened?" I ask, drawing her to me and I feel her whole body tremble. Surely, this is serious. Every day now has its problems.

"Have the school children shamed you?" I want to know.

Mia starts crying when she looks at me, the words tumble from her all mixed with sobs.

"*Ach*, no, Mama — it is far worse. Today, I shamed myself and the whole family, because of our flag."

"Because of our flag?" *Ach, Gott*, my words come so fast and so loud they rumble through the house. My startled outcry upsets Mia even more.

"Honest, Mama, I did not mean to harm the flag. Honest! You must believe me — the teacher will not."

Mia's whole body quakes with fright and remorse. I take hold of her shoulders and look at her. "Sure, it is a terrible thing, my child, to dishonor your flag," I say to her. "Especially in these times when we are hated so." My voice is not kind, for I do not like that this has happened.

"Mama, I did not know I was doing wrong," she says, clinging to my hands. Round tears roll down her cheeks. "I only took my pencil and shaded over the stars and stripes of the early American flag in my history book. I did not scribble it. I just darkened it over neat. But the boy sitting in back of me told the teacher I was ruining it. She says I must bring you to school tomorrow, Mama, because I must apologize before the principal." Mia can hardly finish. Each word is racked with pain.

I am sick all over. I can no longer think or feel or speak, and I must sit down before I fall.

When I arrive in school the next day they are waiting for me: Mia's teacher, the lanky principal, and Mia, herself. Conveniently, all the other children who would be in the room are out on the playground. I walk toward a chair near the principal's desk, as is expected of me. And I think my legs will not carry me.

*Ach*, holy God, how quiet this room is! The waiting eyes are like burning fire on me. In the stillness I become aware of the wall clock, belaboring its day's work. Tick!... Tock!.... Tick!.... Tock! Each harsh sound is like a hammer blow. I feel as if shackles are clanging about my feet, making my steps awkward and heavy. Never have I felt such shame, such disgrace.

Then, I sit down.

They waste no time, but ask Mia to stand.

"Now, Mia," the precise teacher commands, "give us your definition of a good citizen." There is no kindness in her voice. Nor is there kindness in the principal's serious eyes.

They wait.

But Mia does not know what to say. Her hands twist themselves into the folds of her skirt, and her tormented eyes are like an animal's caught in a trap.

"This is a very serious matter," the principal's voice cuts the silence. "It sets a bad example for the other children to follow. Give us the meaning."

Frantic, Mia looks from one to the other. She is speechless.

*Ach!* How tormented she is. I can see the pain in her soulful eyes when she turns to me, searching my face for an answer.

Speak, my child, my heart cries out to her. Speak! Tell them we are good people, worthy of America, the land of the free and the

260

brave, as your school books teach you — America, where all men are equal. But no! They are not all equal. We are not equal; we are outcasts — outcasts from the very land that is to be a haven for my children.

"Mia, are you a good citizen? Give us an answer." The teacher commands her to speak.

My knuckles are white, so tightly I hold my hands in my lap.

Mia is trying. Her eyes are wide in their frantic search for an answer. Surely, my child has met her Gethsemane! A coldness goes over me. Near stopping is my heart. I look on Mia's face and all at once the image blurs before my eyes and all her pain runs together, caught in my hot tears. My heart is breaking! Still I cannot be bitter. It is only fitting. The teacher is right. A land can be free only when its citizens are loyal. And we are loyal. Yet, how can my child say it? It is not always easy to find the right words when the mind thinks in one language and you must speak in another. I can see Mia is trying.

Then I see a light of inner peace come over Mia's face. She squares her slight shoulders and raises her right hand and looks straight into the eyes of her teacher. And she speaks of the beautiful hymn, "True-hearted. Whole-hearted. Loyal forever!" Nothing else. Just this.

Now that the words have been said the teacher's eyes fill with slow tears and she looks shamed. Then acting on an impulse, she gathers my child to her in a frantic act of love.

The principal clears his throat in embarrassment, closing his desk and locking it without looking up. Then presently, he offers me his hand, wishing me well. But Mia's teacher does more. She grasps both of my hands and holds them to her bosom. And as we stand thus a tear falls from her cheek and runs melting through our fingers, forging a new bond of understanding.

# CHAPTER 20

## *Forward*

After this my children are treated better in the classrooms and on the playgrounds. But as is to be expected the teachers have no control over the coming and going, and soon Mia, too, loses her desire for school. And though David and I persuade her to go — which takes no small effort on our part — the savor is gone.

Neither is it an easy thing to keep sending our children to German Bible School, during the summer months, at our church in town. Every day now they bring us news that pressure is put on town officials to shut it down. "How can learning God's Word have anything to do with war?" I say to David, my head full of futile questions and no answers. "It is so important that they learn the way of the Lord. How can they close down the temporary Bible classes?"

David can only shake his head. Then he says, "It hasn't happened yet. In the meantime the children will go."

And though animosity toward our Volga-German people mounts from day to day, we, living here within one mile of town, reap a good share of respect from the people. Mia has been asked to room and board and work after school, in the home of the mercantile owner. David, too, is esteemed by all who know him. And, because of this, clerks in stores treat me with respect — not so with others less known. Those who cannot speak the language simply do not get waited on in some stores. The loss of trade to overly-patriotic merchants seems to be of no consequence. This is one thing I fail to understand.

More and more tales begin to spread about insults to our people. One is that Frau so-and-so in a neighboring town was slapped in the face by a hot-tempered clerk. Her foreign words said no more than what was right: that she had had no opportunity to learn the language, and that she became as hungry as the next person. She was there to buy food!

Others, who believe themselves ill-treated grow resentful and fight back saying, "Why, can you not understand that we have nothing to do with Germany? We are not German militarists!"

Soon our own community is alerted to a tale of horror. It is hard to say if it is a rumor, or true fact; there are so many conflicting versions of the tale. They say a German from the wild bluff area of the Smoky Hill River sold a load of dry beans treated with arsenic. The warning is out not to eat beans bought after such-and-such date. There is great concern among the people. Then, when at last the story has played itself out and not a single person has died of poisoning, there follows yet another version. This time it is simply that the demented fellow had not sold the beans, but rather that he ate them and died. Try as one will, one cannot get the straight of it. Yet, it has added more fuel to the fire.

Not long after this, my Hester's heart is broken because of the awful rumor. Now that Mia stays in town to work, Hester must herd the younger ones home from school. I see her tears and notice the bewildered look on the younger children's faces. "What is it, Child?" I ask. "What has happened?"

Hester's sobbing words tumble out, "Is it true Mama, that all Germans, like us, can eat poison and not die?"

"*Ach*, no, how foolish you talk, for a big girl. And tears, too. Tsh, tsh. Now, wipe and be done with it," I say, handing her the corner of my apron. I keep my words light, hoping that Leah is not within hearing range. But my hoping is in vain. One side-long glance tells me that Leah is standing grim in the doorway.

"Come, tell me," I beg Hester, not letting on to Leah that I can read the feeling that is welling up inside of her. But all my light coaxing does no good with Hester, the deep sobbing in her chest will not let her speak.

"It is the same thing all over again," says Leah with a tight throat, stepping forward, her own eyes welling with tears. "First me, then Mia, and now, Hester. Mama you cannot fool youself any longer, book learning is never meant for us."

"Hush, Leah, do not say it; do not say it," I say, all mixed up with this constant pulling against the stream.

Turning around, I look at the faces of my children. "What have we to do with poison?" I ask.

Maria is quick to pipe up, "Mrs. Audley's Gloria says we eat poison and don't die."

"What made her say that?"

"Hester offered some leftover cookies to the poor children who live below the tracks and Gloria yelled, 'Don't take them, or you will die.'"

"Did they take them?" I want to know, knowing now why Hester's feelings are so crushed.

"No," says Maria, shaking her head. "They backed away from her, as if she were a witch."

Now Davie, too, finds his tongue, "Yeah, she said her mother told her all Germans go around poisoning people. I saw Mrs. Audley's ugly face peeking out the window, and she didn't even tell Gloria to be still."

"Is it true about the children?" I ask Hester, looking closely on her face.

"Yes, Mama, it's true. Then they wouldn't touch my cookies. Oh, Mama, it hurts." New and terrible sobs rack her body and I feel them tremble in my own being, stirring my heart to rebellion.

I cannot help it. I feel like Leah. I want to go to Mrs. Audley and shout at her, "This is not patriotism. It is being a hypocrite. Better that you teach your child higher things. America does not need patriots such as you!" All this I would shout at her. She, whom I have given many free eggs, and lard, and gallons and gallons of milk. But I do not. Instead, I hold Hester to me, stroking her hair, soothing away the pain — my eyes looking out the window to the hazy, far-away sky, void of any friendliness. And Leah, without bidding, brings a cool wash cloth to wipe away our smarting tears.

At supper time the children complain bitterly to David. "Why, Papa? Why do they do this?" they want to know, their faces dark with misery. "We are good people aren't we?"

"*Ja*, sure, we are good people!" he says, trying to hide the terrible hurt he has kept inside of him so long. "And we will continue to be good. Just remember, those who treat you mean mistake rudeness for patriotism. They are jealous for their country. They want no unworthy outsider to spoil it for them."

And though David has great concern that school children spit in our young ones' faces and call them Huns and German spies, he admonishes them, "Always, in everything, behave yourselves. Honor your country, and respect your flag."

"Yes, Papa," they answer him.

But to me, on the side, he says it is all the more urgent that he get his citizenship papers.

Then on the day that David finally takes his test at the courthouse we all run down the roadway to meet him as he comes home from town. The children are all shouting, "Papa, did you make it? Papa, did you pass?"

"Yes, yes," he answers from afar. David is standing up in the wagon box, waving a slip of paper. "Now, we are truly American citizens," he shouts. "Each and every one of us!"

The children laugh out loud and tumble over each other. They run down the road and climb into the wagon with him. *Ach*, such happiness!

Before we go to bed we see the certificate of citizenship framed and hanging beside George Washington, the draped red, white and blue flag, and the screaming eagle. Now, this is something to treasure for a lifetime!

With the winter comes an epidemic of influenza, menacing and terrible. With it all unnecessary visiting comes to a stand-still. No longer is my dining room clean and tidy, with laughter and singing running through, as before. No longer is there a white tablecloth on the long table, but David's carpenter tools lie there making it a workbench. Wood shavings lie thick upon the floor. David is making coffins for the dead. So far, thank God, the sickness has not struck us.

Sober-eyed and sure of hand David fashions coffin after coffin for our people who cannot afford to buy them ready-made. Large ones. Middle-sized ones. Small ones. *Ach*, it breaks our hearts. Some are so tiny, you can carry them under the arm, like a doll box. When this is the case there is almost always a bigger box to go with it, for child-bearing at this time is a deadly thing.

There is sadness in our house. Saws rend through gleaming new boards, emitting a mournful tune. New boards, with a new, clean smell, are whole, but not for long. How can we know, who will drive in next?

It makes me afraid to look to the roadway. It frightens me when I wonder, who will David take by the hand next, with one arm around the shoulder and lead to a chair that tear-blinded eyes cannot find for themselves? I know how it goes. David will stand by patiently then, waiting, until tortured speech can clarify the dimensions.

266

I watch my children with a furtive eye, hoping that they will not get the sickness. All are home, except Mia, who is working up town and going to school. Will she be careful? *Ach, Gott!* It is not the first time that David has made coffins for his own. In Russia he made three for our little ones, nailing the covers on tight, each hammer blow shattering his heart! *Ach*, I cannot think of it. I will not think of it.

No sooner has David finished with the coffin, then I cut panels of black sateen from the bolt of cloth that David has brought from town. I fit the cloth smoothly to the outside boards and tack it on with round, silver-headed nails. I set them neatly apart along the slanting edge and ends of the coffin. When the work is finished it is truly beautiful. Then I line the inside with pure white cloth. Some people choose a silky kind, while others who can afford no more pick the cheaper white muslin. At the top edge where the lid fits down I tack a three-inch white lace flouncing that sways gently as I move about my work. I also make a soft pillow and give it a cover with lace frill on all sides. When this is finished, David puts on the gleaming handles, three or four on each side if it is a grown person, only two when it is a little one. The casket stands on the table while we finish it, and oftentimes the grief stricken person who claims it sits hunched-over, gazing down dully at the wood shaving lying at his feet.... *O, Traurigkeit! Wie schwer!*

The next day, our country church overflows with mourners. There are no flowers for adornment, only the sun streaming in the window catching the smooth sheen of the coffin, stenciling sun-drenched lacy motifs of forget-me-nots onto the sombre black cloth. The minister speaks words of comfort, and the organ starts up the burial hymn from the *Wolga Gesangbuch* that promises life anew with Jesus, *"Jesus ist mein Lebenslicht..."*

> *...Jesus ist mein Lebenslicht,*
> *Jesus ist mein Auferstehen;*
> *Jesus lebt, drum sterb ich nicht,*
> *Nein, ich werde zu Ihm gehen.*
> *Jesus ist mein Paradies. Meine*
> *Wonne Ruhm und Preis.*

Burial takes place in the church cemetery one-fourth mile south, in a spot where the virgin sod is broken for the first time since the world began.

These are hard, busy days, indeed. When I am not nailing cloth onto new coffins I am washing, ironing, mending. Or I knit sweaters and woolen socks for the Red Cross to send to our soldiers overseas. When I am not doing that I am cooking and baking; it takes much bread for my family. There are eight of us now that Mia stays in town.

I worry a lot about Mia and when I ask David to bring her home he says, "A promise is a promise, Evaliz. I cannot go against my word."

"Then what if she foolishly goes to a picture show and gets the flu?" I argue, knowing how unthinking young people can be.

"So we will warn her against it, when next we see her," David says, bluntly. "Don't worry, she will be all right."

But there is no time to warn her. Before the day is out a new automobile drives in, and Davie who has run out in the yard comes right in again.

"Mama, it is Mia. She looks sick."

"*Ach, Gott!*" I cry, trying to remove the sticky bread dough from my fingers. "Where is your papa?"

"He is out in the pasture hauling feed to the cattle with the sleigh," my children say in unison.

Before I can get my hands clean the man from town is bringing Mia in, wrapped in a quilt. He lays her on my bed.

It is true. Mia has the fever. David must not come in the house.

"It is better that you go to the Haldeman's, for who else would take care of the milking and outside work if you got sick," I tell him when he comes in from the pasture.

Now, at last, the hammering and sawing in our house has come to an end. Once more the dining room is set in order, yet no one appreciates it — for in time we all have the fever.

David comes every morning and evening to do the chores, placing kindling, eggs, milk and water inside the screened-in porch where I can reach it from the kitchen door. Whenever necessary he drives to town to get us medicine and groceries, never entering the house. But when I get too sick to hold my head up he threatens to come in, and I must ask Leah to lock the door against him — thinking first of our neighbor; of David; and of our cattle who must be fed and milked.

The pain rages hard and long in my body, yet I drag myself out of bed to see to my ailing children until I fall in a heap. When this happens, Leah leaves her sick bed to take care of the work and family. She keeps the fire going and brings us hot broth.

After many more days, David comes home to stay. The sickness has gone, leaving us with a peculiar weakness. But God has truly been gracious to us: we are all alive!

It is always a happy time for the children when David loads the wagon with grain and drives to town. They know he will come home with something new and exciting. Oftentimes I feel the same as they. There is no telling what David will do when he gets a sum of money in his pocket.

Today is such a day. Already they see him coming down the road, and run to line up on the front porch, waiting for him to drive in the yard.

"What do you think he is bringing?" they question each other, happy as larks — the younger ones jumping up and down.

As he comes closer, I see by the look on his face that it is something, all right.

"What do you think I bought?" he calls, driving in off the main roadway, giving the children no time to ask. He is waving a small paper in his hand.

"That I wouldn't know, I'm sure," I say, seeing the merry twinkle in his eyes, almost like a naughty boy's. "Not a spring buggy I can see, or you would have it tied on in back." Then a fear grips me and I am afraid to know. That David!

Our children are so excited they can hardly wait until the wagon stops. They are eager to climb in and see for themselves.

"No, by golly, Evaliz, I bought a Liberty Bond, instead. This is the only way we can help fight the war. I figure joining the National Guard is not enough. Here, take it."

*Ach*, so it is a Liberty Bond, is it? I cannot be mad. It is a small exchange for the sons others are giving. I reach for the paper and my fingers tremble.

In the wagon bed there is a clamor as the children crowd each other to see what else he has bought.

"Mama, a washing machine!" they cry, surprised, pulling the cover from it.

"A machine, with a handle to push back and forth, Mama," cries Maria, looking down, her face beaming.

"*Ja*, Mama, and a wringer goes with it," pipes 'Linda, with the thick brown hair and cutoff bangs. "Hurray, Hurray! I get to push it first."

"No, me, me --" Everyone wants the first try.

I stand in the yard and take in their joy. I smile at them vying with each other. In my hand I hold the Liberty Bond that makes us all Americans!

"And more." David breaks into the racket. Grinning, he pulls a large sack of candy from under his coat. A shout goes up from big and small alike that can be heard all the way to town and back again.

With a new summer come good crops! Once again the long wheat trains go rolling by, bigger and mightier than ever, writing their smoke trails across the Kansas blue skies.

It is also a summer of harvest-hand shortage and labor strikes in the far cities, the year of the I.W.W! Some say that I.W.W. stands for "I Won't Work." But David explains to me that the initials mean Industrial Workers of the World. They are a wartime radical group made up largely of factory workers from the big cities who take their vacation to work the western wheat harvest.

They lodge, two hundred strong, with their meager belongings under the cottonwood trees, either in the Courthouse Square or at the depot, and threaten to run any man through with a pitch fork if he accepts a wage lower than they specify. Their demand is twelve to fourteen dollars per eight hour day; stackers, eighteen dollars.

In our fields, besides David and our three oldest girls, we have three such men. They are Russians who speak very little English. They were drawn to David because he knew their language. At first they did not show their devious nature. Yet, as the harvest reached its peak they demanded more and more pay. They knew David would find it hard to replace them.

Finally, with enough of the rabble in town to bolster their action they become even bolder. They tell David they will walk off the job unless he pays more.

"What will you do?" I ask David, concerned about our girls and the work still ahead.

"Let them go. That is what I'll do. They are Bolsheviks — Communists! They favor world-wide revolution! I will not harbor them in my yard."

"Nor will I, if that is the truth."

"It's the truth, all right. Pity the Chicago meat packing companies," David says.

Trouble comes soon enough. Saturday night when David pays the men, these three, Ignatz, Leon, and Vasilla, refuse to be fired. What is even more, they refuse to take their belongings or the checks made out to them when they leave for town and the week-end celebration. They smile confidently and say they will be back for Monday's cutting.

"If you do your things will be out by the mailbox," David calls after them in Russian.

Angered, as never before, David follows out his threat. He puts the checks, marked in full, in the suitcases and carries them out by the roadway, where they stay all night and half of the next day.

When we come home from Sunday services they are gone.

"Goodness, that was easy," I think to myself.

270

But on Monday morning the drive shaft on the header is broken and the note pinned under the broken pieces reads, "Lucky for you this isn't your head."

The county sheriff, too, has his problems. The situation in town is out of hand. He is compelled to summon the help of the entire farm community to drive the trouble makers out. The farmers respond with pitchforks, clubs, and guns as soon as the emergency call of six short rings is given over the phone by "central."

And before night, they drive the I.W.W.'s on foot, down the railroad track, nine miles east of town where they are loaded into cattle cars, awaiting the next train to take them out of the country.

Now again, as in that other year of good crops, huge threshing outfits move into stubble fields that reach from horizon to horizon. And again heavily loaded grain wagons begin to move. Now, as never before, prospering farmers are filling new granaries to over-flowing, testing, at long last, their mighty strength. Others wait selfishly for higher-than-ever war prices. But still the surplus crop must trail to town in unending streams. So much greater is this year's harvest!

Even though two more town grain elevators have risen into the sky — our landlord having invested in one of them — time does not permit all wagons to unload. They are bound over into the next day. And still the wagons come.

Soon, the wide open space around the elevators becomes a gypsy camp. Harassed operators hustle about chalking numbers on wagons to maintain rank and order.

At first there is good talk among hardy men, sitting on their wagon seats proudly, for wheat is bringing $2.42 per bushel. Men bring out their pipes and cigarette paper and exchange light banter that they will stay all week if need be. The young-bloods, on the other hand, take out their pocket knives and set to carving out whistles and pistols.

Then, as the days grow hotter and the oncoming throng ever greater, there is a constant shifting and reshifting for better positions until tempers rise and wrangling runs rife. The first-comers refuse to be hedged in on. Even though the low numerals on their wagons would indicate that they be served first, how can they be, if they are blocked in?

Pressured by their owners, heavy work horses begin to jostle each other, ripping harness against buckles and hobnail trim. Wheels lock into wheels, grinding shrill notes, tipping and spilling sheets of pure gold from wagon tops. Hot-headed youths come to blows, rolling in the hot powdery dust among their wagon wheels — goaded on by friend, and cursed by newly-acquired foe.

The situation worsens until at last "central" is called upon to sound her six short rings throughout the countryside, asking that no more wheat be brought to town.

From our land owner's fields the golden grain rolls forth, enough to line his pockets with riches. Enough, also, for us to pay our old debts, with something left. I cannot believe it! Neither can David.

"What is happening to us?" I say to David, unable to keep my glad voice in check. "Can it be that, at last, we will make something of our lives?"

"It can. And it will, Evaliz," he says, his eyes off into the future. "This is the beginning of the Becker's owning their own land."

We look at each other and we laugh at such a crazy, sweet, and foolish thought, still not believing that anything as good as this could actually be happening to us.

Nevertheless the wagons hurry to and fro from our fields, as they did in that other year, pouring wealth into the granaries our landlord provided. Wagons are filled, and emptied, to be filled again. This work is even harder than the harvesting, because of the constant flow. And Mia and Leah are needed alongside the stout men. Two years of growth have added to their usefulness.

Our girls do not mind the work. Indeed, they insist on it. They are as happy as larks in the springtime. Dressed in overalls and blue chambray boy's shirts and wide straw hats over plump braids they drive the creaking loads into the yard and shovel the wheat into the granaries. Then they are off again with a rumble of wheels, standing in the empty wagon bed, singing their school song at the top of their voices:

> . . We crossed the prairies as of old
> The pilgrims crossed the sea,
>     To make the West as they the East
> The homestead of the free.

Smiling, I stand out in the yard after I have helped them and wave them on. It is a happy song — "The Song of the Kansas Emigrant" — and so fitting for us. My children love to sing it. I know the meaning of the words well, for Leah has made them clear to me in her patient way. Indeed, I am proud of my girls, because of their happy outlook on life.

Not only is this year's wheat crop the greatest we have ever had, but the yield of oats, barley, rye, sorghum and corn is equally heavy. The storing of corn has become a problem since the cornbins are neither big enough nor strong enough to hold the tremendous yield, and farmers throughout the country are piling the husked ears on the bare ground in tall mounds, thirty to fifty feet long.

CHAPTER 21

# The House Shall Stand

T oday is a great milestone in our lives. An honor has come
    to our house; a recognition has come to our people.
    Governor Arthur Capper of Kansas who is a friend to our
    industrialist landlord has come to town to address the
people of the farming West. But first he comes to our house to eat.

"Quick, Evaliz, the best of everything," says David, rushing
home from town ahead of them. "Already the landlord has told him
what a good cook you are."

"*Ach, Gott,*" I say, putting my hand to my forehead and
brushing back my loose hair. "How can anything so good and also so
dreadful happen to me when the house is in a mess — the ironing all
over the house."

"You have maybe two hours," says David, going out to
straighten up his blacksmith shop.

In a time like this, it is good to have many children. I am already
deciding how each one must help.

"Quick, Leah," I say, "away with the ironing. Go to the cellar
and bring up potatoes, dill pickles, jams, and cabbage, and thick
sweet cream, while I start the berry pies.

"T'linda, plenty of dry cobs for the fire — hurry, Child! And
Katta, *Liebchen*, you sweep the dooryard clean.

"Hester. Maria. Catch me six roosters. Call your brother to help you. First close the chicken house door before you check, so they do not fly out. If none are there then you must run them down in the yard — so hurry, catch me nice ones."

"Hurrah! Come Maria!" Hester shouts, "Davie is in the haymow. Now he has a chance to prove he is the best runner."

"Mia," I continue, "swat the flies and scrub the floors."

"I scrubbed them yesterday with lye water," she protests.

"No matter," I tell her, "scrub them again, and pull down the shades for added coolness. Then put on the good white tablecloth and set the table just so."

We all work so fast. Every minute or so we glance down the road toward town.

When the two worthy gentlemen finally come the chicken is browning just right. The blackberry pies are cooling in the window sill; the potatoes are ready to mash; buttermilk biscuits are ready to slide into the oven; tender garden beans are simmering slowly in sweet cream; and the table with its dash of color in the freshly-scrubbed room is good to look upon with dilled cucumbers, round red slices of pickled beets, bowls of gold and crimson jams, and large pats of butter embossed with roses.

The coming of this guest to our house has cast a solemn spell over all. It has brought a Sunday atmosphere to an ordinary week day.

Quietly my children, dressed in their second-best and scrubbed clean, withhold themselves until they are spoken to. Yet the landlord draws each one of them out in special recognition; each in turn must speak up, saying, "Welcome, to our house, Mr. Capper," and extend a hand to him.

Proudly, David stands to one side, while the new acquaintances are made. Then, amid the fluffing of the mashed potatoes, I, too, get the pleasure of taking the hearty handshake of the Kansas Governor! His voice is wreathed in friendship.

"It is a pleasure to meet someone so highly praised as you, Mrs. Becker."

Embarrassed, I cast a side-long glance at our landlord, but he smiles and nods as though saying, "Yes, yes, it's true." Then I look at the pleasant face with the deep eyes, the hair combed neatly from a left part over his high forehead, and I know he is a man of intellect and rare human understanding.

"Please, go in and sit. Dinner is ready," I say in German, knowing that he will understand, as will our landlord who speaks the language.

It is not until David and our son come home from the afternoon speech in town that the feeling of real honor strikes us. David is beside himself with well-being.

"*Ei*, Evaliz, you should have heard the Governor's address. He spoke eloquently of the equality of our farmers, whether native-born or foreign. He especially praised and thanked the staunch character and foresightedness of the immigrants who first brought kernels of hard winter wheat to this country."

"He said that?" I marvel, not believing that anyone, least of all an eminent man, like Mr. Capper, would take the time to praise the likes of us, after all the set-backs we've suffered as misfits.

"*Ja*, sure, he said it. What is more, he assured his listeners that it is a recognized fact in congress that the diligent efforts of the immigrant here in our farming West has been, and is, an instrumental factor in feeding our armed forces and allies overseas. Therefore, each farmer however great, or small, should receive his rightful share of the nation's gratitude."

"And did the people of our community hear him?" I ask, my mind still in a muddle.

"Why wouldn't they hear? They were there, eh, Davie? And they applauded."

"Applauded?" I cannot believe it. Perhaps I have done the people an injustice.

"*Ja*, Mama, Papa is right. There were about two thousand."

"My, my!" I look at the two beaming faces before me.

"It is enough cause, eh, Evaliz, to hold our heads high," David says, then adds, "not only as good Christians but as loyal American citizens!"

"*Ach, ja,*" I say, thinking and reflecting on the years of strife, the proving and the testing. And I am reminded of the old hymn, "How Firm a Foundation," that speaks of life and trust in God:

*When through fiery trials thy path-way shall lie,*
*My grace, all-sufficient, shall be thy supply:*
*The flames shall not hurt thee; I only design*
*Thy dross to consume, and thy gold to refine.*

Times are changing. The years have gone by. My family is growing up. We have a houseful of obedient children, all good looking and full of happy ways. There are eight now, ranging in years from three to nearly twenty. They are Leah, Mia, Hester, Maria, David Phillip, Theolinda, Kathi, and now Sonya. Sonya is golden-haired and blue-eyed, pretty as a doll.

Whenever Frau Shuster comes she looks at my grown girls with the eye of an appraiser, and says, "*Ech*! What a string of weddings that will be once they start to go. Too bad I haven't a son, or I'd get me one."

"*Ach*, go on with you," I chide, jokingly, yet seeing the double meaning behind her beady eyes. "What would you do with a girl?" I ask.

"More than I do now," she says, bemoaning her lot, eyeing Leah as she kneads out fresh bread loaves and puts them in greased pans.

I watch Leah myself, thinking it's no wonder Frau Shuster would like to have her to run her house. Leah, very pretty, five foot five, is as good at housework as she is in the field. She will make someone a good wife when that time comes. Nor has Leah let up on book learning, I remind myself. She can recite the classics with a candor that matches David's. The small allowance of egg money, and her will to do, have made book buying and self-study possible.

*Ach*, the soul contentment in me is so great that I completely forget about my guest. I try to amend. But it is too late; Frau Shuster's voice explodes.

"*Na Donner*, speak what is on your mind," she commands. "What you thinking, huh?" Frau Shuster will not be left out of anything, if she can help it. But I only smile and lay my hand on her gently, so that she will take no offense. I take one tiny stitch, and yet another, and say nothing.

Truly the years have gone by like the ticking of a clock, neither hastening away the sad hours, nor pausing, briefly, to mark a wee measure of perishable joy. Ticking ever onward. Ticking, ticking — minutes, hours, days, weeks, months, years. Marching with the seasons. Cold, warmth, hail, drought. The laughing, and also, the deep sighing. Plowing. Sowing. Reaping. Learning. All these things and more.

World war has come and gone. And long ago the bedraggled rag dummy that was Kaiser Bill in a street celebration has been cut down from the high pole above the curfew bell on the Courthouse Square, the deliriously happy crowd having given him the honored spot in the funeral parade, his battered head limp and shaggy, hanging on a thin neck like that of a dead sparrow.

Sons of war have returned to their homeland, while still others sleep quietly in poppy fields on foreign soil. And new songs replace the marching songs of old, "Oh welcome home — ye living sons — your glorious task is done. . . ."

And though our prairie town and outlying farm lands gave sons in death, as did countless others, it nevertheless bore its sorrow with pride and dignity. Indeed, it is no light thing to say that tolerance and understanding have, at last, mellowed the varied citizenry of our plains!

Yet, lest we in our house — and the Volga-German people in general — should take our inheritance of liberty and freedom too lightly, we have another lesson forced home on us. And it takes Leah to remind me of my old dream to make of my children, good Americans!

The lesson comes out of Bolshevik Russia in the form of letters, some of them written in blood. They are letters of famine and death in a land torn by revolution. Many are from our relatives who remain there. Others are for our people further out in the country, but addressed to David. This is because David, in the past, has helped our people, by writing the addresses on their mail in the Russian script.

Every day now, it seems, the children come running in from the rural mailbox shouting, "Mama. Mama, here is another letter. Can Papa send them food, too?"

"Wait," I say, "till your papa comes from the field and reads it."

The children are very excited and concerned. Their eyes are veiled with misty anxiety.

I reach for the large square envelope with the many Russian stamps affixed to the front and an extra sheet of them folded double on the back, and my hand trembles, for I do not know who the letter is for nor what terrible message it contains.

My children press close to study the foreign stamps. The stamps are red and white in color, each bearing the imprint of 1000 pyb. meaning rubles, no doubt, for money in Russia has no value since the Bolsheviks demolished the governing body. Overly plump wheat-heads wreath an octagon that encircles the anvil and long-handled fire tong and sledge offset by a rising blaze of heat waves.

"*Donner Wetter*," shouts Davie, "look at all those 1000 ruble stamps. There must be thirty or forty. That would buy plenty of food."

"What do you mean, food," says Leah, putting him straight. "There is no food in all of Russia. There is only worthless money and people eating their own dead, thanks to the bloody Bolsheviks!"

"Leah! Leah, no more talk like that," I say. But Leah will not retract her statement. To her the situation demands airing.

Leah continues, "Mama, how can we not speak of these things, when they are true?" Leah's deep burning eyes are on me. Her fierceness is not for me, but for the terrible truth of it all.

Leah is right. For the moment my wish to shield them from the sordid has over-powered my better judgement. I can only admit my error in silence.

Leah is not through yet. "We cannot deny all those other things Papa has read. Someone stole your sister Katrin-Lizbet's last pillow. Then took all her clothing as well, leaving her nothing to wear but an old shirt that belonged to Uncle Gottfried before the Bolsheviks killed him. All this in the dead of winter."

"No, of course not, we can't deny it," I say, and the pain of knowing, that I have harbored inside of me, rises up in my throat and makes my nostrils smart with unshed tears.

My tormented thoughts race back to Katrin-Lizbet in her youth, always so proud and courageous. It is hard to believe that she has nothing but a rag to hide her nakedness.

"*Ach*, yes, Children, learn a lesson from this," I say, looking for a chair to hold me up. "Only by the grace of God, have you escaped the same treatment."

Leah quickly brings me a chair and puts it under me. My eight children crowd around me.

"Mama, you tell us the rest," they beg. "Mama, please. We would rather hear it from you."

There is nothing to do but finish it, although the ending is the saddest part of it all. The children wait with bated breath. I begin. "As Leah has told you, there is no food in all the Volga region — no dog, no cat, no bird, nor any other living thing. The people have devoured them all."

"Even the worms, Mama?" the little ones want to know, looking big-eyed and unbelieving.

"*Ja*, even worms, and all insects, flies, bugs. Some people eat common earth. Also, they have stripped all the trees of bark, to brew a poor tea. Worst of all, according to the letters your papa has read, people are eating their own dead."

"Ugh!" The children grasp their throats at the last remark.

I cannot tell the rest, but Leah carries on.

"Yes," Leah says, "Mama is right. On the night our aunt's twelve-year-old son died, someone stole his body for food."

No sooner has she said the words then a spasm of convulsion comes from the throats of the little ones. "Ock --ou - r - rck!" They are ready to vomit.

"Enough of this," I say to the oldest. "Go, now, dress warm and do the chores early. Hurry, all of you, so that you do not miss hearing the letter, when your papa comes home with a load of feed."

Although I busy myself in the kitchen, my little Sonya close by, playing with doll clothes, I cannot forget the famine among our

278

people. With every bit of food I touch, I am reminded of the hungering, freezing masses.

As soon as David is through unloading the feed with Davie helping him, the girls are through milking. They hurry to the house on wobbly legs, slushing milk over the top of full buckets. Separating is next, but first the letter!

All eyes are on David as he uses his pocket knife to slit open the letter addressed to him. His stubby, work-worn fingers have a time getting the flimsy paper out and I can hardly wait. Impatient, our children begin to fidget, their shoulders, arms, and fingers twitching as though trying to help. Finally David unfolds the letter. He takes a quick look and his countenance falls.

*Ach, Gott,* what is it? I think. It must be something terrible. My heart nearly stops. Then David speaks. "This letter is not for us," he says. "It belongs to Johann Sterkle. Leah, go call them on the phone."

Leah obeys immediately, then reports, "They will come as soon as their evening chores are done." Then she adds, turning to the older girls, "Come, let's get the cream separating done. And T'Linda and Kathi, you milk feed the young calves so we'll be ready."

They all hustle about with their work, and even wash the cream separator afterwards.

The Sterkles live seven miles out in the country, but that is no problem; they have an automobile. Still it will take awhile before their chores and supper are over with. We know that.

Outside the night sky is grey-black with low scudding clouds. And intermittent gusts of wind are tearing at the eaves of the house. The hour is getting late, but our children insist on waiting up.

When the Sterkles finally arrive they have their six children with them, three boys and three girls, ages five to fourteen, full of laughter.

But tonight there isn't the usual joy running through the house. Strangely quiet, Leah herds the tow-headed, freckle-faced and pig-tailed youngsters to the stairway corner where there are steps to sit on. Our children sit on the floor, except Leah, Mia, Hester, Maria, and T'Linda who take their places on the bench behind the table.

We grown-ups, too, waste no time with small talk. We take our places on straight back chairs, facing David by the table near the hanging lamp.

For the moment there is no sound in all the house except the ranting wind reaching down through the chimney to provoke the kitchen fire, causing the tea kettle to drone in irritable displeasure.

The melancholy sound brings tears to my throat. And I feel I should go and put the tea kettle on the back of the stove, but I dare not delay the letter any longer. I steal a shy glance at the Sterkles and it is hard to tell if the impudence of the tea kettle has added to their anxiety.

Grete is so frail, yet she sits so straight, her dark hair smoothed back from her face in a tight knot; her intent eyes glistening with terrible expectancy; her fingers twisted like rope in her calico lap. Johann, moustached and red-headed, with a body of steel, his deep furrowed face baked hard as the dry earth, now sits hunched, infinitely gentle, with downcast eyes waiting for come-what-may. The letter is from his aged mother. The words are German. David begins to read:

"*Kratzke*

*Geschrieben den 7 Dezember 1921*

"*Zuerst seid recht herzlich gegrüszt und im geiste geküszt ihr unsere lieben Kinder.*

"First, may heartfelt salutations and spiritual kisses be unto you, my beloved children.

"Circumstances compel, me to take pen in hand and write into a remote land, to make supplications that you, my dear children, come to our rescue and save us from death by starvation.

"It has been a long time since we have had any word from you. But, God, in a dream, has revealed to me that you are well and still among the living. I am constrained therefore, to write to you for help, for the famine is widespead and terrible. . . ."

The words in David's throat sound heavy and tortured, and he pauses to swallow, hiding his embarrassment in pretending to bring the quaking paper into better focus, under the hanging lamp. I see the veiling mist in his eyes.

But that is nothing compared to what Johann Sterkle is trying to hide. Without looking, I can tell he is holding down convulsions that are threatening to strangle him. Grete's knuckles are bone white.

Only the tea kettle alone is brash enough to shrill its high and mournful sound throughout the house. David goes on reading the letter:

"We have eaten our last horse long ago and hunger's-death stands before our eyes. And as there are three of you, surely you will not let this happen, for many can help a few. If you cannot send for us then perhaps you can send packages, or a few dollars, so that we can help ourselves.

"It is impossible to live. We have had total mis-crops these last two years, consequently we have absolutely nothing. You can well imagine how it is with us. Many have died of hunger. Yakor has died, also, but he died of typhus.

"Truly, the judgment of God has overtaken us, but few heed the times and God's word has found its fulfillment: O Lord, *are* not thine eyes upon the truth? *thou* has stricken them, but they have not grieved; thou has consumed them, *but* they have refused to receive correction; they have made their faces harder than a rock; they have refused to return. Jeremiah 5:3."

The Bible text is too much for David. It chokes off his voice and brings great tears to his eyes, and he must stop reading for awhile. Loud sobbing sounds come from our older girls, their tear-stained faces glinting in the lamplight.

Unashamed, all of us weep in our own way, Sterkle and his wife, David and I. Our little ones, seeing us weep, begin to stir in their semi-dark corner and soon they are crying too.

Sterkle makes the first abrupt movement. He pushes back his chair in rising and stalks out of the room, through the kitchen and out into the cold, blustery night. I hear him blow his nose hard. When he comes back in, brushing his wind blown hair smooth with his hand, David continues with the letter:

"We have no bread and we have not the wherewithall to buy any. A *pud** of rye bran costs as much as four times one hundred thousand ruble. A good horse costs up to two million ruble, the cow the same, a sheep up to 500,000 ruble. There is enough money in Russia for those who have it. The money is carried around in the market place in large sacks.

"America has now set up relief kitchens in the villages, but they are only for children — but what profits those who are too weak to crawl, or if there is no one strong enough to carry them? They can only lie and gaze with soulful eyes into that direction.

"Yes, the hunger is perilous and terrifying. May God, in his mercy, have compassion upon us poor sinners. In closing, we again salute you. Live in health until we meet again in happier times. If not here on earth, then, under the golden canopy of heaven. Amen.

*Von mir eurer Mutter und Stiefvater.*

(signed) Your Mitzen"

The letter is finished.

Johann Sterkle reaches for his blue bandanna and openly wipes his eyes, first one and then the other, each time with a firm

*Pud* — Russian measure, about 36 pounds.

281

outward stroke. He replaces the handkerchief in the back pocket of his overalls and sits unmoving, staring before him.

His tiny wife folds and unfolds her hands in her lap. She is mumbling a prayer barely audible, "Oh, God, have mercy. Oh, God, have pity."

Our combined children, who weep because their parents are weeping, huddle together by two's and three's, their heads touching, patting each other in solace.

Finally, Johann Sterkle bestirs himself to look at David. "Thank you, friend," he says. His voice is deep. "Will you be so good as to read it again. It is too much to grasp in one reading."

"I will do it gladly," David says, picking up the letter and beginning at once.

And though David went to the bank the very next day and sent an order for staple foodstuffs, such as flour, dry beans, rice, lard, and the like to be filled in New York, using the check Johann Sterkle left him, the final outcome, in time, was more dreadful than the beginning.

In the end Sterkle's aged mother wrote only one more letter. She was writing it, she said, under the terse direction of a Bolshevik official who commanded her to write that the food received had been replaced with stones. And that upon delivery, she had been beaten to within an inch of her life. What was more, should she again ask the bourgeois *Amerikanski*, that last inch would not be spared!

⚘

One by one the seasons surrender their lingering hold upon the land. Each time the last is forgotten by the opening of a new door. And so it is with our lives.

Blue-eyed Mia, now a grown young girl, does not finish grade school as I promised she would; the need of field work was always too great. Neither does Hester, nor Maria. Nor Davie. Yet, all these, like Leah, are not standing still. Every evening when work is done they sit at the table, under the lamplight, their books open, being coached in various ways by David and Leah. Here they learn to spell, to work arithmetic, to draw maps of the world, to put on paper the intricate details of the anatomy. They learn to read and write in German, studying Bible history and Luther's Catechism. They learn many Bible verses by heart. Thus they gain the power of words in both languages!

And even though the first five of our children have not finished grade school, Theolinda's chance to do so is now at hand. Theolinda, my brown-haired one with gold flecks in her eyes, has grown to fine maidenhood, proud and straight.

Already I am sewing the white dress she will wear on Commencement Day. She says, in high school, she will study to be a teacher and apply for a job in one of the district schools in our farm community.

"My, a teacher you will be, like your papa once was — and his father, and his grandfather before him," I say, proudly, hardly believing that we have finally come to this.

T'Linda goes and leaves me to my stitching, alone in the house. A meadowlark out on a fence post perches just long enough to thrill its three silvery notes, letting them trail away on a passing breeze. Three notes like three steps, our steps: one to citizenship, one to obtaining knowledge, one, still unfulfilled, that of eventually owning our own land.

A shaft of sunlight comes through the window to lean warm and comforting against my knee, reminding me, with its growing warmth, that I am sitting here in my rocker, dreaming. *Ach*, and why not? I think.

I lay the white stuff I am stitching on in my lap and gaze at the framed document hanging on the wall. The same splinter of light has spear-pointed it with brightness, so that I must take notice. The document is to tell all who see it that David is a United States citizen, and we, joint heirs, with him! The document pledging true allegiance to the United States of America is signed in David's own handwriting. How well I remember the tears of joy we all had when he finally achieved it.

Sitting here now, I marvel that our dream, my dream, has turned out so well; not all of it, it is true, but good enough. The rest can come with the generations that follow. I sit here and rock softly, softly.

". . . . *Liebchen, die Zeit bringt Rosen*," the rocker seems to be telling the floor boards. But it is the remembered voice of the old *Hausfrau* speaking to me, philosophizing that time, indeed, brings roses. "*Wart' nur*, wait," she said to me then, but in my troubled youth I had no faith in her words.

Coming back to reality I hear the faint sound of my children's voices, far off, in the direction of the melon and potato patch where they are hoeing. Before they come home I will make them some lemonade I tell myself. But for now I pick up the ruffles and continue with my sewing.

The graduation dress is of crisp white organdy. The butterfly collar tapers down to the waistline to be caught under a sash. The sash ties in a six-inch bow in the back. Rows of ruffles are to decorate the full skirt. T'Linda will look beautiful in it, highlighted by her bright countenance, her flattering brown bangs, and the long hair-braid down the back. So very clean I keep my hands. So very fine I set the stitches. I decree this dress shall be a monument to learning!

In the evening, after the dishes when the lamp is lit, the dress is ready to try on.

"Come, T'Linda, try it on so your *Baba* can see," I say, happy that the time has finally come. Theolinda comes quickly, her eyes bright, a soft whistle escaping her lips. She takes the dress lovingly.

"Hurry, put it on, then come out immediately."

The four older girls, Leah, Mia, Hester, and Maria, dash after her into the bedroom. I hear them chatter busily as they help her on with the dress. Then, the door opens and T'Linda stands before us! David registers surprise. Our little ones oh-and-ah, while the older ones show hearty approval.

"Well," says Theolinda, spinning around on her toe. "What do you think of it, Papa?"

"*Ei, Ei*, what can one say other than, that it is angel bright! Unstained, like a new promise!" His face is aglow. "Your mama has done herself proud on this one."

"I think so, too." Theolinda smiles and gives me a wink. She continues. "My only hope is that I can be worthy of a teaching position, and of all the work Mama has put into this."

"You will be worthy, when the time comes," David says. "Only strive and believe."

This is the time of the year when my brother Friederich buys an automobile — a shiny red Minute Man — and drives out to Colorado to visit. Friederich with a half-dozen sons, much land, and three tractors can well afford it. David, on the other hand, still drives and farms with horses, saving the money it would take for an automobile to invest in a section of land of his choice. I am pleased with David's reasoning. Soon, he will have enough money to sign the contract.

The place he is counting on is a good farm, with sound buildings set among trees. It has deep cultivated fields. A tenant whose term expires next spring is living on it now. But already we are planning, planning.

How good it will be to live there, a family still intact, before our girls start marrying off.

"It is only right," I say to David, "that they should share the reward of our combined labor, if only for a brief space of their young lives."

There is great excitement as David makes ready to go sign the papers on the new farm. But, even so, he takes time to read the Word of God, as he does every morning, and night. While our eight children settle themselves around the long table David reaches for *Die Heilige Schrift*, where it rests besides the tall mahogany clock. He turns to Psalm 127:

> *Except the Lord build the house,*
> *they labor in vain that build it:*
> *except the Lord keep the city,*
> *the watchman waketh but in vain . . . .*

After the Lord's Prayer, David solemnly closes the book. "Yes, except the Lord build, there can be no future in anything," David says, and I know his thoughts have gone far back in time as have mine, far back to *Russland*, to a time when there seemed to be no hope. Then seeing our children's heads still bowed, David says quickly, "Eat, eat. This is a day to remember, as long as we live!"

When the horses are hitched to the light spring buggy and he goes driving out of the yard, the children run after him, waving him on. Our dogs do their share of jolly barking.

"Good-bye, Papa. Good-bye, Papa. Hurry back with the good news."

"That, I will," David calls back, flicking the rumps of the bays just once with the ends of the lines. "And when I do, all of you will be landowners!"

*Ach*, how sweet the taste of success, I think. How great, the satisfaction of having made something of our lives.

I stand in the farmyard, my hands wrapped in the hem of my clean apron, and watch David go, unmindful, for once, that the rollicking wind is loosening my smoothly combed hair and tumbling it playfully about my shoulders. A sigh of a thousand qualms escapes my lips. Tears of joy fill my eyes and slowly dim their vision. Then there is only the faint whirring of wheels on the roadway, blending with the glad soughing of my heart, and the faint strains of remembered music played by a tall dark and handsome Gypsy fiddler.

How strange was the way we lived in the past. We labored with no thought of praise, and received none. We mingled with, and were viewed by all, yet no one took the slightest notice. We strove for knowledge, but the door of learning seemed forever shut,

285

locked with the key of insurmountable adversities! And yet I feel content, for who needed praise? And who was there that craved notice? Was the door of learning really closed? I say no. And, again, I say no. It was the testing that induced strength in us all.

In my heart there is no remembering of ill will. There is only peace and contentment. It is a good country, our America! Like a stepmother she may rant and rave, but when she smiles it melts away the tears.

# Epilogue

Catherine the Great, Empress of Russia, desiring to populate her vast steppes, gave birth to a whole new people. . . . *Die Wolga-Deutschen*, Volga-Germans, or Germans of Russia.

Premier Joseph Stalin, on the other hand, fearing that the German colonies might harbor Nazi spies when paratroopers landed behind the lines of Tsaritsyn (Stalingrad), banished the entire republic almost overnight — a group of people, men, women, and children numbering up to 390,000 souls according to a September, 1941 world press release, but estimated anywhere between 750,000 to one million by displaced persons (DP's) who were fortunate enough to escape the purge.

The Volga-German region was an autonomous republic situated between the lower Volga and Don Rivers, with Saratov on the north as its provincial capital. The territory covered approximately 10,300 square miles, reaching slightly eastward and south of Saratov to within about 300 miles of the Caspian Sea, and from the same northern point westward to the Don to about 500 miles of the Dnieper riverfront (Ukraine).

Later maps chart the Saratov Oblast as having 39,000 square miles with a 1946 population of 2,400,000. Following the 1941 purge of the German-Russians, the vacuum filled with a multi-mixture of Russia's 175 nationalities.

As a direct consequence of Hitler's axis forces invading Russia in the early fall of 1941 the Volga Republic was dissolved and the German population deported to Siberia. The decree signed at the Kremlin Aug. 28, by President Mikhail Kalinin directed that the vast resettlement be carried out at once under the supervision of the defense council headed by Premier Joseph Stalin.

The migration decree provided in writing that the Volga Germans were to be resettled some 1,600 to 2,000 miles farther east to the Omsk and Novosibirsk regions in western Siberia, the Altai region of the Kazakhstan republic, and "neighboring localities rich in land."

The imagination bogs down in trying to envision such a trek — the very young, the very old, the sick and the dying — across the great Russian plains and through the icebound Ural Mountains, to say nothing of the lack of foodstuffs, of household provisions, and needful machinery to start a new life. Russia, at the time, was desperately in need of rail cars to move her materials of war, so in all likelihood the people were later chained together and forced to march much of the way.

The following excerpt is from an interview the author had with a Volga-German displaced woman (DP) who reached the United States:

Question: What happened in September 1941 when the Soviets set out to capture all Volga-Germans to send them to Siberia?

Answer: Large army trucks drove up in the street, a soldier stood at each of the four corners, and into this the people were thrown, regardless of whether they had their family with them. If the baby was in the house sleeping the mother dare not go bring it. It was a Soviet scheme. In order to break the strength of the people they had to separate man from wife, mother from child.

When the trucks were full they drove to the rail yards where freight trains stood on the sidings, and the people were loaded into the cars. Sometimes a line of cars stood for a week before they were full — people were getting harder and harder to catch. Many people died in the cars before they got started. I saw miserable people hiding in forests. I saw them living in deep bomb craters. It is anyone's guess whether they were caught, or died of hunger and the inclement weather.